NATURAL CREA
OR NATURAL SF

Born in 1944, John Davidson has had a lifelong interest in both
the mystical and the scientific. Graduating from Cambridge
University in 1966 with an honours degree in biological sciences,
he took a post at the University's Department of Applied
Mathematics and Theoretical Physics, where he worked for
seventeen years.

Whilst studying for his degree, he had come into contact with
the teachings of an Indian mystic and in October 1967 he made
the first of many trips to India to meet him. He has continued in
search of the mystic reality since that time.

He left the University in 1984 and presently runs the *Wholistic
Research Company*, which supplies books and products related
to living healthily in a modern world. Many of these products are
of John Davidson's own design.

Since 1984, he has also written a total of ten books, including
a series which attempts to demonstrate that *all* human experience lies within the framework of a greater mystic reality. His
particular interest has been to show the true place (and value) of
modern science in relationship to that reality.

By the Same Author

SUBTLE ENERGY
THE WEB OF LIFE
THE SECRET OF THE CREATIVE VACUUM
NATURAL CREATION AND THE FORMATIVE MIND

NATURAL CREATION OR NATURAL SELECTION?

A Complete New Theory of Evolution

JOHN DAVIDSON
M.A. (Cantab)

ELEMENT

Shaftesbury, Dorset ● Rockport, Massachusetts

© John Davidson 1992

First published in Great Britain in 1992 by
Element Books Ltd
Longmead, Shaftesbury, Dorset

First published in the USA in 1992 by
Element, Inc.
42 Broadway, Rockport, MA 01966

All rights reserved.
No part of this book may be
reproduced or utilized in any form or by any means,
electronic or mechanical, without permission in
writing from the Publisher.

Designed by Roger Lightfoot
Front cover photograph: *Soft coral, Red Sea*
Georgette Douwma, Planet Earth Pictures
Cover design by Max Fairbrother
Typeset by Cambridge Photosetting Services
Printed and bound in Great Britain by
Dotesios Ltd, Trowbridge, Wiltshire

British Library Cataloguing in Publication Data

A catalogue record for this book is available
from the British Library

Library of Congress Catalog Card Number Available

ISBN 1–85230–240–2

CONTENTS

To the great biologist,
Charles Darwin
Who helped free us
From the influence of religious dogma.

It is now time to free ourselves
From the influence of Charles Darwin.

NATURAL CREATION
AN INTRODUCTION TO
THE SERIES

Natural Creation is a series of three books continuing the author's presentation of the world of science and humanity within a context of universal and natural mystic philosophy. The three books in the series are entitled:

Natural Creation and the Formative Mind
Natural Creation or Natural Selection?
Natural Creation: The Mystic Harmony

They may be read in any order, though they were written in the above sequence.

Natural Creation begins with the premise that this physical world is only a level of perception, a plane of consciousness, a dance of *continuous manifestation* or creation, a play of the Universal Life Force, a realm of being within the all-encompassing Supreme Being.

It points out how the Universal, greater or *Formative Mind* is the architect of all patterns and rhythms, of space and time, demonstrating that physical science is presently only the study of superficial relationships upon the 'surface' of this Golden Womb of creative manifestation. It shows the way forward for man and his science to work in harmony with natural law. It suggests a radically different perspective on the true nature of science.

Natural Creation portrays the world of our fellow species as living and engaging beings, possessed of mind and consciousness. It shows how strictly Darwinian suggestions concerning evolution as an explanation of the fossil record, and of how we come to be here, cannot be the whole story since they deal only with bodies, ignoring the inner dimension of Life and the great creative power of the Formative Mind.

The author points out that present scientific and mechanistic descriptions of the universe are not so much incorrect as lacking in their perception of this inward formative dimension of being. They are therefore fundamentally incomplete.

He shows how everything is integrated and ordered into the most beautifully exact cycles and patterns, from atoms to galaxies; how the planetary surface constantly moves and recycles itself for the continuous support of living creatures. He presents a logical yet mystical perspective of life on Earth throughout the millions of years of our planet's history. And he explains fully the tremendous formative impact of the most significant of all cycles upon planetary circumstances: the ebb and flow – with a periodicity of several million years – of Mind and Consciousness, of the Life Force itself. Evidence of this great cycle is clearly etched into the Earth itself, for all to read.

He directs attention to the evidence that, on a geological time-scale, we are nearing the 'end' of this cycle and may 'soon' experience a springtime of consciousness, the like of which we can hardly begin to conceive. He presents the mystical experience as the highest of all experiences, showing how it is, and has been, common to all peoples and to all cultures. He ends the series with a full description of the mystic hierarchy of creation, according to the teachings of the highest mystics.

ACKNOWLEDGEMENTS

It would not be possible to mention by name all those who have contributed to this book. Many have helped unknowingly, and in so many ways. But in particular, I have quoted from the writings of those listed below. I am grateful to the authors, translators and publishers for the use of this material. Full details are given in the bibliography.

Address to the 1962 Yale graduating class, John F. Kennedy, 1962.

Bacteria Take the Chance out of Evolution, Jeremy Cherfas; *New Scientist*, 22 September 1988 and a paper in *Nature* (vol 335, p142), published by John Cairns, Julie Overbaugh and Stephan Miller.

The Dinosaur Heresies, Robert Bakker; first published 1986. Excerpts from pages 410, 413, 414. Reproduced by permission of Penguin Books Ltd. (UK and Commonwealth), and William Morrow & Co., (USA and Canada).

Life Pulse, Niles Eldredge; Facts On File Publications, New York and Oxford, 1987.

Mathnawi, Jalalu'ddin Rumi; translated by R. A. Nicholson, Luzac & Co, London, 1926.

The Origin of Species, Charles Darwin; J. M. Dent & Sons, London, 1928.

Spiritual Heritage, Maharaj Charan Singh; Radha Soami Satsang Beas, India, 1983.

Ammonite fossil, photograph by Richard Revels; courtesy of Natural Science Photos.

Compsognathus, reproduction of a model by A. Hayward; photograph courtesy of Natural Science Photos.

The Earth's present lithospheric plates, after Frank Press & Raymond Siever in *Earth* (W. H. Freeman & Co, New York, 1982), after *The Oceanic Crust* by J. Francheteau, copyright 1983 by Scientific American Inc. Plate motions modified from the work of J. B. Minster and T. H. Jordan.

Emma Kunz and marigolds, photograph copyright by Emma Kunz Zentrum, CH-8116 Wurenlos, Switzerland.

Human skeleton embedded in Miocene limestone, published in *Philosophical Transactions of the Royal Society*, London, 1814. Photograph by permission of the Syndics of Cambridge University Library.

Tyrannosaurus rex, reproduction of a model by A. Hayward; photograph courtesy of Natural Science Photos.

Particular acknowledgement must be given to the work of Niles Eldredge. It was he, together with Stephen J. Gould, who highlighted the continuous cycles of extinction and proliferation. In my discussion of the palaeontological evidence for this cycle I have relied more on Eldredge's work than any other. His popular book, *Life Pulse*, lays out the fundamentals of his case in a thorough yet readable manner. In fairness to him, however, I should point out that most probably he does not endorse such notions of life and being as I am suggesting herein. I would not wish to spoil his reputation!

Thanks are also due to Christian O'Brien, Holly Gothard and Julia McCutchen who went through the manuscript making valuable suggestions, to Nancy Mangan who did much of the typing, and to Dennis Halls for the neatly executed drawings.

I may here premise, that I have nothing to do with the origin of the mental powers, any more than I have with that of life itself.

Charles Darwin
The Origin of Species

As every past generation has had to disenthrall itself from an inheritance of truisms and stereotypes, so in our time we must move on from reassuring repetition of stale phrases to a new, difficult, but essential confrontation with reality.

For the great enemy of truth is very often not the lie – deliberate, contrived and dishonest – but the myth, persistent, persuasive and unrealistic. Too often we hold fast to the cliches of our forebears. We subject all facts to a prefabricated set of interpretations. We enjoy the comfort of opinion without the discomfort of thought.

John F. Kennedy, 11 June 1962
To the 1962 Yale graduating class

When the eye is entirely perfect it sees the root (cause),
But when a man is squint-eyed, it sees the branch (effect).

Jalalu'ddin Rumi
Mathnawi, translated by R. A. Nicholson

INTRODUCTION

It is commonly observed that, as the nineteenth century gave way to the twentieth, the Western mind became increasingly impregnated with the mechanistic or 'scientific' view of life and nature. Even before this, however, religious dogma viewed the world as a mechanism created by God, and from which He remained remote. He had created it and all creatures, and had then withdrawn to a safe distance. In many respects, there is not much difference between these two apparently competing theories of life.

Mystics, on the other hand, whether of East or West, have always pointed out – on the basis of their *experience* – that the Supreme Reality lies within us. That we are a part of that reality and that the creation is a continuous show, a continuous projection or play of this Supreme Power of Life or Consciousness.

They say that God is present in every particle of His creation and yet He is also separate. But this is not a philosophical statement to be taken as the basis for an intellectual discussion. It is a pointer to the highest reality which needs to be directly experienced in mystic transport in order to be understood. Intellectual debate, say the mystics, is like discussing the theory and nature of flight without ever going up in an aeroplane.

Western man of recent centuries, however, has mostly considered himself superior to all the mystical philosophies prevalent in 'subservient' cultures, strongly adhering to a mechanistic world view – whether he considered the world to be of divine or natural origin. To 'go native', either in philosophy or social habits, has been severely frowned upon.

It was from this milieu that Darwin came, embracing an ideal of science equated with a mechanistic world view and struggling with a religious dogma based upon a story related in an ancient Jewish book. A story which many of the Jews themselves, especially their mystics, took largely as an allegory, but which the less imaginative Christian mind had accepted as literal and mechanistic 'fact'.

The scientific view held that man was entirely a mechanism consisting of physical substance. Religious dogma decreed much the same, adding that somewhere in the offing was a soul which somehow gave the whole affair a religious flavour. The world, maintained the Christians, was created in seven days by a Divine Being who then kept Himself aloof. But in both points of view, the participatory roles of Mind and consciousness in the creative process were completely overlooked. The life within was utterly ignored. It was all rather unsatisfactory.

The irrationality of this religious dogma must have infuriated the logical and scientific minds of the late nineteenth century. It is a matter of little surprise, therefore, that when Darwin suggested a mechanism which seemed to explain the origin and diversity of the species without involving the external intervention of a totally incomprehensible Divine Being, the idea was seized upon by the scientific intelligentsia of the day and actively promoted to replace the bizarre and illogical religious doctrine and its associated creation myth. Scientific minds must have felt great relief when the constraints of such a belief system were lifted. But the battle between the two has been raging ever since.

Time, however, has moved on and a century of geological study and a detailed examination of the fossil record has failed to demonstrate the veracity of Darwin's hypothesis of gradual evolutionary change mediated purely by a process of *natural selection* and *the survival of the fittest*. Rather the reverse is true, for there appears to be no evidence at all of slow, mutational, evolutionary change amongst the old fossils embedded in our ancient rocks.

So Darwin's theory – though still widely accepted – has remained only a belief system, a theory or suggestion put forward to explain how species change and why a myriad creatures, known only from dead relics in the fossil record, no longer exist today.

Even in a world where religious doctrine and the idea of a geocentric universe were once deeply entwined, when people did finally become accustomed to thinking of the earth and the planets as moving round the sun, it all seemed very obvious. There were no significant dissenters, no contradictory evidence or facts to worry about, and no alternative theories. Even the theologians adjusted their beliefs to fit the facts. Not so, however, with Darwin's explanation of the fossil record. The field is still wide open and the debate still continues.

There is no doubt that well over 99 per cent of the creatures whose physical remains are to be found in the fossil record do not exist on earth today. And of today's creatures many have arisen in their present forms only within the last 10 million years. So *some* agency of change must be at work. Yet there is no evidence at all of the extensive kind of evolutionary change that was predicted by Darwin.

Limited changes within certain boundaries have certainly occurred. Over the last 400 million years, for example, small scorpions have become large scorpions (up to 5 or 6 feet long!) and back to small ones once again. And there have been more extensive changes amongst the vertebrates. The various forms are individually classifiable as separate species and represent a gradation and gradual change in the species over time. But no missing links have ever been found between any of the major classes of creature nor even between families within a class. Scorpions have never showed any tendency to be anything but scorpions.

Moreover, even these changes appear to take place in fits and starts. There seems to be a cycle spanning many millions of years, synchronously involving all species and characterized by rapid extinction and proliferation phases of variable extent, followed by long periods of equilibrium where very little alters. And during these proliferation periods, apparently new species or radically different variants of old ones can appear suddenly. So the question still remains: *What on earth is going on?*

Whenever man has found himself faced with such paradoxes, when all the best minds have failed to suggest a really convincing solution, it usually means that some essential factor or dimension is being overlooked. Often, that factor is very simple and 'obvious', lying right under our noses all the time. We may be looking right at it, yet be missing its relevance to our problem. *Natural Creation or Natural Selection?* attempts to add this missing dimension to considerations of geological cycles, species change and the fossil record.

The missing dimension is that of *being*, of Life and the Formative Mind, a topic discussed more fully in *Natural Creation and the Formative Mind*. 'Adding in' this dimension reveals a picture of life on earth which puts evolutionary concepts into a far wider perspective than ever before presented.

This dimension of being is a real dimension, more real even than those of space and time. It is the inward or vertical, pattern-making and manifestational dimension, the projection process by which the physical universe and all physical bodies come into existence.

It is the *ontological dimension*, the dimension of the Formative

Mind, taking its origin or source from the Supreme Being. It is thus the backbone of a dynamic, continuously existent, creative process that exists within all living beings. And, as with so many good ideas, when this perception is applied to existing explanations and descriptions, we find that no one was wrong, just that the previously acknowledged boundaries required expansion.

Conventional evolutionary theory deals only with a subset of the relevant data. It ignores the role of the Life Force and the greater Mind. It ignores the existence of Mind and soul. It ignores the mystic nature of God.

Can we afford, then, to ignore the dimension of being in any study of living beings, even if we are studying only their external physical forms? *Natural Creation or Natural Selection?* attempts to show that we cannot.

John Davidson

1. WHAT ON EARTH IS GOING ON?

In *Natural Creation and the Formative Mind*, I tried to show how the physical universe is a projection of the Supreme Consciousness, patterned by the greater or Formative Mind into a hierarchical structure of energy and being. In effect, this adds an inward dimension to the study of physical existence – a dimension of Life and Mind whereby it may be comprehended how all physical forms come into existence as outward expressions or crystallizations of more inward patterns of a greater Mind. The individual minds, possessed by all creatures, are just one aspect of this greater Mind. And enlivening it all is the Supreme Being, the life and being within all things.

Once this is understood, we come to realize that attempting to describe physical forms or patterns whilst ignoring the inward formative dimension is like trying to understand the nature and functioning of an image upon a screen whilst ignoring the projection system. It is like trying to describe the physical universe as if space possessed only two dimensions, rather than three.

Many of the anomalies and paradoxes of science, indeed of all aspects of life, become understandable when allowance is made in one's thinking for the existence of this inward dimension or projection process. Many other mysteries which we thought we had understood are also more fully illuminated. For life and mind, which lie within, cannot be understood simply by the study of outer form. The workings of the projection system and the light within it must also be taken into account. Nor can the origins of the 'laws of nature' governing inert matter or living forms be comprehended without a perception of the formative dimension of existence itself.

As physicists have pointed out, we are *participators* in the universe. But the *degree* of this participation is far more than most physicists have ever imagined. In the present book, then, we re-evaluate the geological and fossil record in the light of this formative dimension. And the picture which emerges is both fascinating and revealing.

WHAT DARWIN ACTUALLY SAID

It comes as a surprise to many folk to learn that Darwin never suggested that life evolved out of inert matter. This was a later extrapolation, made by others. It is a theory for which there still remains no evidence, but which is adhered to with a tenacity that almost gives the idea the status of a religious belief. It is also a creation myth which no other human community, throughout the length and breadth of recorded belief and legend, has ever previously suggested. It makes one wonder who is really the more accurate observer of nature's miraculous processes – the scientist or the 'savage'?

As a theory concerning the origin of life, it appears to have its closest ties to European beliefs held as recently as the last century: that mice (for example) were spontaneously generated in cupboards containing soiled linen! Similarly, many other creatures were thought to self-create themselves out of the habitat in which they were found. Frogs from ponds, fishes from lakes and streams, and so on.

Darwin's idea was that all living creatures have evolved from one or a few common ancestors, through *natural selection* by *the survival of the fittest*. But as to *how* the common, pre-existent ancestor or ancestors got there, he declined to comment. In fact, he specifically stated in the opening paragraph of chapter 8 in *The Origin of Species*, on *Instinct*, that he was purposely saying nothing regarding the origin either of mind or of life itself. Darwin is very clear about this:

> I may here premise, that I have nothing to do with the origin of the mental powers, any more than I have with that of life itself. We are concerned only with the *diversities*[1] of instinct and of the other mental faculties in animals of the same class.

[1] Author's italics.

He also acknowledged the difficulty inherent in understanding how instincts arise:

> Many instincts are so wonderful that their development will probably appear to the reader a difficulty sufficient to overthrow my whole theory.

His honesty is disarming. Clearly, Darwin was troubled by the existence of instinct, behaviour and mind function, as well he should have been. For how is it that a cuckoo is born with the instinct to lay its eggs in another's nest? Or how did the cuckoo's offspring develop the instinct – by random mutation – to turn their unfortunate fellows out of their own nest within three days of hatching? Are instinct and behaviour so well understood by scientists that they can be assumed to evolve by random fluctuations in the DNA? They are not.

Without an understanding of the nature of instinct, how can we say that it arises by random mutations? If we do not know the nature of a thing, how can we suggest that we know how it evolved or came into being? Especially when there is no evidence that behaviour and instinct are programmed either into the DNA or the brain or anywhere else in the physical body. It is only an assumption of materially-minded scientists, just as it is assumed that our human mind and consciousness arise from activities within our own brains. 'Where else,' they argue, 'Can life, consciousness and mind come from?'

In fact, Darwin's further comments on instinct do not even attempt to elucidate the true nature of instinct. He, himself, says:

> I will not attempt any definition of instinct.

He then goes on to say, more or less, 'We know it when we see it.' But as to the nature of such 'mental powers', he makes no further suppositions. He intentionally avoids the question because he freely admits that he does not understand it.

Furthermore, since Darwin did not consider his theory to be an account of the origins of life and mind, he also did not consider his ideas to challenge a belief in or an understanding of God. That Darwin was an out-and-out materialist is again a popular misconception. In fact, he makes a point, in his closing sentences to *The Origin of Species*, of specifically referring to his belief in a Creator.

> Thus, from the war of nature, from famine and death, the most exalted object which we are capable of conceiving, namely the production of the

higher animals, directly follows. There is grandeur in this view of life, with its several powers, having been originally breathed by the Creator into a few forms or into one; and that, whilst this planet has gone cycling on according to the fixed law of gravity, from so simple a beginning endless forms most beautiful and wonderful have been, and are being evolved.

So though I may not personally agree with him that God created all living forms by introducing one – or just a few – lower species which then set about diversifying, his ideas concerning life, mind, God and evolution are certainly of a totally different order to those put forward by the majority of Neo-Darwinists.

Darwin's observation of the similarities between life forms was correct. But his interpretation viewed life purely from a horizontal, mechanistic point of view. It missed the essence of life, the inner spark of consciousness, for he himself had put upon one side considerations of mind and life.

So, the modern conception that life evolved out of dust and water is *radically* different, in its fundamental assumptions, from what Darwin actually thought and wrote. In essence, Darwin was saying, 'I don't understand the origin of life and mind, but it does seems as if all these life forms had a common ancestry.' While the moderns say, 'Life and mind are the result of molecular complexity and self-organization, and everything has evolved from there.' Darwin said that God created the first lower forms. The moderns say that the first forms arose in ancient muds. The two are separate theories, bundled together as one.

The lack of awareness of life and mind, however, is quite in keeping with the perceptive limitations of our present age and consequently the one theory is considered to be an extension of the other. And the relevance of the inner dimension is altogether missed.

During Darwin's time, considerable new attention was given to the evidence of the fossil record. The hold of the Church had to some extent been relaxed and men felt more free to pursue rational rather than scriptural explanations concerning the nature and origins of life. Many naturalists, therefore, were grappling with the same data, attempting to understand the fossil record from within the prevailing climate of thought. Similar 'solutions' were therefore bound to have occurred synchronously.

So, it is no matter of surprise that the originator of the expression, *the survival of the fittest*, was not Darwin at all, but an eccentric philosopher, Herbert Spencer. In fact, the phrase did not even appear in *The Origin of Species* until its fifth revised edition.

Similarly, the title of Darwin's book was taken from the writings of a naturalist of humble background, Arthur Russell Wallace, who published a paper one year before Darwin's book was published, containing in complete form what has become popularly known as Darwin's own theory. In the early days of the evolutionary theory, it was known as the Darwin–Wallace theory of evolution and Darwin himself does make it very clear that it was Wallace's ideas that finally gave him the missing pieces of his puzzle.

Wallace, however, was born into poverty and never had what was almost the only opportunity of crossing the great class barriers of the day – a university education, for that required parents of sufficient wealth and 'connection'. So he never had the time or facilities with which to undertake the extensive field research for which Darwin is so justly famous.

Moreover, Wallace, along with Sir Arthur Conan Doyle, John Ruskin and Lord Tennyson, frequented the spiritist circles of the day and as such was suspect in the eyes of the scientific orthodoxy. It was not long, therefore, before Wallace's name was dropped from the theory.

To be fair, Darwin's work is so full of data and considered thought that it was indeed his work, rather than Wallace's, which made the theory so well known and acceptable. Darwin's work as a field biologist and careful, honest thinker is to be deeply respected. *The Origin of Species* is a classic of observational detail and applied thought. He is by no means a flashy salesman or showman, glossing over difficulties. He approaches all the areas where he knows his theory to be on shaky ground. And many more difficulties have arisen since then, of course, especially in the realm of understanding the genetic processes supposed to underlie his theory.

So I may not agree with Darwin's main convictions, especially those concerning the derivation of all species from a common ancestor, and the roles of chance and natural selection, but I have deep respect for the work of a great man.

Darwin felt sure that further search amongst the fossil record would reveal the evidence he required to prove his theory. Yet the reverse has been the case. There are now more problems with his theory than there were in his day, for a quite different picture has emerged, as we will see.

In fact, it would be very interesting to know what Darwin's

reaction would have been to many of our modern discoveries, especially the difficulties associated with determining the nature and origins of genetic change, as well as the continued absence from the fossil record of any missing links between the species.

Let us, however, start this tale from the beginning. We will first examine some of the more philosophical considerations surrounding evolutionary theory and then, in subsequent chapters, have a look at the fossil record and the geological story.

HOLISM[2], NATURE AND EVOLUTION

Nature is a whole, a complete system. Similarly, each creature is a whole, yet integral part of this system. It is our limited conceptual minds which conceive of nature as being comprised of linear pathways. This being so, it is not possible for nature to have evolved the outer forms of creatures by a linear, piecemeal process. This is not the way nature operates; it is the way our limited minds operate. We confuse the way the totality functions with the nature of our thoughts concerning that totality.

Both Darwinian and Neo-Darwinian theories are more indicative of the nature of our rational, intellectual minds than the circumstances of nature. The theory evolved in the minds of Darwin and his successors, not in nature, and was adopted by other scientists of a similar mind. In fact, it found such a resonance amongst like-minded people that it spread like a new political ideology or social custom, where the ground is ready for new input: the first edition of Darwin's *The Origin of Species* (3000 copies) sold out within just two days. A publisher's dream! Now Neo-Darwinism is taught in schools, together with the other scientific, religious and social beliefs of our culture.

But prevalence and acceptance do not make an idea correct. History can vouch for that. It is the fertility and readiness of the ground that makes an idea grow with such vigour, not necessarily its essential correctness. Nazism is a good example of this, from more modern times. Yet, historically, very few ideas last for long. It is only the mystical and spiritual philosophy, based upon inner, repeatable experience, and an expression of man's true being, which surfaces

---

[2] The word 'holism' was first coined by the South African prime minister Jan Christiaan Smuts (1870–1950) and was a concept used particularly in his book *Holism and Evolution*.

repeatedly within all human communities. This would seem to be the only perennial philosophy.

Nature, then, is a whole and we should bear this in mind especially when analysing particular connections and relationships.

In science – whether we are studying life forms or subatomic particles, whether we are looking at 'substance', behaviour or mental activity – we are looking at patterns, rhythms and relationships. When we observe a whole flower, for instance, we perceive its pattern and manner of functioning at that level. When we study its parts – the individual petals, the anthers, the stamens, pigmentation, cellular structure, biochemistry and so on – we are examining patterns at another level. We may even decide to examine the whole plant or the whole ecosystem in which the plant and its flower are enmeshed – this is an even more encompassing level than that of the whole flower.

When we take a flower to pieces and examine those pieces, that is all we are doing – examining the pieces. We are not investigating the *whole* flower, as a functional whole, nor the whole plant, nor the place of the plant within the fabric of nature. In fact, one could say that the *larger* the pattern or the piece under study, then the more *fundamental* is our enquiry. And that the largest and most fundamental pattern of all, to be studied as one entirety, is the whole of creation.

Our analytical, reductionist mind, addicted to 'manyness', cannot understand this. It seems too simple. Such a mind considers that it is the process of analysis and division which will provide the most fundamental answers. But to understand the universe one has to expand the frontiers of one's mind to take in the wholeness of the pattern. Then one sees that the greater whole *functions* as a whole – not as the multitude of little 'pieces' almost arbitrarily defined by our intellectual minds.

If something *functions* as a whole, then, although an analysis of its parts may still be of great value, the deepest understanding will always come from a complete perception of that whole. In fact, the development of such a perception becomes an ever deepening life *experience* leading ultimately to true mystical experience.

The ultimate whole is the Oneness of the Universal Consciousness, of God. Situated as we are, at the nethermost pole of creation, we are dealing with the divisions spun out by the greater Mind. But the concept of wholeness, or holism, intuitively appeals to us because it reflects the nature of Reality, the essence of our innermost self.

In this physical realm of multiplicity, the simplest and most primal pattern of the greater, Formative Mind is that of polarity and division, and is found reflected in every derived pattern. The creation is not manifested by a *linear* process of division but by means of a *multireflective*, *multifaceted* process of patterns forming patterns from within out. That is why we can observe this fundamental 'law' of polarity in everything from the positive and negative electrical charge of subatomic particles, to the rhythm of the seasons, to birth and death, to the cyclic creation and dissolution of the Universe.

Polarity or duality is the primal division in all things. And this dynamic process of patterning within patterning is also why we see the same patterns repeated throughout nature and appearing in so many different forms. The spiral of DNA, for instance, is repeated in the spiral formation of petals in a flower, of leaves on a stem, in the whorls of *nautilus* shells, and in the ordered formation of the star-laden galaxies.

What happens, then, if one attempts to understand this vision of nature's wholeness in terms of conventional evolutionary theory, a theory very much in the analytical and reductionist vein? One is immediately led to wonder how such wholeness could have arisen from linear and random processes. Nature is a whole; we analyse her into pieces according to a preconceived theory, and then insist that she obeys the conclusions of our analytical intellect. Something is very unsatisfying about this approach. Nature does not function in a piecemeal fashion and therefore any theory which presumes that she does must, at best, be incomplete.

Let us take a specific example: the evolution of a spider. The question is: how could a spider have evolved by random mutation? A spider exhibits a host of integrated biochemical, physiological, neurological, anatomical, behavioural and instinctive adaptations. It is able to manufacture perfect silk; to spin and weave it into perfectly organized webs and traps; to know how to walk in a sticky web without getting entangled; to know how to wrap up a fly, but to identify and leave a wasp alone; to understand the importance of waiting patiently at the edge or centre of the web; to paralyse prey with so perfect a toxin that it does not then poison itself when it sucks out the body juices with specialized mouth parts – and much else besides. The spider and its way of life are so whole-some!

So, musing upon how a spider could have evolved so many integrated skills and biological systems from some unspiderly ancestor, are we to suppose that the earliest spiders wove rather poorly structured webs out of inferior silk; got stuck occasionally in their own webs; could not distinguish between dangerous hornets and house flies; used poor toxins which only partially killed or paralysed their prey whilst later giving them a tummy ache or worse; and that they were ill adapted for actually eating and digesting their prey and so they only relied partially upon their spiderly ways for making a living, anyway? In short, that they were pretty much of a mess, still needing considerable time, not to mention several million 'chance' mutations, to get their act together? Surely such a process would be worse than design by committee!

If this were the case, and since such evolution is still supposed to be in progress, why are there are no semi-evolved creatures living now? Why are there none in the fossil record? In fact, 300 million year old spiders with web-weaving spinnerets have been found in the fossil record, yet nowhere has any fossilized species been found which is on the way to becoming a spider. It's spiders or something else! All creatures, not just spiders, are well-structured wholes. It is our own linear, divisive minds which perceive them as comprised of parts and linear processes, then insist that they must have also evolved in that way.

Indecision, as any member of a human family or any business executive can tell you, leads to just muddling through with nothing particular ever being achieved. If you try to go in too many directions all at once, you end up getting nowhere at all. Evolution by chance and by miniature steps would pull a creature in a host of different directions until all life forms became like string and sellotape constructions. A bit of this and a bit of that. For one cannot attribute any *goals* to a materialistic view of evolution. Nature cannot be assumed to know where she is going in such a philosophy of chance and chaos. And in the absence of any consciousness, vision or volition, how could such perfect design as we see around us have come into existence? Yet somehow we are asked to believe that living creatures, who most clearly possess volition, desires, goals, mind and consciousness, have arisen by random processes from dust and water which exhibit none of these.

Materialistic evolutionary theory is forced to assume that there is no apparent purpose to life and that natural selection is not selecting for some future, intelligently conceived goal; it is a selection only conferring advantages in the current moment. How then could some radically new species design emerge purely by chance and over an immense span of time, yet exhibit such a multitude of integrated characteristics? 'Progress' by tiny random steps would surely be one of constant indecision and change of direction, leading to imperfection and destruction rather than perfection and integration?

Forms, structures, processes, systems, membranes, molecules, atoms, subatomic particles and forces – these are all *effects*, patterns spun out in space. They are also only *our* analysis, *our* mental compartmentalization. Our human kind of sensory perception and mind-brain activity is required for us to see them in the way we do.

In simple terms, our mental analysis in words and language is different from the thing itself. Nature is one – we can experience and realize this within ourselves, but we can never adequately express it. For as soon as we express, we divide. We separate ourselves from our experience, and then we mentally and verbally divide up that experience.

We can never describe the colour red, we can only experience it. Likewise with the whole of nature, the whole cosmos, the whole of experience. Ultimately we are forced into the realm of personal *experience* – mystic or mundane – if we wish to really understand *anything* in the fullest possible fashion. No amount of reading a recipe book will ever bake a cake!

Similarly, we can examine the fundamentals of Darwinism or Neo-Darwinist evolutionary theories. For Darwinism presupposes that not only can whole systems and cycles be genuinely reduced to a number of interconnected pathways, but that they actually *evolved* in that way.

Even the addition of one single behavioural tendency requires more than just the change in a single gene, even supposing that instinctive behaviour is genetically linked, which is by no means even demonstrated. The chance mutation of a single gene – a rearrangement of energy patterns at a molecular level – even if potentially 'useful', is only capable of integration if the whole of the rest of the organism is able to cope with it. The sudden appearance of feathers on a reptile or even of fluffy scales as a starting point would be of little use to it. It would be more of an aggravation. One piece of wood does not make a piece of furniture, nor even an indication that a new piece of furniture – of a very particular type – is on the way. You are more likely to trip on it and hurt yourself. There is no 'on the way' in nature – everything is already there.

And if, as some modern theories in physics and the ancient mystical philosophy both suggest, all manifested substance is actually only patterns of energy in space, *spun out under the influence of our minds*, then how did the cosmos get started in the *absence* of life, consciousness and Mind?

Without the minds and the karmas of the souls inhabiting this world – and that means all of its creatures – the potential energy of space remains unruffled. It rests purely in potential form.

SCIENCE, MIND AND HOLISM

Our science is based on the fallacy or illusion that the ideas and concepts of our linear mind are a genuine description of nature's totally non-linear processes. But the greater truth lies in the non-conceptual understanding of experience or direct perception of the wholeness, not in our analysis of the details. If physicists, evolutionists or biologists think that analytical science will reveal the final secrets of 'life, the universe and everything', they are misled. Such an analysis cannot even tell us the real nature of the mind which is performing this analysis.

There is no harm in intellectual analysis. It is a part of the way our human mind is put together. But it must be seen for what it is. It can be a very powerful tool, just as one's legs are useful for getting about. But the problem is that generally, we have no control over our mind and no sense of expanded consciousness to enliven our thinking with mystic insight.

The result is that our mind becomes so habituated that we cannot even tell the difference between our thoughts or concepts, and the objects of our perception. The word 'experience' comes to mean less and less to us. It is only as we awaken from this deep slumber of illusion that we begin to place more emphasis on our inner life and automatically experience and realize many things concerning the nature of our own mind.

Man's science knows nothing that is truly fundamental. Our science observes and analyses only patterns or processes, but we have no idea how these processes are integrated into one whole. And there is no end to their analysis.

We may know something of biochemical pathways and relationships, but we have no understanding of *how* even a nose is formed in the shape it is. Or how any other organ or system in the body comes to possess the shape, function and characteristic that it does, let alone the whole mind-body system, complete with its subtle, emotional and mental energies. Modifications to the DNA may lead to modifications in the shape of the nose, or of biochemical pathways. We may even see some aspect of this in action by way of protein synthesis and so on. But how each and every atom and subatomic particle is patterned into a body in the way it is – this is as much a mystery to science as ever it was.

Nature, then, is a whole. That was our starting point. And conventional evolutionary theory makes no allowances for that. Clearly, something is missing.

DARWINISM AND THE INNER LIFE DIMENSION

To many of those who are aware that their inner life is not created out of complex biochemistry, but rather that the inward Life Force is itself responsible for the integrated and complex patterning of physical substance into living bodies, conventional evolutionary theory seems, at best, incomplete. For it only addresses the physical exterior of life.

Neo-Darwinian theory approaches life as if it were a by-product of material substance. And if we doubt that fundamental premise, then we must doubt the explanations of materialistic evolutionary theory. Even the conclusions of quantum physics, that the perceiver is integrally linked to the perceived, should have disturbed evolutionary theorists. For if the perceived exists only within the mind of the perceiver, then the concept of a universe devoid of a perceiver becomes untenable and the proposition that life evolved out of dust and water becomes meaningless.

Actually, modern evolutionary theory misses two essential factors that are apparent to mystical experience and perception. And – some would say – to ordinary common sense, as well.

Firstly, that life or consciousness precedes form; that life creates form and not vice versa; and that the purpose of life is the evolution of consciousness. The evolution of consciousness implies the spiritual progress of the individual through personal struggle against the attraction of matter, through escape from the illusion of form into a knowledge of the One.

Secondly, that in terms of energy, outward energies are created from within; that the outer, physical 'world' is a creation out of the more subtle states within ourselves; that what we call physical substance is actually only a level of experience or being in a grand hierarchy of such levels, all within ourselves.

This means that creation did not happen a long time ago but that the *creative process is continuous.* The Universal Being is intimately involved in every small particle of the creation in a supremely dynamic and continuous act of projection, manifestation or creation.

Regarding evolution, therefore, the essential problem facing us is summarized in the comment of the old school teacher looking sternly and questioningly at some offensive object, demanding an explanation from his silent audience: 'But someone must have put it there!' We are alive; we have minds; there is a physical universe; we are intimately involved in the show of creation; there is a multitude of creatures who have left their fossilized remains behind. So how did all this come about? How did it all get there?

The facts are that the species which exist at this present time bear resemblances, but yet are clearly different, to most of those which have left their fossilized remains for us to puzzle over. And there are many long-departed species in the fossil record which seem to bear very little resemblance to anything which exists today. Why? What are they doing there? Why have they changed? Or have they changed? And if so, how?

Without the realization that there is an inner dimension to things, there appear to be only two potential explanations. Either the present species have evolved out of past species by chance and in a purely mechanical fashion. Or an aloof Divine Being, quite separate from His creation and quite beyond the wit of man to understand, has found it necessary to occasionally replenish the stock of earthly creatures by acts of Divine intervention, quite outside the normal laws which He has otherwise provided for the maintenance of His creation. An odd sort of arrangement.

The thesis which I am presenting, however, takes the inward side of things as the primary reality, out of which all else is derived. Therefore, the explanation of how such a diversity of species both within the fossil record and in present times, has arisen, is given a radically different perspective, for we have a formative dimension of being to consider.

If in this physical domain we really are only looking at patterns on a screen, then to try and understand how things happen here by an analysis of these patterns alone, never addressing oneself to the projection process, is to miss the essence of how things come to be. It is as if, while watching a movie, we had become so deeply involved in the drama that we had entered the screen, taking the screen characters as the ultimate reality, analysing the how and why of their behaviour and of the screen 'substance' itself, without ever considering the projection process by which all the images, patterns and rhythms come into being.

And this is where the analogy fails us. For in reality, that projection system lies within us.

EVOLUTION OR CHANGE?

It needs to be pointed out here, discussed more fully later on, that the fossil record, though showing ample signs of *change*, shows no evidence at all of *evolution*. That is to say, there is no doubt that species do change in outward appearance over the course of time, but there is no real evidence that the species which are alive today are in any way *higher* or *more evolved* than those found in the fossil record of hundreds of millions of years ago. The only possible exception is man.

In fact, it seems as if every species is perfectly adapted to its particular environment and is part and parcel of its time and place. The common misconception, for example, that dinosaurs died out because they were a poor and inept design has been discounted in recent years by palaeontologists (fossil experts). Dinosaurs, in fact, seem to have exhibited perfect adaptation to their particular environments.

Evolutionary theories are really addresssing two primary issues, which often get confused. Firstly, the origin of life. Secondly, the attempt to explain and interpret the fossil record – does it exhibit a continuous spectrum of species, continuously *evolving* to some 'higher' condition, or does it simply exhibit *change*? And, in either case, what mediates those changes – natural selection of random genetic mutations or some more integrated, ordered and subtle process of life altogether? The two issues are linked, of course, but it is useful to remember the differentiation.

So to explain the fossil record and get us up to modern times, both theories require extensive evolution and diversification. Both theories begin with a *few* species and end up with *many* and *various*. Both therefore suppose a process of evolution, a progression towards something higher.

The more metaphysical or mystical approach, however, which acknowledges the difficulties of understanding time and creation in intellectual terms, realizes that it may not be so meaningful to speak of a 'beginning' to time and a physical 'origin' to life – that even the fact that we are grappling with such conundrums is telling us that we have reached the edge of our intellect's capacity to understand things.

SOME COMMON OBJECTIONS TO EVOLUTIONARY THEORY

There is no doubt that living creatures have existed upon our planet which are not be found at the present time. We have fossils of the great dinosaurs, for example, and *millions* of other extinct species. Some palaeontologists suggest that of all the creatures which have existed on this planet, over 99 per cent are now extinct, and from the fossil evidence there is little reason to doubt it. The figure is probably closer to 100 per cent.

Moreover, when considering the species which presently exist, many of them date back no further than 10 million years in a fossil record spanning nearly 700 million years. Or 3.5 *billion* years if you count fossilized bacteria and the remains of ancient seaweeds.

So neither the extinction of species nor the advent of new ones is in dispute. Man's activity upon the planet has clearly shown that catastrophes and mass extinctions do occur: we are presently in the midst of a mass extinction, due to man's activities. But observations of extinction and renewal do not necessarily go hand in hand with a belief in a Darwinian kind of evolutionary process.

There are so many flaws, logical, observational and evidential, in Darwinian theory, that a number of books have appeared in recent years by adventurous scientists and independent thinkers. Some point to the mechanistic logic of Darwinism and its failure to embrace a holistic view of things. But many are written by creationists with as strong a dogma to promote as the avid evolutionist. And many of them stretch credulity, logic and evidence to the extreme of interpretation, especially when it comes to attempting to prove that the world began in 4004 BC.

There are, however, a number of arguments that are commonly put forward and some of these are sound. Indeed, many evolutionists agree that their theory is not without considerable difficulties. But what, they argue, is the alternative? The creationist/Genesis scenario hardly appeals to reason, nor even receives support from the fossil and geological record.

It is not my part to present these more well-known arguments in any detail and I would point any interested readers in the direction of

Michael Pitman's *Adam and Evolution* (1984) as well as Ian Taylor's *In The Minds of Men* (1984), both of which have many interesting things to say, though I do not always agree with their interpretations. And neither of them offer an alternative explanation of the fossil and geological data.

It is worth summarizing some of the more obvious objections to Darwinism. Firstly, the logic employed as proof of evolution is often circular, being based upon evolutionary theory as if it were proven fact. That is, fossil data is always interpreted to fit the theory. Such methodology tends to automatically preclude the recognition of 'anomalies'. Rock strata, for example, are often dated by the fossils found within them, while fossils are dated from the rock strata within which they are found. This becomes embarrassing when certain *index fossils* such as the now famous *coelacanth*, for instance, previously used for dating fossils to an age of at least 70 million years, turn up hale and hearty in fishermens' nets off the coast of Madagascar. Or when a thirty foot creature bearing a striking resemblance to a *pleisosaur* (a marine dinosaur) is photographed in fishermens' nets off the coast of Japan, and described by their on-board zoologist. The Japanese took the incident seriously enough to introduce a commemorative postage stamp, while the Western world largely ignored it, scientists and all.

Such findings should not be ignored, but previous scientific research based upon invalidated dating standards is never really updated properly afterwards. There is so much of it and everyone is interested in his own work, not in putting previous records straight. Old fallacies are thus perpetuated.

Even radioisotope dating techniques are based upon a number of assumptions that could be incorrect. It is assumed, for instance, that the rate of cosmic ray bombardment and atmospheric conditions have been stable for millions of years; that radioisotope ratios in rocks and living creatures are the same now as they were then; that the artefact has not been disturbed by the processes of fossilization; and that the rate of decay of radioactive isotopes has remained the same. There are just so many unknown factors that are impossible to account for when dating really ancient specimens.

It is purely an assumption that nature's constants are indeed constant over long periods of time. In a world where everything else moves in cycles, why should not the 'universal constants' also alter cyclically over vast spans of time? If we do not know how the laws of nature and mathematical values we consider to be constant actually come into being, how can we assume their utter constancy? The universe itself is supposed to be expanding, and perhaps will one day contract, though the evidence for both is inconclusive. But if we can countenance such strange ideas as the expansion and contraction of space, then surely a rhythmic change in the universal 'constants' should not be too hard to envisage? Or perhaps there is an ebb and flow in the subtlety and density of physical substance, itself resulting in a cyclic change of certain 'universal constants'.

If something along these lines turned out to be correct, then all our physical assumptions regarding astronomy, physics, geology, evolution and the like would be due for reassessment. But then, viewed from an historical perspective, this is indeed the pattern of change in man's ideas regarding himself and his environment.

But generally, I have no quarrel with radio-dating methods. It is pretty much all we have got to go on. And at least we are likely to have got the *relative* dates correct. Even if 100 million years ago turns out one day to be 50 million or 200 million years ago, at least *all* such dates would be shifted accordingly. So only the time *scale* would be altered, not the relationships of the data. But it is wise to be aware that there are many unknowns in science which are assumed for want of any better information.

These days, with our human race, especially in the West, centred on personal self-seeking and competition, Darwinism is interpreted by reflecting such psychology onto nature – the gene is considered selfish and organisms, competitive. But are we really supposed to believe that complex molecules originate the 'self' and behave 'selfishly'?

In Japan, on the other hand, there is a school of thought which emphasizes the co-operative nature of organisms in a Darwinist scheme of evolution. Creatures are seen to move into unoccupied niches as a co-operative use of resources. Clearly a reflection of the Japanese culture and social attitudes.

So we automatically see things through the screen of our own mind patterns, through the tinted colours of our own mental envelope, just as people, generally speaking, tend to 'believe' in the religion or social ideology in which they have been raised. Where then is the 'objective' view of reality?

The biological objections to Darwinism are equally sound. There are, for example, no missing links, alive or in the fossil record, between any of the major classes or even families of species. There are no bland, unspecialized creatures awaiting development. All biological and ecological systems are linked, integrated and complete. There are no species in the process of developing a new sense organ – say 5 per cent of a new kind of eye – or most of a complex biochemical cycle with only a few enzymes missing! These things do not exist. There is only a highly complex and *already complete* biological tapestry. Nothing in nature appears to be wasted.

There are also problems in the formation of the fossil data itself, for only certain creatures and certain locations are conducive to fossilization. The fossil record therefore presents only a distorted and very partial reflection of the ancient biosphere. Creatures with mineralized exoskeletons such as lobsters, crabs, trilobites and shellfish are more readily fossilized since these remains are inedible. Soft-bodied birds and mammals, or insects whose protective coat is made of purely organic materials, rarely leave any traces. Bones, organic material and soft tissues are good food for bacteria, fungi and many other hungry creatures and do not normally survive for very long. But there are few customers for shells and exoskeletons, so they more readily sink into the sediments, to be preserved as fossils.

For the preservation of soft-bodied creatures, conditions need to be just right. A catastrophe – local or planetary – is more or less essential to prevent the soft-bodied remains of dead creatures being immediately gobbled up by the hosts of other living organisms, each in search of dinner. Volcanic ash, scalding volcanic water, floods, mud-slides and quicksands – all these and more are represented in the fossil record, preserving messages from the past. But they are not everyday phenomena.

This is why many of the 'whole body' fossils and remains have been found in postures indicating sudden death: a perfectly preserved fossilized perch in the act of swallowing a herring; an *ichthyosaur* (marine animal) feeding her young and another in the process of giving birth; buttercup seeds in the stomachs of dead mammoths, not to mention the erect male organ, several feet long, of a mammoth who clearly had something other than disaster on his mind at the moment of his untimely demise and instant deep refrigeration! What a way to cool your ardour!

Whatever catastrophes befell these creatures, it was enough to kill them outright without destroying their body structure, whilst at the same time preserving them from destruction by environmental factors or other living creatures.

So the creatures living in those areas, at those times and with those bodily parts most suitable for fossilization have become the fossils we find today. But we cannot then extrapolate from these meagre remains to describe the entire flora and fauna of those times. Not all evolutionists appear to be aware of this somewhat obvious fact. Most evolutionary texts faithfully propound the gospel taught to the authors when they were at school or university, speaking almost as if only those creatures who left us their fossilized remains existed at that time. 'Trilobites were the dominant animals in Cambrian seas', declares one well-known text, 'Constituting 60 per cent of the known inhabitants of those seas.' Trilobites were arthropods, members of the same family as lobsters, spiders and insects and possessing a hard mineralized exoskeleton, ideal for preservation. Moreover, they shed their shells periodically as they grew, so each trilobite was able to leave several fossils of his (or her) existence. Those are the reasons why so many of their fossils have been discovered, not because there were more of them than any other species or because they were the 'dominant' species.

And I wonder what they all ate? Clearly they were not alone in those ancient seas! For the trilobites to have been so numerous – and some species of this large family grew to a length of two feet – the oceans must have teemed with other life.

So it is not surprising that apart from one unusually rich fossil site in the Burgess shale off British Columbia, shells and exoskeletons are practically the only remains of the Cambrian era, the trilobites' heyday – a period of about 65 million years. Nothing else survived. We do not even know the extent of the oceans and land masses of those times and where to look for other fossils, even supposing that some could have survived.

In recent years, these imperfections in the Darwinian approach have been acknowledged by many biologists, with the result that Stephen Gould and Niles Eldredge came up with a variation upon the Darwinian theme – the theory of *punctuated equilibria*. This theory effectively suggests that very little evolution actually occurs under normal conditions. It is based upon the evidence of the fossil record itself which indicates that the proliferation of species takes place in waves every several million years or so, after a preceding period of extinction, often extensive. But why this should be so remains a matter for speculation.

This is a considerable admission, for what is really being acknowledged is that there is no evidence in the fossil record for the continuous and gradual change of one species to another. As we have said, this lack of conclusive evidence has long been a weakness in Darwinian theory and would have sounded the death knell of the idea long ago, had there been any satisfactory alternative to account for the fossil data.

So Darwinian theory is riddled with imperfections both in its factual and theoretical basis. And interestingly, it is this very observation of punctuated equilibria which provides evidence for a rational and alternative point of view, as we will see in succeeding chapters.

But before we embark upon that adventure, let us first consider what it is that constitutes a 'species' or a creature, a topic introduced at some length in *Natural Creation and the Formative Mind*.

2. THE SUBTLE SIDE OF SPECIES

In *Natural Creation and the Formative Mind*, the role of the *tattwas* in forming the subtle species blueprint and in differentiating creature from creature was described in some detail. And though the subject is also discussed in chapter 8, let us briefly consider these inner energies that form the creatures of our planet.

The term 'tattwas' is Sanskrit and comes from the Indian yogic and mystic descriptions of the creation, where it is used in a number of different ways. As the term is used here, the tattwas are the five primary modes of subtle or mental energy. Arising first in the causal realm as the subtlest of mental essences, the tattwas decrease in subtlety of vibration as they descend, until we find them as the five states of gross physical matter: solid, liquid, fire, air and ether – the energy of vacuum or space.

A physical body – both its subtle and gross aspects – can be considered as a *tattvic configuration*, a projected image of an inner pattern. Species differ because their subtle tattvic configurations differ. But all creatures are made from allied patterns inside, and so all bear resemblances to each other in their outer form. The basic biochemistry of all species is clearly of the same essential nature, for example. Were this not so, creatures could not eat each other as food.

This subtle formative configuration is a microcosm that enables the creature to reach out into the macrocosm. Man is a complete microcosm: he has the potential to access all parts of the creation, inner and outer. Other subtle microcosms of other creatures are only partial in their constitution. They are thus specialists: they live and have their being only within a particular sphere. They are conscious or aware only of what their mind and body configuration permits them to understand and to perceive.

It is variations in these microcosmic configurations which constitute the intrinsic differences between higher and lower species, giving them greater or lesser intelligence. And only man, the highest of all, can rise above his human instincts in mystic transport. Other creatures cannot. Even their ability to learn about the things of this world is within the very fixed boundaries of their instinctive habits and behaviour patterns. The less complete the subtle microcosm, then the more instinctive is the creature.

To work in full consciousness in this world, we need a full and active complement, in our subtle make-up, of the tattwas which comprise it. We cannot be aware of or possess the ability to contact in the macrocosm that which we lack in our subtle vehicle, in our microcosm, in our reflected image, in our instrument panel. Consequently, the greater the number of active tattwas in a creature, then the higher the level of consciousness of the creature and the greater its intelligence.

Just as there are only three spatial dimensions, there are only five primary states of matter or energy at both subtle or gross levels. Species of the plant kingdom have only the water element active within them. Invertebrates possess fire and earth, fire and water or fire and air. Reptiles have fire and earth in their make-up, and fishes have fire and water. Birds have three active tattwas: fire, air and water, while mammals and higher animals are comprised of fire, air, water and earth in their active states.

Only man possesses the active tattwa of *akash* or ether. Akash is the primary tattwa from which the other four are derived. In the physical realm, akash is the space within which all else arises as patterns and rhythms. Hence, with this tattwa integrated into his inner make-up, man has the intelligence to do things in space and time denied to other creatures. If a man chooses only to express himself through animal instincts, then he has already charted such a destiny for himself in his next life. Mentally, he is already drawing closer to those forms and, on death, it is to the most appropriate one of them that he will automatically be attracted. The fluid and subtle mind then crystallizes as an appropriate outer form.

If he aspires to lead a 'good' life, to be a human being in the highest sense of the term, then he will be reborn as a human. The higher the aspiration for spiritual understanding, the better he becomes as a human in future lives. And the purer and clearer his mind becomes, then the more opportunity is given him to lead a spiritual life.

It is these primary tattvic divisions that have resulted in the major classes of creature found on earth. This is why there are not many more classes of creature, each merging imperceptibly into the other. It is the addition of the third active tattwa, for example, which underlies the jump from the cold-blooded reptiles and invertebrates to the warm-blooded and more intelligent birds. The incorporation of the fourth tattwa gives the higher mammals their still greater intelligence.

It is multiple variations in the configuration of these tattwas that result in the myriad outward forms we find both today and in the fossil record. And it is these subtle, tattvic configurations which constitute the fundamental species types which inhabit our planet. We can call these fundamental and subtle configurations, *super-species*.

Fluid in their subtle structure, pregnant – like the Mind of which they are a part – with flexibility and potential, the super-species are expressed outwardly in the many changing forms we find amongst living creatures and in the fossil record.

Many people, unfamiliar with this way of looking at things will no doubt find the idea of the tattwas unacceptable. However, it is neither whacky nor outdated. It is deeply coherent and satisfying, if one takes the time to understand it.

Man may have discovered more than a hundred chemical elements, but the nature of the physical universe remains the same. It is still comprised of solid, liquid and gaseous states, interpenetrated by the activity or energy of 'fire', and all contained within the envelope of space. There are only five primary conditions of matter, not one or two or six or seven. Why? How? There are only three spatial dimensions. Why and how? Is it a simple coincidence? Is it by design? Whatever it is, the whole of nature is comprised of such apparent – yet fortuitous – coincidences.

SUBTLE MICROCOSMS AND SUPER-SPECIES

Scientifically, we define a species according to the characteristics of its physical body. The mind and soul within are ignored. But from the mystical point of view, the soul is the source of life. This is the innermost essence, a drop of the Divine, and around the soul lie the multilevel, projected energies of the Mind, in ever-decreasing subtlety. Ultimately, it is these Mind energies which are crystallized and outwardly expressed as the physical body.

A soul is a soul. Life is life. And from the highest mystic point of view, all souls are the same. All are drops of the same Ocean. Whether the soul is encased in the body of a plant, a bacterium, an insect, a reptile, a bird, a mammal or a man, the essence of life is the same. This is why we feel an affinity towards all living creatures, because we are all of the same Source.

It is the mind and body surrounding the soul that vary. It is this that we perceive outwardly as different species, different bodies, different behaviour patterns and different instincts. In this scenario, then, how do new species come into existence?

It is clear from our discussion that the mystic understanding of a species will be different – though allied – to that of conventional science, for the mystic perception takes into account the pattern-forming dimension of Mind. Inwardly, one species is differentiated from another by the particular patterns or complex vibrations comprising the tapestry of its more subtle energies or tattwas. Scientifically, the characteristics of a species are thought to be entirely contained – in encoded form – in its DNA. The DNA is considered to be the primary genetic pattern of a species, though it is a pattern which can vary to some extent from member to member within a species and within certain limits. Esoterically, however, DNA is only a partial reflection of the dynamic, subtle energy configuration constituting the species. It is only a part of the means by which the inner patterns become the outwardly projected image on the screen. It is the greater Mind which is the primary pattern maker, the primary former of energy patterns and relationships, in this multilevel, multifaceted and wholly integrated dance of energy we call a mind and body. DNA is only one aspect of the way in which physical patterns are formed.

Every normal cell of a particular creature contains identical DNA. DNA is not only involved in the genetic transference of species-specific information, it is also the organizational centre, at a physical level, of all cell function. There are billions of cells in a human body and there are hundreds of thousands of integrated molecular and atomic inter-reactions per cell per second. DNA lies at the heart of this amazing and incessant activity. Exactly how it functions is still a matter of great mystery, but the fact that each cell contains the same DNA is no coincidence. It must be a part of the manner by which bodily processes are so beautifully integrated and organized. DNA is like a microcosm of the physical body. In some way, it functions as an image of the whole, providing coherence and 'intelligence' at a physical level.

Just as the Egg of Brahm, the Universal Mind, constitutes the whole of the Mind, just so is each individual creature like a shimmering egg of intricately-structured Mind energies, enlivened from within by the soul. It is a vibrant microcosm of being, where the relationships are closer than we could ever intellectually understand. DNA is only one vibration in this multilayered, multirelated patterning system. For not only are the patterning of mind and body parts of this inwardly dancing egg, but the apparently outward circumstances, the destiny or life events of the individual, are also woven into it.

The shell – the physical body – of one of these microcosmic eggs comes into being because of what is going on *within* that egg. If we do not know that the egg has an inside, then of course we are confused and come up with some amazingly bizarre ideas in our attempt to explain the nature of these intriguing 'shells'. Physical bodies, then, are the external shells or end results of a dynamic process of manifestation from within.

Now it is quite evident that adaptability to change is the key to survival over long periods of time. It is also clear that species can adapt or change, sometimes so considerably that at first sight two members of the same species may even be taken as individuals from different species. Look at the variations amongst dogs, for example. Man also has the potential to be black or white, tall or short, and so on. (Dark skin pigmentation is a useful adaptation to living in areas of strong sunlight, while pale skin is helpful in areas of reduced sunlight.)

It seems possible, therefore, that the subtle energy pattern which underlies a species contains far more than its actually manifested expressions at any particular point in time. We have called this subtle microcosm a super-species. It may be expressed as variants within what are scientifically defined as one species, such as the variations in dogs, or as the spread of variants that are present in all species populations. But it will also be the underlying subtle form common to all closely related species. And over the span of geological time, this same super-species will be expressed as different and outwardly changing species in the fossil record.

Thus, to take an example (see Figure 2.1), the super-species which is presently expressed physically as the two extant species of elephant (Asian and African) may actually include all the recently extinct forms of elephant – the mammoth, the mastodon and so on. Within the super-species lies the potential to be woolly during an ice age (i.e. a mammoth or mastodon) and bare-skinned when living in the tropics.

And throughout the course of the fossil record this same super-species will have been manifested in many different outward forms. But the common link between them is that they are all expressions of the same super-species. The super-species is therefore an arch-chameleon, having the potential to manifest physical forms that are totally at one with their environment, totally at home in their niche in the planetary ecosystem, totally a part of their time and place.

Now a super-species is made up of a particular configuration of subtle mind energies. Consequently, all the expressions or

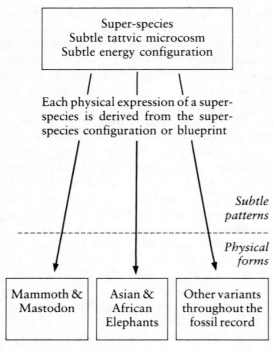

Nature is comprised of creatures at a multitude of different levels and expressions of consciousness. Physical bodies are the outward expressions of subtle or mental energies, while species are the expression of particular configurations of these energies. We may call these configurations the super species.

Each physical expression of a super-species is derived from the super-species configuration or blueprint

Subtle patterns

Physical forms

The gross physical expressions of a super-species may not always be so apparently similar as the forms of an elephant. Going back in time they may become increasingly difficult to recognize as expressions of the same super-species. What provides the continuity is the inner mental character and the niche they occupy in nature.

| Mammoth & Mastodon | Asian & African Elephants | Other variants throughout the fossil record |

There may be more than one representation of a super-species at any time, e.g. Asian and African elephants, divergent island sub-species, and so on.

A species as it appears at any one point in time is only one possible expression of the super-species.

Environmental conditions in both the subtle and the gross physical world, integrated within the total balance of nature, result in the outward expression(s) of a super-species at any point in time. Environment, mind energy patterns and physical form are interwoven aspects of Formative Mind function and expression. The super-species are aspects of the Formative Mind energy projection system.

Figure 2.1   The nature of a super-species.

manifestations of a particular super-species will possess fundamentally the same mental characteristics, the same kind of instincts and pretty much the same way of being. And they will occupy essentially the same niche in the natural economy whether now, 200 million years ago or 200 million years into the future. In a sense, the outward form is not so very important – that will be a reflection of the times and external circumstances. What really constitutes the creature is its configuration of subtle mental energies.

It is obvious that the super-species blueprint and its particular expressions as individual species are also closely linked to DNA function, which we discuss in Chapter 7. But it should be noted here that DNA function is so sketchily understood that 95 per cent of the DNA appears to many geneticists to perform 'no useful function'. This means that there is a lot going on within the DNA that we do not understand and that the relationship of DNA to the subtle super-species blueprint is a deeply intriguing one.

Please note that I am not advocating a religious doctrine of immutability or permanence of super-species, even at the subtle level. To suggest the existence of the super-species is enough of a hypothesis! In some way or other, however, the spectrum of super-species does represent a complete economy of all possible expressions of consciousness.

But just as DNA has built-in species integrity and resistance to change, if the more encompassing super-species operated under similar constraints, this would neatly explain why selective breeding and microevolution never result in radical changes. The species always retains its fundamental character.

There is always a resistance to change in nature. Old habits – physical or mental – die hard. So, as the fossil evidence indicates, it would not be possible for species to move from class to class – from reptiles to birds, for example. Nor does it even seem likely that rabbits, squirrels and mice all had a common rodent ancestor. So there is something akin to species integrity even at the subtle level.

Nature is remarkably specific in its breeding and fertility. Although there is some degree of fertility between interrelated species, the progeny of such liaisons are usually infertile or cannot be in-bred. Even if the progeny is fertile, the union does not occur under normal circumstances, but is induced by man. There is an inherent *behavioural* (i.e. mental) aspect which maintains differentiation between all closely related species.

As breeders of any species will tell you, all species, when left to themselves, have an inherent tendency to revert to the 'wild type' within a few generations. Arthur Koestler related that even the fruit fly, *drosophila*, favourite of genetic researchers, when bred into an eyeless strain, reverted to a normal-eyed type within a few generations, even when the eyeless strain is in-bred. Or feral pigs once again develop tusks, their hides become more bristly and their youngsters once again exhibit the coloured stripes of their wild cousins.

It is as if there is a constraining, spring-loaded mould upon a species which automatically reshuffles the DNA until the more natural type re-emerges – the 'natural' type being the most harmonious expression of the subtle species pattern relative to the environmental circumstances of the day.

The genetic system itself seems to have very specific, built-in biochemical safeguards to protect the species integrity of the DNA. It seems as if it is almost a 'law of nature' that changes in the DNA do not normally progress beyond recognizable 'species boundaries'. I imagine that these 'species boundaries' are subsets within the total potential of the super-species, representing the particular expression as defined by the DNA content at that time. But, as we said, DNA function is hardly understood, despite the advances of genetic engineering and molecular biology. The science, I believe, is only in its infancy.

Incidentally, when one considers that evolutionists suggest that eyes developed through a multitude of partially-sighted mutants, on a multitude of separate occasions, it is indeed surprising that the reversion in fruit-flies to an eyed form is so *instant*. When the reversion appears it does so in one generation, there are no semi-eyed intermediates, even though the possession of eyes and all the associated neurological, biochemical and brain functions are clearly mediated by multiple changes to the DNA. Even though the expression of eyes may be bred out, the potential for eyes still exists, either in the DNA or in the subtle super-species blueprint from which the DNA is derived. Or both.

In fact, as we will see, DNA has the ability to 'turn on and off' large areas of itself. But what turns these keys is not understood. Perhaps it is here that the subtle side of things can be seen in operation.

MICROEVOLUTION

The potential for change within a species, is known to evolutionists as *microevolution*, a process which can actually be observed in nature. The divergence of island species, over geological time spans, into a number of very similar species is a good example, or the slow change of one species over the course of time into larger or smaller variants. On a shorter time-scale, bacteria becoming resistant to certain antibiotics, or flies to DDT, are further examples of a similar natural process in operation.

Note, however, that from physical observation alone one cannot tell whether the driving force behind such changes is natural selection of random mutations – as decreed by conventional theory – or an ordered, determined and natural response of the creature to a changing environment. But even in microevolution and small-scale adaptive flexibility to the environment, we cannot ignore the part played by the formative processes of the greater Mind. For the underlying super-species is comprised of Mind energies.

At a physical level, one can say that DNA provides a potential whereby some adaptation to environmental conditions is possible. It also permits all members of a species to be at least marginally different from each other, from a physical point of view. This provides useful tone and flexibility to the system.

But while horses have increased in size over the last 55 million years, also changing their feet from toes to hooves, and variations on the spider theme have existed for over 300 million years, there is no evidence at all of horses becoming cows, or spiders changing into scorpions, or any similar changes. Even the ultra-fast-breeding bacteria do not become other radically different species in order to escape adverse environmental conditions. They simply adapt, whilst retaining their identity as a species.

This is one of the major areas where the fossil evidence that Darwin hoped would be discovered has never been found. Despite a rigorous, extensive and continuous search, all such 'missing links' in the fossil record have remained missing. There exists no evidence whatsoever for the evolution of all species from one or a few ancestors. Nor is there any suggestion that the older forms of a species were more primitive or less well adapted than their modern equivalents. Times have changed and so have the creatures, that is all. Each creature appears to have been a perfect reflection of its time and place.

ECOLOGICAL NICHES AND THE NATURAL ECONOMY

Adaptation of species to particular ecological niches is another observable aspect of species differentiation, for each species exists by virtue of its ability to play a particular role within the natural economy. Each such niche or space is, in a sense, a complex subtle vibration which is matched by the mental vibrational character of the creature.

In human sociological terms, to take an example, this is like the *need* for a person with a certain personality and skills being fulfilled by the apparently fortuitous *appearance* of the right individual. The niche is essentially of a subtle and mental nature, a pattern and 'space' in the Formative Mind, and it is 'filled' through resonance and unconscious matching at a subtle level. The right individual then appears upon the scene, at the right time. We observe the outer effects while the subtle causes remain hidden.

When an environment changes suddenly, so too does the nature of these niches. Under these circumstances, the speed of adaptation is accelerated as the species automatically adapt themselves both inwardly and outwardly to match the new conditions. Those that cannot adapt go into decline and may ultimately become extinct. But the underlying super-species never becomes extinct because it is a pattern or even a principle in nature.

In other words, when there is a gap or a space or a change within the subtle realm, the niche may automatically be filled out of the pool of already existing species. Microevolution is hence automatically accelerated at such times, just like water filling the space behind you when you get out of a bath. But the fossil record also indicates that even microevolution proceeds in fits and starts. Really, it is the Gaia principle at work – the inherent balance in nature in which all things are integrated into one whole.

And we must also remember that outward circumstances are not coincidental to the existence or forms of creatures. Within the greater integrated complex of the Formative Mind, they are part of one energy system. It is not correct, therefore, simply to think of creatures struggling to adapt to changing environments, as if the creature and environment were totally separate in the manner by which they come into being. The 'environment' is actually formed under the combined influence of all its creatures through the power of the greater Mind. We do not outwardly perceive this process in operation, but we get intimations of it when we become aware of how fittingly things are arranged and put together. The hidden, inward mind of a creature, human or otherwise, fits its body and its destiny like a hand in a glove.

Thus, in our previous example, both the job or niche and the person arise simultaneously and are automatically drawn together as a part of the integrated way in which the greater Mind functions and the way we all jointly create our own physical reality. If we looked only at the physical structure and appearance of the individual, we would miss the deeper reasons of why and how he was fulfilling that particular role. It would seem almost coincidental.

Similarly, a species fills a niche in nature according to its subtle nature – its mental attributes – which manifest outwardly as its body. And both the niche and the species filling that niche arise together out of nature's deeper and hidden integrated processes.

From a higher point of view, one can look on nature entirely as the dynamic manifestation or creation of God. God is the Supreme Being, the Supreme Consciousness or the Supreme Life Force. He lies at the heart of every living being as the Source of Life. Mystics say that He has created His creation in order to express Himself, in order to experience Himself. Since He is also the Supreme Ocean of Love, His creation is also His way of playing the game of Love with Himself.

What we call the natural economy of creatures is actually a complete spectrum of all the potential ways in which this great Life Force or Consciousness can be expressed. 'Nature' is thus a reflection of a more subtle complex higher up in the Mind regions. For consciousness is always one and the same, while it is the Mind which creates the patterns and constraints, producing the various configurations or modified conditions of consciousness which we observe with our physical senses as physical creatures.

Essentially, what is being said is that nature is one whole. At the physical level, we see her as the planetary ecosystem. At the level of the super-species, we see her as a dancing integration of subtle mental configurations, varied microcosms for the Life Force, providing the potential for all levels, qualities and experiences of consciousness or life, and acting as the blueprint for the associated physical forms. Moving higher up within the Mind regions, we find the seed or pattern form for the whole of nature. And beyond the Mind we ultimately find the pure oneness of God.

The different perceptions result from viewing the creation from different levels. It is a question of one's own level of consciousness. And note that even at the physical level, if one's own mind is deeply divided, disharmonious and entirely given over to analysis, then nature is not even intuitively perceived as a whole, but as a lot of little pathways and pieces. In fact, the mechanistic view of the creation is entirely predicted by the suggestions I am putting forward! It is one of the potential levels of consciousness and is meant to be that way.

LIFE, MIND AND ECOSYSTEMS

Perceived physically, each creature occupies a niche in the planetary ecosystem. It has a way of making a living and it also fulfils an important role in nature. We can define the niche according to what the creature does – according to its acts and behaviour, what it eats, where it lives and so on. We may describe it as a ground-dwelling forest carnivore or a large-size, grazing herbivore of the open plains – or whatever it may be. We can take each creature, great or small, and analyse its interactions, dependencies and contributions to the creatures amongst whom it lives.

We can also see how each species modifies the environment according to its own needs. At the simplest level, even building a home and leaving territorial markers is reshaping an environment for personal ends. But all creatures act together. The forest plants and trees trap energy from the sun, shade the soil and hold it together, keeping it moist and friable. They drop their leaves around them and, by the agency of moulds, bacteria, worms and a host of tiny creatures, the quality of the soil is maintained, and the cycle is continued. Many creatures live in the forest, each doing its own thing. As a creature it lives for itself, but in the wider economy of things it is performing an essential function so that all creatures can continue to exist.

Similarly, the ocean species keep the level of marine minerals in a state of perfect balance, helping to recycle them back onto the land in cycles varying from the instant moment (by way of iodine-rich gases, for example, produced by some seaweeds) to millions of years (in the sediments that accumulate upon the ocean floors, becoming rocks in eras yet to come).

Ecosystems have both local and planetary aspects. My garden is a local habitat where many species live in concert. But without the oceans, the mountains, the rivers and the forests, and all the creatures living in them, there would be no garden. The planet acts as a whole to keep the atmosphere, the temperature and much else in a delicate and dynamic equilibrium, fit for the continued presence of life.

An individual creature may think that it is acting in a personal way, looking after its own needs, but all creatures act together as fellow members of an orchestra, each playing its own instrument, creating what we call a physical ecosystem. And globally, all creatures are combined, creating one planetary ecosystem.

There is wonder in this view of things, yet our observations of the physical only scratch the surface of what is really going on. Lying behind the acts of every creature is its mind. Without the mind, creatures do not act. It is the integration of their minds which is outwardly expressed as the physical ecosystem. An ecosystem exists at the level of the mind before it is expressed physically. It is the joint expression of all the minds of all the creatures. Although the minds may be concealed in forms, it is at the mind level that an ecosystem is first manifest.

But the Mind itself is not the highest level of reality. Mind is only the creator of pattern and rhythm in space and time. The highest reality is the Supreme Being, the Universal Consciousness, the Source and Wellspring of Life. The creation is the manifested Will of this Supreme Lord to express Himself. The Mind is His henchman, His administrator, the one who divides the Oneness of the Supreme Life into myriad ways in which that Life can be experienced. These myriad ways are the myriad species – the myriad levels and expressions of Life or Consciousness or Self. But Oneness lies within it all and thus the myriad forms that Life takes on are all intermeshed and integrated.

Looked at physically, we call this creation a physical ecosystem, and wonder at its balance and integration. Looked at mentally, we see how all expressions of the Mind are melded into one complete system in which every mental tendency and instinct is an essential aspect of the whole. Looked at spiritually, we see how all that oneness arises and why there should be such a multiplicity of life forms.

MORPHIC FIELDS, SUBTLE BLUEPRINTS AND THE FORMATIVE MIND

What we may see as an evolutionary response of creature to environment is actually only a shift of emphasis or a simultaneous modification of patterns at many 'levels' within the Formative Mind, just as the changing image on a screen is due to changes within the image in the projector.

The DNA, being a part of this energy matrix, naturally responds with the necessary 'mutations', but such 'mutations' are quite deterministically ordered, according to the nature of changes within the subtle blueprinting processes of the Formative Mind. In a very real sense, therefore, one can say that changes to the DNA are triggered by mind energy. The process at work is not one of random mutations and natural selection. It is a process of response and change within the integrated spectrum of mental and physical energies.

The many 'morphic fields' of Rupert Sheldrake are also to be found in these interconnected and multilevel fields of mind energy. He suggests that what we have usually termed innate behaviour or instinct is actually learnt, over periods spanning generations, and is encoded automatically into the morphic fields associated with that species. Behavioural patterns as well as outward forms are thus built up over the millennia as 'habits' or 'memories' within the inner structuring of the morphic fields, or – I would say – within the greater Mind. Habits are simply patterns of subtle mental energy, established by repetition.

Just as individual mind has its memory of past events, so too does the greater Mind have its memory. The former is a reflection of the latter. Habits are simply memories that have been played back over and over again until they pop out automatically, with little or no triggering.

This process neatly explains, for example, how bluetits from different geographical areas all learnt how to remove aluminium foil milk bottle tops very rapidly after the initial discovery had been made in only one particular area. It also explains how the memory was retained even after all the individuals who would have remembered the technique had died. For during the Second World War, the aluminium foil was replaced by an alternative. Yet after the war, when foil caps were reintroduced and long after the last of the original bluetits in the know would have died, the habit was rapidly resumed.

It is a similar process which underlies the way in which new ideas, social or scientific, are generated almost simultaneously though 'isolated' from each other in different parts of the world. It is an essential part of the integration of nature at all levels. It is a part of the outworking of the Formative Mind, for all individual minds are drops in the ocean of Universal Mind, just as all souls are drops in the Ocean of God. A wave will break in many places independently. If one cannot see the wave, this seems like a coincidence. But when one can see the whole wave, it is predictable.

Everything is connected, within, to make up one mystic whole. Yet conventional neo-Darwinists, looking only at the material level of energy, and believing entirely in chance mutations of DNA as the source of adaptation, find such a viewpoint heretical.

From a conventional, materialistic point of view, the retained memory of bluetits is impossible to explain, for how can *learnt* behaviour or *acquired* characteristics be *genetically* transmitted through the DNA? For this reason, the Lamarckian theory of evolution, which believes that characteristics *acquired* by the parents during the course of their lives can then be *transmitted* to their offspring, is considered incorrect by modern evolutionists. This is because acquired physical characteristics (eg. a sun-tan) are not observably transmitted to offspring, and because the genetic mode of organism formation is held to be the only means by which characteristics can be transmitted.

But in fact, both Darwinian and Lamarckian explanations lack the fundamental insights concerning the nature of life, consciousness and the greater, formative nature and manifestational dimension of Mind.

DNA is only one aspect of the total energy complex comprising a living creature, as we have discussed. It does not demonstrate the ability to generate form all by itself. Rather, the form of DNA is itself a reflection of patterns within the subtle blueprint. After all, something has to pattern the DNA!

An understanding of this permits us to see that both genetic and acquired means of inheritance are only aspects of change in the subtle patterning. They are brought about by activity with the total, multilevel 'environment' of the Formative Mind. In other words, when an environment changes, living creatures possess formative processes which enable them to adapt with it as one whole entity. For the formative patterns of both creatures and inert substance are blended, as it were, at the subtle level, where energy relationships are more integral and instantaneous, transcending the spatial barriers of the gross physical domain. It is the exact nature and relationship of these subtle formative processes which will probably occupy the attention of breeders and geneticists of the next century.

The precision of this subtle activity is, however, quite as exact as any process of this world. Its sparkling clarity and immediate response to change is a built-in part of the integrated design underlying the physical world. Everything happens exactly within the one whole egg of the greater Mind.

When one gets a graphic, mental image of the multilevel, integrated nature of total Mind function, then one also realizes that the distinction between 'inherited' and 'acquired' characteristics is not so rigid as was once thought. For *neither is a fundamental process*; both are only outward aspects or effects of more inward patterning.

Thus the subtle atmosphere of an environment as well as the gross physical environment itself, are totally at one with the nature and quality of the life forms found therein. For it is the 'karmas' of the life forms which create their own 'environment', because the so-called outer environment is actually a subjective experience for each living creature. Even the outer world is an aspect of the Formative Mind; it is a world of the Mind.

So, for example, in China we find that the intricate, natural sculpting of trees and landscape, the unique character of Chinese family and social relationships, the nature of their philosophical and artistic expression – all these and more are imprinted with a similarity of pattern, a constant integrating theme running throughout, however varied the outward appearances may seem. It is like a lady whose individual outfits are all different and suitable for different occasions, yet all bear the integrating stamp of her individual personality and mind.

This same process is present in all things, whether within the life of an individual or a household, the characteristics of an area or of a nation, or the composite 'mood' prevalent at any time upon our planet earth. As this 'mood' – local or global – changes, then everything changes. It is all one vibrating and whirling dance. It is just one process, ebbing and flowing, pulsating from within with rhythm and form – modulations of time, space and energy.

IS EVOLUTION PSYCHOSOMATIC?

One can approach the matter from a simpler and less metaphysical point of view. Most people acknowledge that many aspects of health and illness are psychosomatic. This to say that bodily conditions are influenced by mental and emotional factors. In my previous books, I have devoted many pages to pointing out that contrary to common attitudes, the energy of the mind really exists as a powerful force and that to discount something as 'merely psychosomatic' is to miss the point entirely.

In fact, it is not just heart disease, digestion, asthma and other ailments which have psychosomatic aspects. All bodily functions, from waggling a finger to the complexities of cellular biochemistry, involve the interaction of mental and physical energies. This being the case, then why should not the genetic material presented by the reproductive organs for the next generation be influenced by mental factors? That is, 'Is "evolution" psychosomatic?'

Though we will return in a later chapter to a discussion of genetic processes, let it be said here that if mind energies can be so fundamentally involved with biochemical and neurological activity, then there can be little doubt that they will affect the male and female germ cells presented by the parents of any species for the next generation. Mind, however, is both influenced by the environment and, in a wider context, is also a part of the process by which the 'environment' comes into existence. One can see, therefore, how present circumstances, since they both arise from as well as influence the mind, can be expected to influence any 'mutations' or changes in the DNA. In this sense, therefore, I am suggesting that evolution – or rather, change – amongst the species is psychosomatic.

This, of course, is the essence of this book – the involvement of Mind factors in the continuous changing of the species – and we will be continually circling around this theme.

SPECIES, KARMA AND REINCARNATION

The real essence of life within all creatures is the soul or consciousness. Surrounded by accumulated mind patterns, the soul is then projected forward into physical body after physical body, according to the tendencies of and attractions of the mind. This is the law of karma, according to which both the physical body and its individual destiny are apportioned automatically, according to past actions and thoughts, the seeds of which are impressed upon the mind in previous lives. The constraints placed upon a soul when born into this world are thus entirely of its own making, a direct reflection and 'reward' or 'punishment' for past deeds and desires.

Bodies only exist on this plane by virtue of the karmas of the souls inhabiting them. Everything is created and patterned from within and apparently outward processes are only responses to these multifaceted karmic demands. Everything in the physical universe is simply the outworking of this great law of cause and effect, while the real life and motive power come from within.

The details of these inner processes are hidden from us. They are a part of the outworking of the multilevel Mind which, as we have seen, includes our individual mind, our physical body, the physical plane and all the events of a lifetime.

Because the soul is the same whatever the body in which it takes birth, the real evolution is of that soul progressing through birth and death – reincarnation and transmigration – from species to species, until it comes to man. There for the first time it has the potential for God-realization. But, by karmic law, 'progression' can be downwards as well as upward.

Within this multilevel arrangement there are numerous ways in which mental characteristics and energies are actually manifested physically. Genetic inheritance is only one of many. No-one suggests, for example, that we genetically inherit the events which come to us during the course of a lifetime. Yet it is obvious that such events are determined to a large extent by our mental characteristics – by our personality, talents and so on. We automatically do that which our mind is interested in doing.

Do evolutionists, then, consider that psychological characteristics are genetically inherited? Mostly, they do not, for it does not accord with observation. Every parent, for example, will tell you that their child demonstrated at a very early age the essential personality which continued throughout their life, which may be very different from that of their parents. So our basic mental qualities are something with which we are born. Yet they are not inherited from our parents.

The materialist must attempt to explain such fundamental observations if his theory of 'all is molecules' is to deserve any credence. He must proffer some solution as to how our minds and their personalized characteristics arise.

Actually, they arise from the mental impressions of past lives. But by dismissing any understanding of reincarnation as unscientific, conventional science has no satisfying answer as to the origins of mental characteristics. It is, of course, acknowledged by scientists that the linkage between the daily experience of mind and brain is not at all understood. But without an understanding of inner mind patterns, consisting of dynamically active, inner and subtle fields of energy, this is not surprising!

Amongst chimpanzees too, indeed amongst all the creatures I have ever come to know, personalities become clearly discernible right from birth. And as with human beings, these personalities are not genetically related to their parents.

Chimpanzees play, laugh, display, cower and use a wealth of facial gesturing and body language. In association with man, some prove boisterous, clumsy or extrovert, whilst others are tidy or introvert. Some will soon break things, discarding the old and the broken, whilst others will use things carefully, stacking up cups or items not in use, even trying to put broken items back together again. Such differences of personality are also evident in the wild.

Mozart did not genetically inherit the ability to play the piano at the age of four. Child prodigies do not inherit their mathematical or sporting genius. No-one inherits his own psychology and capabilities. Bluetits do not genetically inherit the ability to remove milk bottle caps.

Our thoughts, talents and emotions are not to be found within the physical matter of our brain cells, any more than the web-making instincts of spiders, the nest-building capabilities of birds, the song of a robin or even man's comprehension of language can be found in any processes of the genetic or central nervous systems. All these are part of the mind and its expression as the subtle energy blueprint of the creature. Each organism is an individual, with its own individual history of past lives and experience. And this experience is carried forward in a general way, from birth to birth.

So many confusions and enigmas are resolved when one understands that each soul carries its own personal memories with it from past lives, whether human or otherwise. The particular incidents and personal aspects are forgotten, but the general impressions on the mind remain.

In laboratories, researchers breed generation after generation of rats and other creatures. Each one is thought to be a brand new individual. But then researchers report that successive generations learn to run a maze faster than their predecessors. Or they find that different rats in a laboratory elsewhere pick up where the previous and geographically unconnected experiments in rat learning had left off.

Physically, there appears to be no link, but mentally there is. It is so easy to overlook the dimension of the Mind, the power that moves the souls from body to body. It may well be that the same souls are returning again and again into the same associations and circumstances. 'Old hands' at the game are being reborn, carrying their talents with them in their own personal mind. So it does not take them long to renew their familiarity with the game. Maybe this is how bluetits remembered how to lift the metal foil caps off milk bottles after the war years were over.

Again, just as we humans – consciously or unconsciously – telepathically transmit our thoughts to each other 'on the ether', similarly the subtle fields of energy are patterned by other creatures. And these patterns are then picked up by fellow members of that same species, for their minds are akin to each other. They are all tuned in to the same 'frequency'. Memories and behavioural patterns can then be transmitted across otherwise insuperable geographical boundaries and between generations. They may even remain in the subtle energy fields in the absence of any access by the living species of that time.

All this subtle mind activity is a part of the 'mood of the times', a subtle field of energy patterned by the minds of all living creatures, integrated in its formative substratum and manifesting to us as our physical reality. We not only copy others in both thought and outward fashion, but we are all riding the same communal and subtle wave, all immersed in the same formative sea, all linked unconsciously at a level deep within our own minds. This is how new styles of clothing or fashions of music or facets of social behaviour all emerge independently at the same time in separate regions of the world.

Furthermore, because the creative, akashic levels of energy retain a memory, a pattern or vibration of all that has gone before, so may we and other souls draw unconsciously upon the past. This phenomenon is well known to breeders, where the sudden re-emergence of an old pattern – often the wild type – is referred to in genetic terms as a *throw back*, a *reversion* or an *atavism*.

Materially minded evolutionists insist that such memory from the past must be encoded genetically, since they refuse to believe in anything not perceivable by the five physical senses. But in the wider mystical perception and drawing upon our understanding of the ontological dimension of Mind, we find that genetic processes are only one facet of what makes a creature what it is. Such old patterns may be locked away in the DNA as well. So little is really understood of DNA function that almost anything is possible. But DNA is not the only place where old memories can be lodged.

It seems to be only a matter of common sense that such spontaneous or rapid reversion from a form which took so many generations of highly selective breeding to produce, cannot be a matter of 'chance mutation'. The 'wild' form must still be hidden within the creature – either in its subtle blueprint or in its genetic coding or both. Perhaps it is only fed through into the DNA from the subtle patterning as the reversion occurs. But it is clear that somewhere in the system lies a blueprint, more subtle than the DNA.

Acquired or learnt characteristics could therefore be transmitted within a more general field of mental energies outside that of the individual mind, as well as being conveyed from birth to birth within the mind of the individual.

But how the mind energies function, how its subtle energies pattern, organize and manifest the physical bodies of the individual species, the actual role played by DNA – these and many other details remain a mystery yet to be unravelled. Perhaps they are beyond the limited capacity of our human mind and intellect. It is certain, however, that the fullest comprehension can only come by mystic experience, by which time interest in physical processes will have declined in favour of a far higher pull.

ARE THE DINOSAURS STILL WITH US?

Breeders recognize that there are two kinds of variation that occur within a species. Firstly, there are the minute changes which, when added up from generation to generation, constitute a large change. The shape of a dog's ears or the size of carrots, for example. The original wild carrot is thin, tough and fibrous in comparison to today's offerings in the vegetable market. The size and texture of the domestic carrot has been achieved, it is assumed, by a long and selective breeding procedure. Similarly with the characteristics of dogs.

Secondly, there are instances, like reversions or sports, when a species spontaneously appears in a form which, were only random mutations involved, would have required a major reshuffling of multiple elements within the DNA, not just one random mutation. That such multiple changes would all occur together in integral synchrony and by chance is unlikely. The process seems more like a fundamental change of state. Some hidden key is turned, an automatic reshuffling occurs and a previously hidden pattern emerges – or re-emerges.

The question therefore arises: what causes these changes to the DNA? Can any of these changes – major or minor – be induced by radically modifying the environment in which the parents are breeding? Can genetic processes respond intelligently to the environment? In the early 1950s, the biologist C. M. Waddington performed some experiments upon the ill-fated fruit fly, *drosophila*, which indicated that they might. The fruit fly is used extensively for genetic experimentation because it breeds rapidly and freely, and because its DNA has been well studied.

In one series of experiments, Waddington heated young pupae to a temperature of 40°C for a period of four hours. It is within the pupa that the amazing metamorphosis takes place in insects as they change from larval into adult form. Waddington found that some of the emerging flies possessed abnormal wings in which cross-veins were absent.

In a similar experiment, eggs were exposed to ether fumes for twenty-five minutes, about three hours after being laid. Fruit flies normally have one pair of wings located on their second thoracic segment. But after exposure to ether, some of the subsequent flies, emerging after passing through their usual larval and pupal stages, were of a four-winged variant in which the third thoracic segment, normally wingless, was a duplicate of the second, complete with wings.

Note that in both cases, it is the *environmental stress* of temperature or ether which causes modification to the resultant form. There could have been no mutation of the original DNA, for the eggs and therefore the DNA were already determined when the stress was applied. Now the modification of later form due to environmental factors at an earlier stage is not unknown in nature. It is observed in the natural and seasonal variants of certain tropical butterflies, for example, where it is the weather conditions during pupation which determine the emergent form. In these circumstances, the environmentally induced variations are considered normal.

That, in itself, is interesting, but watch what happened next. Waddington selected the abnormal flies as parents for the next generation, subjecting them to the same stress factors as before. The offspring were again selected in favour of the same abnormalities and breeding continued in this selective fashion. He found that in each successive generation, a greater and greater proportion of flies were of the abnormal type. In fact, after a relatively small number of generations, as little as eight in one instance, the abnormal parents gave rise to abnormal progeny, *in the absence of the environmental stimulus.*

That is to say that characteristics ACQUIRED by adults due to environmental conditions were then TRANSMITTED, genetically, to the offspring.

Either the DNA transmitted from one generation to the next has changed by responding to environmental stress through a process other than natural selection of randomly mutated features. Or overall form is not found entirely in the DNA, but lies in some other blueprint. Or both.

Do fruit flies, then, contain within them the potential for a four-winged variant, one which is not normally expressed at the present time? It is not recorded whether the variant was fully functional as a four-winged flyer, but then Waddington was not replicating normal changes to the environment. It would be interesting, however, to know whether being four-winged would be of value to the fruit fly under certain environmental circumstances. Would it enable it to fly faster to escape certain predators, for example, or to be a more efficient flyer in wet or hot weather?

Since, geologically, conditions on earth have been known to change dramatically and will no doubt continue to do so in the future, could we assume that fruit flies possess the latent ability to appear in either form, depending upon environmental circumstances, just like seasonal variations in butterflies? And, most importantly, that if those circumstances persist, then these adaptations are actually built into the genetic code so that their progeny are automatically adapted to the altered environment?

Observing how supremely well adapted and organized creatures are to their environment, it seems so much more reasonable to suppose that their genetic processes are also organized for intelligent adaptation rather than relying upon chance in this one, yet so important, area of their existence. Is this how bacteria can so rapidly develop an immunity to antibiotics, for instance? Not by a lucky chance mutation but by a coherent process? We will see later that there is strong evidence for this.

We have said that, in the mystic scheme of things, the physical universe and all its forms are patterned from more subtle inner blueprints. That DNA is not the primary pattern-maker. That whatever we may observe in the DNA is a reflection of what lies in the more subtle sphere. Do all species, then, possess in their subtle morphogenic fields the potential to be far more than we presently observe in them, a capacity for metamorphosis even greater than those life cycles which are already such a marvel to us?

And do the subtle blueprints or the DNA – or both – retain a memory of all that has transpired before? Are potential dinosaurs or other creatures of the remote past still lurking in our modern species, in the outward forms more resonant with our modern times? Are ancient forms still hidden in some of the reptiles, birds or even mammals of today? Is there any evidence for this?

What is it, after all, which makes the vibrational atmosphere of one's time and place? It is an aspect of our minds, all linked in some deeply formative substratum. What is it then which changes as time goes by? Again, it is our minds and the greater Mind. And since the body is an integral part of the outworking of this Mind, I am suggesting that the body automatically follows suit. But are the forms of the past still remembered in the subtle energies of the Mind? Are old expressions still held as memories within the super-species complex? Are they even lying dormant in the DNA? A racial memory no-one could ever have imagined?

For part of an answer to this intriguing possibility we can turn again to the phenomenon of reversion, atavism or sports. Here, for example, we very occasionally encounter wings on normally flightless insects, vestigial toes on horses, tiny rear legs on whales and two or three inch 'tails' on baby humans. One can even persuade the embryonic tooth tissue of unhatched chicks to grow tooth buds if suitably transplanted to another area of their body. No modern bird possesses teeth, but some of those who lived in the time of the dinosaurs certainly did. And 50 million years ago, horses – then no bigger than a dog – had toes.

Surely this must mean that, whether in the DNA or in the subtle patterns, change has a memory, suggesting underlying processes far wider than those permitted by the theories of random mutation and solely DNA-based genetic inheritance. For reversion requires changes to an amazing complexity of biological processes, beyond the 'control' of just one 'gene'. Even if DNA is involved, turning inner keys and switching on areas of itself that have lain dormant for millions of years, does this not suggest that something more than a random process is at work?

If the system were purely mechanistic, why should there be a memory? How could a random evolutionary process have discovered that it is sometimes useful not to throw things out? That they might just come in handy once again even if in modified form? Whether this is the reason why old forms are remembered is unsure, but from a higher point of view, memory is an aspect of consciousness and experience. There is no point in experience if it is immediately forgotten and discarded. But in a totally mechanistic scenario, such motivations cannot be ascribed to DNA.

Nor is it absolutely certain that all reversions arise only from a memory of the past history of that particular species. Toes, teeth and tails are still in common use. Can there therefore be a sideways influence, one presently existant pattern influencing another at a gross or subtle level, as in the apparently unconnected occurrence of similar happenings?

Additionally, each individual carries in his own mind the deep personal impressions relating to his past births. So, a human baby born with a small tail may be anatomically recalling a previous life rather than expressing the hidden memory of some evolutionary ancestor.

Certainly, a soul only receives as a physical body that which its karmas or inner mind dictate. This is a primary reality for all souls taking birth and cannot be overlooked in any complete understanding of the natural world. If a baby is born with a small tail, or a horse with toes, it is in the karmas of that individual. It is a natural expression of what lies within the mind of that individual. But exactly what that cause may be will differ from individual to individual.

Memory and potential seem, then, to be common themes in the processes of life and reversions are indications of potentiality not normally expressed, but capable of manifestation when merited by the times and circumstances.

Reversions, either to ancestral forms or simply to the wild type, are not the only sudden changes observed by breeders. The other kind are sports – the emergence of a form which is significantly new, a pattern which cannot be related to an old memory. These represent the pure, previously unmanifested potential of the species. Even Darwin speculated that the germ:

> is crowded with invisible characters... separated by hundreds or even thousands of generations from the present time: and these characters like those written on paper with invisible ink, lie ready to be evolved whenever the organization is disturbed by certain known or unknown conditions.

In Darwin's day, of course, the nature of what constituted the 'germ' had by no means been defined. Even our present, very rudimentary understanding of genetic processes was not at all understood and it may not have been outside Darwin's original conception to have included something like our subtle energy blueprint.

It is only a recent addition to evolutionary theory that insists on the primary implication of DNA in all aspects of biological inheritance. In Darwin's day, there was no understanding at all of the subatomic structure of matter, though ideas concerning the formative nature of the 'ether' of space were prevalent and acceptable. Darwin put on one side questions concerning the intrinsic nature of mind and instinct. The obsessive insistence upon an absolutely material explanation of everything in terms of so-called solid matter is an idiom only of our present times.

Note, too, that Darwin's conception of the germ, crowded with potential forms, is a different proposition to that of random mutation. In this passage he is not implicating chance as a primary factor in his scheme of things. He is suggesting, like myself, that potentially new forms already exist in seed form.

But the real source of these potential forms lies hidden, not in the DNA nor in any gross material substance, but in the vast potentiality of the Mind.

At the present moment, the crystallization of both mind and matter into dense, habituated patterns largely precludes the emergence of new species. Thus we observe only extinctions. But if nature had a cycle which included finer and more spiritualized eras, what we observe today as occasional and spontaneous sports and reversions may then be only a small part of a spectrum of biologically regenerative processes we would find hard to imagine.

PARALLEL AND CONVERGENT EVOLUTION

Having had a good idea once, nature is apt to repeat it, say Richard Dawkins and other neo-Darwinists, troubled by the frequent appearance of almost identical species or biological characteristics where no geological link can be identified to account for their presence, or where no evolutionary line of connection can be traced. They call the phenomenon *parallel evolution*. But the question remains, how? How does nature repeat her 'good idea'? Can random processes really be said to possess the memory, intelligence, organization or just sheer good luck to repeat good things.

Australia has been disconnected from all other continents for far longer than modern mammals have existed, yet the parallels between marsupials and mammals are too close to ignore. From flying squirrels and jumping rodents to burrowing moles and hunting wolves, the only differences in form and physiology appear to be in the marsupial and mammalian methods of rearing their young. Their instinctive habits – even the specific behavioural details of how they use their limbs and teeth for digging, hunting and foraging – are almost identical. Even social and courtship rituals are very similar between these two groups of higher animals.

And yet the geology of the earth does not permit that the two groups had a common ancestor. They must, say the evolutionists, have evolved quite separately and – 'by random mutation of DNA' – have hit upon almost exactly the same physical form and behaviour. And not only that but they are thought to have independently evolved their similar anatomy, physiology and biochemistry: their endocrine glands and their hormones, their brains and their nervous systems, their skeletal structures, their blood cell types and their immune systems. For almost all of these and much else are very similar.

If one examines only the biochemistry, the structure and function of muscle, nerve, endocrine, blood, lymph, kidney, liver, spleen and brain cells in marsupials and in their mammalian counterparts, there are millions upon millions of identical features. Yet, so says the theory of parallel evolution, they were all independently lighted upon by chance variations in the DNA. And this is supposed to have taken place amongst ancestors who were already highly specialized and successful, in little 'need' of evolving into anything else at all.

Troubles abound just as much when similar comparisons are made between the marsupials of Australia and the Americas. For they are denizens of two continents which have had no physical contact for as long as marsupials and mammals are supposed to have existed. So how come there are marsupials in both continents? Parallel evolution again? Does it not seem too coincidental that marsupials are only found in these two *neighbouring* continents. Why not Europe and Australia? Or Africa and Australia?

Amongst mammals, the problems for evolutionary theory are no less. In fact, the porcupines of South America and those of Asia and Africa are so similar that G. R. Taylor has been forced to suggest that they crossed the Atlantic on rafts of matted vegetation, presumably in pairs. Such explanations are clearly signs of desperation!

Many might suppose that man brought creatures with him on his intercontinental adventures, but though this may indeed have been the case, it is not acceptable to conventional evolutionists, for it would need to have taken place long before man is supposed to have appeared upon the scene.

In this respect, one wonders what future palaeontologists will make of European rabbits and wild dogs in Australia in a few million years time! Or American grey squirrels in Europe! Or wallabies in England, escapees from wildlife parks and presently making their home here.

No less surprising and difficult for the ardent evolutionist to comprehend is the similarity of certain organs in creatures otherwise so dissimilar. Evolutionists call it *convergent evolution*. The eyes of the intelligent octopus and other cephalopods are remarkably similar to those of vertebrates, for example. Is it really just the coincidental repetition of a good idea?

Sheldrake suggests that once a form or pattern has evolved, it is spread by 'morphic resonance', making it easier for geographically distant evolutionary processes to adopt it. This theory is appealing, but where are these morphic fields?

From the mystic point of view, they lie within the subtle structure of the creature and within the multilevel energies of the Mind. Within the context of a multilevel creation in which the life principle is the primary creative force, patterned by different configurations of Mind from within-out, it seems reasonable that the same patterns will be repeated over and over again. The same inner projection system underlies all creatures, so the same patterns will naturally recur, just as electricity and atomic structure are the same not only in Australia and England, but amongst far distant galaxies, too. It is all a part of the Formative Mind, the great universal pattern-maker.

Island species provide us with further insights into patterns of change amongst creatures, for many of them are indigenous to particular islands. Madagascar, for example, which split off from continental Africa at least 165 million years ago when dinosaurs as big as a row of cottages roamed the world, now has a high proportion of species which are unique to its shores. This certainly demonstrates, pretty conclusively, that the creatures of the present are physically related to the creatures of the past.

There are thirty unique species of lemur, seven unique species of chameleon, several unique species of deer – and so on. But there is one strange thing. They are all quite clearly members of families or groups found *in present times*, on the African, American, European and Asian mainland. If they have been isolated for so long, why are they not even more different? What has been keeping them in some semblance of step with the rest of the world? Why have they not gone off and done entirely their own thing?

Perhaps amongst the most instructive of all Madagascar's unique wildlife are the tenrecs. Tenrecs comprise a little-studied group of at least thirty-three small species of mammalian insectivores, of which twenty-nine are unique to Madagascar. There are twenty-one species of long-tailed, shrew-like tenrec who behave to all intents and purposes like their shrew cousins in the rest of the world. In addition to their long tails, they even sport large and sensitive ears for use in echolocation, just like 'real' mice and shrews do elsewhere.

Then there are the greater and lesser hedgehog tenrecs who look and behave remarkably like hedgehogs. Their feeding habits are similar and they are, of course, covered in spines. There is an aquatic species which looks like a cross between an otter and a shrew, sporting webbed rear feet. And there are three species of burrowing tenrec who have borrowed more than a simple habit from the moles. But all this similarity, say the conventional evolutionists, has taken place by chance, by 'parallel evolution'. And how did the first pair get there? It must have been, say the experts, on rafts of matted vegetation. . . .

There are also about thirty species of unique Madagascan lemurs whose progenitors are supposed to have arrived there about 40 million years ago. Lemurs have many cousins elsewhere, especially in parts of south-east Asia, Indonesia and the Philippines. And how do they say that the first lemurs reached Madagascar? On rafts of matted vegetation!

Looked at purely from a physical point of view, the multiplicity of coincidences required for 'parallel evolution' would seem too much to countenance. Surely 165 million years – or even 40 million – would have led to an absolutely and radically different array of creatures, perhaps a burgeoning of entirely new classes, perhaps something altogether other than mammals and reptiles, not just variations on familiar mainland themes?

The spectrum of species seem so wholly modern in character. There are no dinosaurs, no really archaic mammals, no really ancient relics of any kind. Though the species are undoubtedly different, the changes on Madagascar and the mainland have remained remarkably in step. How? Surely it is more than just the coincidence of parallel adjustment to planetary environmental conditions?

It all seems rather unsatisfactory. It is undeniable that island species or other creatures living in isolated habitats have developed due to that isolation into unique forms found nowhere else on earth. All the same, surely the causes of a change in species which stills keeps in harmony with the global style are not those of chance, random mutation and survival of the fittest?

The fact that Madagascan species have kept pace with the mainland creatures as regards their general style or form shows that there must be a real connection at a deeper level. There has to be some hidden, cohering and integrating system – we cannot simply fall back on good old 'chance' whenever we are stumped for an answer!

The global integration of style or pattern must mean that there is an energy association at a subtle level that crosses physical boundaries. And, in general, this means Mind, the Formative Mind – the originator and integrator of all forms. The sea of Mind from which all forms emerge automatically ensures association and connection.

Thus, the evidence underlying 'parallel' and 'convergent evolution' – which to the material approach represents a degree of coincidence way beyond the bounds of chance – is actually predictable when seen within the framework of the Formative Mind. Like the global existence of a world 'mood' or social climate, there is absolutely no difficulty in understanding how patterns from distant places bear resemblances to each other, keeping in step with the march of time. Rather, it is to be expected.

BEHAVIOUR AND EVOLUTION

It is a matter of some difficulty for proponents of materialistic evolution to explain why emerging physical forms are already endowed with appropriate behaviour patterns. Birds not only possess wings, they also know how to fly and where to fly. And they have extensive navigational instincts and suitable sensory faculties.

If all change amongst the species is the result of random and unintegrated mutations, then how is it that the physical changes resulting in the acquisition of wings are matched by the appropriate mental, instinctive behavioural and sensory adaptations? How is it that extensive changes to musculature and bodily form are matched even by appropriate modifications to the brain, nervous and sensory systems? The conventional evolutionary theory decrees: by random and fortuitous mutations. That is, by coincidence. Is this a reasonable supposition?

In the materialistic paradigm of 'Life is a by-product of molecular self-organization', behaviour is reduced to biochemical and bio-electronic activity in brain and body. No-one, however, has ever identifed the means by which thought, emotion, memory, instinct and all such mental attributes arise from molecules and electromagnetism. Seen in the light of the multifaceted energy model of mind-body function this comes as no surprise, for mental energies are not to be found at the level of gross physical substance.

Conventional science, however, insists that behaviour and con-sciousness, as well as mind, instinct and emotion, have a physical origin – in humans and in all other creatures. It has, they assume, evolved and is all somehow magically encoded into the DNA. Some molecule that DNA!

But this just does not add up. For every change in outer form there has to be a corresponding change in instinct and behaviour – in both cerebral, neurological and mental function. How, in a world where chance is considered as the driving force, can these multiple elements ever be synchronized?

Changes to one physical characteristic alone require multiple modifications to the DNA. Yet at the same time, we are expected to believe that the infinitely more complex biochemical, cerebral and neurological activity associated with behaviour also change by ran-dom genetic mutation so that the creature remains integrated.

Such a theory is bizarre, for the most amazing series of biochemical and physiological coincidences would be required to arrive at the required perfection. The idea does not bear examination in the light of a modern understanding of the sheer complexity of biochemical processes – a complexity quite unsuspected by Darwin, who pre-dated all but the most rudimentary theories of the atom and to whom the strange world of the subatomic was quite unknown.

Consider how – by chance mutations – a reptile or a dinosaur could have evolved into a bird. Anything other than a completely functional pair of wings would have been worse than useless. Even if the wings were perfectly articulated, they would still require extensive neurological and cerebral changes as well as the mental or instinctive ability to know how to use a pair of wings. The requirement for millions upon millions of parallel, integrated, synchronous yet chance mutations is more than seems reasonable, even given millions of years in which to accomplish it.

It might happen, just for one species, once in a billion years — though I doubt even that — but not for almost every species that has ever existed. For such wholeness and integration to arise by chance, again and again and again, seems too bizarre a proposition to seriously countenance.

How then does integrated change take place? Through the natural, automatic integration of mind and body. Mind is something other than molecular patterns. It forms the multilevel blueprints of the physical form and all its systems. So any shift in one aspect of outer form is automatically integrated with other necessary outer changes. Modifications first take place in the subtle energy configuration of the creature. When the inner pattern changes, then the anatomical, neurological, cerebral and biochemical changes take place automatically.

An image projected upon a screen is always integrated as one image because of the nature of the projection system. When the film in the projector is changed, then the whole image changes automatically.

Consider the fish *Asemicthys taylori*, which lives along the northwest Pacific coastline of America. This remarkable fish sports a specially modified skull bone adorned with sharp spikes. Using its lower jaw as a lever, *Asemicthys taylori* punches holes in snails and bivalve shellfish before swallowing them whole. The pre-punched holes then allow its digestive juices to penetrate the creature.

Asemicthys taylori specializes in eating only those snails and bivalves which are particularly well protected against predators — snails with a hard plate sealing the normal entrance to the shell and bivalves which have an especially efficient seal between their two halves. Snails without this hard shield or bivalves with naturally leaky seals are left for the fish without an on-board hole punch.

Stephen Norton, the University of California biologist who first reported this behaviour, comments that he has no idea how *Asemicthys taylori* even distinguishes the protected molluscs from the unprotected ones and why the fish only attacks the more difficult species. But to conceive that there has been concurrent and coincidental evolution in three separate areas within one species: the simultaneous development of bony spikes, a knowledge of how to use them, and the ability to select only the tough customers, seems extreme. Especially when one considers that each one of these facets would require a multitude of independent chance mutations were one to rely entirely upon the conventional evolutionary paradigm for answers.

This perfect integration of behaviour, instinct and outward form is apparent in all creatures. To the reductionist thinker, there is nothing but chance and natural selection to integrate one aspect of body function or behaviour with another. Yet in nature, we do not see creatures struggling with an instinctive behavioural pattern that is a clear mismatch to their anatomical capabilities. Pigs are not seen leaping off farmyard buildings in the mistaken and mutated belief that they can fly!

Natural selection, conventional evolutionists might say, keeps all random mutations in harmony with a common purpose and a race of pigs who thought they could fly would soon die out, as idle dreamers meeting an untimely end. But there can be no end 'purpose' in a world dominated by chance. And there is something intrinsically, intuitively and rationally unsatisfying about a theory which suggests that harmony, balance and complete integration arise by chance and random fluctuations. Surely such thinking is lacking in some essential dimension.

Strangely it is man, more obviously than any other creature, who exhibits apparently avoidable behaviour that leads to his own demise – warfare, stressful living, ecological stupidity and so on. But there is no evidence whatsoever that in man or any other species behavioural patterns are genetically encoded. They may run in families due to psychological conditioning and exposure, just as religious and socio-political philosophies and attitudes are transmitted. But no-one seriously suggests that temperament and political or religious affiliations are transmitted genetically.

So, since behaviour and physical functioning are so closely inter-woven in every organism, any theory that attempts to explain their origins as independently evolved, with only natural selection of chance mutations as the mediator, is evidently lacking in some fundamental way.

SCIENCE, CULTURE AND DARWIN

What we call science is simply observations of the outward mani-festation of the karmic process – the gross physical realm. Science is an intellectual analysis of one end of what is actually a dimension of being by which increasingly complex patterns are formed and mani-fested. And biology is the study of the physical bodies which inhabit this realm.

To understand what is going on, we have to become aware of the inner processes which are responsible for the manifestation of outer forms. We cannot make an analysis of only the physical form and expect complete understanding.

Darwinism was, no doubt, a useful step towards providing the Western world with an alternative to religious dogma. But the blind belief in a totally materialistic universe which has become associated with his theory is as far removed from the true mystic and spiritual understanding of life as a rigid religious orthodoxy based upon verbal formulae and dogmatic statements of faith. It is time now to move on.

The lack of subtlety in Darwinian thought is reflective of the Victorian era whence he came. The heavy architecture, the giant engineering constructions, the steam engine, the industrial revolution, the impetus for material gain and the great new world of industry and competition; the self-righteousness, intolerance and suppression of feeling and emotion: these were some of the hallmarks of his era and these are the fundamentals of Darwin's thought. These were some of the mind patterns of his culture – which he then projected onto nature.

Even Darwin himself, normally observant, was overruled by his preconceptions when reporting that the 'miserable savages' who 'lived in Tierra del Fuego were quite 'brutish' and that he had only been able to discern eleven words in their language. He saw them through the coloured glasses of his own mind and theory. He wanted them to be the missing link between man and ape. But not long after, a more sensitive and perceptive ethnologist took the time to live with this tribe, became familiar with their extensive language and religious beliefs, shared in their social customs, and found them to be a race of humans as much like ourselves as any other.

Darwinism is a relic of Victorian philosophy. It has had its place and its purpose, but the theory is so lacking in evidence and logical consistency that it is not even good materialistic science.

The fossilized, physical evidence of life long before our times needs to be reappraised within a broader understanding of how life is actually put together. This involved Mind and consciousness as much then as it does now. We cannot expect a coherent understanding of the past if we ignore that.

Concepts and theories in science change just as much as social structures and ideas. The one reflects the other; they are bound together as inseparable expressions of the human thought of those times. And the mood of the times is changing. There is an influx of higher understanding. The role of soul and Mind is being more clearly discerned. Therefore, we can expect that our scientific theories of life and the universe will also change, to accommodate this deeper perception.

INTERLUDE

MY LAW – TIEME RANAPIRI

The sun may be clouded, yet ever the sun
   Will sweep on its course till the Cycle is run.
   And when into chaos the system is hurled
Again shall the Builder reshape a new world.

Your path may be clouded, uncertain your goal:
   Move on – for your orbit is fixed to your soul.
   And though it may lead into darkness of night
The torch of the Builder shall give it new light.

You were. You will be! Know this while you are:
   Your spirit has travelled both long and afar.
   It came from the Source, to the Source it returns –
The Spark which was lighted eternally burns.

It slept in a jewel. It leapt in a wave.
   It roamed in the forest. It rose from the grave.
   It took on strange garbs for long aeons of years
And now in the soul of yourself it appears.

From body to body your spirit speeds on
   It seeks a new form when the old one has gone
   And the form that it finds is the fabric you wrought
On the loom of the Mind from the fibre of Thought.

As dew is drawn upwards, in rain to descend
   Your thoughts drift away and in Destiny blend.
   You cannot escape them, for petty or great,
Or evil or noble, they fashion your Fate.

Somewhere on some planet, sometime and somehow
   Your life will reflect your thoughts of your Now.
   My Law is unerring, no blood can atone –
The structure you built you will live in – alone.

From cycle to cycle, through time and through space
   Your lives with your longings will ever keep pace
   And all that you ask for and all you desire
Must come at your bidding, as flame out of fire.

Once list' to that Voice and all tumult is done –
   Your life is the Life of the Infinite One.
   In the hurrying race you are conscious of pause
With love for the purpose, and love for the Cause.

You are your own Devil, you are your own God
   You fashioned the paths your footsteps have trod.
   And no one can save you from Error or Sin
Until you have hark'd to the Spirit within.

Attributed to a Maori

3. NATURAL CYCLES

ANCIENT TIMES

At Sawtry Fen, close to my East Anglian home, the farmers dig up huge oak trunks every year when they plough the peaty soil of their fields. They say that all the oaks are lying with the same orientation: they lie as they fell 100,000 years ago when the glaciers moved inexorably down from the North felling them like skittles in an alley.

The wood of these massive trees is now too dense to burn on a home fire but it is not yet fossilized, so the farmers pile them into stacks at the sides of their fields. Piles of logs over 100,000 years old! Then, when they get the time, they burn them.

In recent years, the fens have been drained, providing an excellent soil of black sedge peat – 10,000 years of compost, accumulated since the last recession of the ice. But the wind blows the light earth away and every year's ploughing has taken the farmers deeper into the ground. Now they find the ancient oaks, preserved first by the icy grip of the glaciers and then by the boggy, low-lying land above when the ice receded. And strangely, amongst the trees, they find the leaf litter of 100,000 years ago, complete with the wing cases of beetles and the flimsy exoskeletons of insects who flourished there before the coming of the cold.

Ten thousand years or so ago, the glaciers moved back from what are now the temperate zones between the tropics and the poles. They had covered England as far south as the Thames Valley for perhaps 100,000 years before. And before that the ice age stretches back one million years or more, interspersed every 100,000 years or so by 10,000 year interglacial windows, when the ice temporarily receded.

Ten thousand years is nothing in terms of planetary history, but times must have been hard during those icy years for any humans who made their homes amongst the ice. The Eskimos, the

Greenlanders and the Laplanders are perhaps the remnants of these ancient ice age communities. Our present European races are said to have migrated from southern climes when the cold moved back. Man has always been the adventurer and gone where he could. We are descendants of the Aryan race, they say, from Persia and beyond.

But history is lost before 10,000 years ago and even less than that. We know so little of the past. Recorded history is the luxury of an established civilization, with a climate where records will not rot and moulder. China and Egypt probably hold the most ancient records of civilization, with artefacts and art dating back to around 3000 BC – a mere 5000 years ago.

Nature, too, holds many intriguing mysteries. Indeed, it is mostly mystery. A little knowledge can masquerade as much, and we so easily forget our ignorance. Yet we do not know how we even move a finger, how the mind and body interface to perform all the functions with which we are familiar and how the detailed ordering and patterning of the body is maintained and administered. We do not know why every molecule, atom and subatomic particle in the physical creation keeps on moving so incessantly. We do not really know what makes the sun come up.

How little we know through scientific analysis. How little is it possible to know by such thinking. How unfounded are so many of our scientific assumptions and theories. How little we really know of the past.

For a period of nearly 200 million years, until 'only' 65 million years ago, the dinosaurs roamed freely across many parts of our planet. Strange and awesome to our present mind, they inhabited a planet – our planet – where trees sometimes stood as high as 50 to 100 metres, nearly 400 feet, as tall as a thirty or forty storey building.

In Alberta, the dinosaurs flourished in a huge swampy area on the verge of a vast inland sea. And recent finds in China show they lived just as well amongst scrub land and coniferous forest, where water only existed in shallow basins, alkaline and high in soda, as we find in modern times around the Great Salt Lake basin in Utah, North America.

Though some were no larger than a thrush, the size of others was incredible – up to 100 feet long and weighing as much as 35 tons. That is as big and voluminous as a row of maybe three or four semi-detached, British houses. With their long necks, the herbivores amongst them were ideally suited for browsing amongst the tall trees. Standing up on their rear legs, the largest of them could graze trees up to a height of fifty feet. Some of them even took to the air. The incredible *pterosaurs*, which included the *pterodactyls* amongst their number, had short stubby bodies and wingspans of up to 10 metres (30 feet). That is probably two or three times as long as your living room. How on earth did they get off the ground? If we had no fossil records to prove that they had existed, no one would believe us if we suggested that such creatures could have lived and flourished so successfully, so long ago. Under modern circumstances, the larger dinosaurs could not have survived. There would not be enough for them eat, for a start. So what was it that was so different at those times?

Recently, scientists have evolved a technique for measuring the content of the air trapped in small bubbles deep within the polar ice. This is interesting, for it gives us some indication of relative oxygen, nitrogen and carbon dioxide content over the last 160,000 years. But two geochemists, Gary Landis and Robert Berner, have also applied similar techniques to air bubbles trapped in amber – fossilized coniferous resin that can date back 200 or 300 million years. Not surprisingly, they have found that the proportions of atmospheric gases have changed. Previously, scientists had assumed that they had remained the same.

Specifically, air bubbles from 80 million year old amber contained up to 50 per cent more oxygen than we find in our atmosphere of today. Oxygen content in modern times is about 21 per cent, yet a 25 million year old sample from the Dominican Republic had a content of only 16 per cent, while a sample from Manitoba dated from the Cretaceous period, the hey-day of the dinosaurs over 65 million years ago, had an oxygen content of 32 per cent. Some scientists consider that this is a high enough concentration of oxygen to have initiated a spontaneous global conflagration. But then this would also depend upon atmospheric pressure and temperature at that time. And of that, we know little.

The accuracy of this technique is a matter of scientific debate, of course, and some scientists refute it, but suppose our planet has undergone such wide-ranging atmospheric changes of oxygen, carbon dioxide and nitrogen content. It would certainly have had considerable effects upon the living creatures. In fact, it would have been the living creatures of those times who created that balance.

Incidentally, atmospheric pressure would have been automatically higher, which could perhaps explain how the huge pterosaurs, with a bigger wingspan than some light aircraft, got themselves airborne and stayed aloft.

Climatic conditions of the past are almost indeterminable, but at times they have certainly been sufficient to support vastly more vegetation than the earth supports today, together with the entire ecosystem of other creatures that would have necessarily gone with it.

The earth has seen many changes and even sudden disasters. Meteor impacts, volcanic dust clouds, comets, arrival of antimatter from space, shifting of the earth's axis, cyclic reversal of magnetic polarity, cyclic activity within the sun spread over long periods, the 225 million years it takes for our sun and its planets to circle around the centre of the galaxy – all these and more have been implicated in both the sudden and the slow changes to climatic conditions which have so clearly affected our planet during the long course of its history. And many more such ages have yet to come and go. Many disasters, many more good times.

Our present technological and deeply materialistic civilization is turning out to be a planetary disaster. It cannot last forever, or even for very much longer. It has only been going for a few hundred years or so – hardly noticeable on the cosmic time scale. All things change and go into decline and new conditions emerge.

Nature rolls on inexorably, and the souls come and go in the endless cycles of birth, death and rebirth. We were here at the outset, for we are still here now. For us, the ultimate spiritual lesson has yet to be learnt. Life has a meaning and a purpose and time is only our illusion. A lifetime goes by so rapidly, though it may seem so full of pains and happinesses. One hundred years of it is usually more than a man can endure under present conditions. His body and mind are worn out well within such a short time span. Even after just one day, we need many hours of sleep to restore our mind and body. Yet if evolution were so good at creating highly adapted life forms, why do we not live on forever? Why are our lifetimes so short? Some creatures live for less than a day. Only trees, with their more peaceful presence, can live for hundreds of years.

We are lost and ignorant in this world. But ask any human if he is lost and most will say 'No, I know where I am! I am at the supermarket!' (or wherever!) But what are we doing there? How did all this come about? What on earth is going on? Life is meaningless to us if we do not ask ourselves these ultimate questions and seek for answers deep within ourselves.

CYCLES OF THE LIFE FORCE

Ancient Indian, Greek and other mystics have divided cosmic time by the depth of the spirituality prevalent on earth. There is, they say, a regular cycling of the spiritual and the material spanning many millions of years.

According to the Indian seers, as recorded in the Sanskrit Puranas, one full cycle of these ages or *yugas* spans 4.32 million years. The *Sat yuga*, when man is aware of his innately spiritual heritage, comes first, lasting for 1.7 million years. Just as spring sets the scene for the ensuing seasons, so too is the Sat yuga the driving force which gives impetus and life to the following, less spiritual, yugas.

But slowly, the intensity of its spirituality declines. There then follows, said these sages, the *Treta yuga*, lasting 1.296 million years, then the *Dwapar yuga* spanning 864,000 years, and finally the *Kal yuga* of 432,000 years. This is the period through which we are now passing, occupying just one tenth of the total time of one full cycle. These periods are not sharply demarcated but are only a simple way of dividing time and drawing attention to the steady ebb of spirituality.

Life is spirit and without spirit, there is no life. When the quality of life and spirituality in the Kal yuga finally becomes untenable, then there is a change of state, a sudden flooding of the physical domain with the Life Force, as a Kal yuga once again gives way to a Sat yuga. Winter has ended and spring has come.

Exactly where we are in the present Kal yuga is a matter of speculation – some authorities say we have only just begun, others declare that we are in the middle and the more optimistic ones say that we are nearing the end. There is – as ever – a difference of opinion.

But when that great influx of life energy flows into the physical domain, then all biological processes are quickened like an old man receiving the elixir of youth. Perhaps this comes about by a cyclic 'movement' within the whole Egg of the Mind, when the astral and causal regions come into closer vibrational resonance or synchrony with the physical domain, a mystic periodicity within the higher energies of creation. After all, if there are cycles here, there must be cycles and patterns there, as well.

Man is said to live for 100,000 years during a Sat yuga, so conditions then must be a tremendous improvement on present circumstances! Most folk could not tolerate the thought of going out to work, nine to five, for the next 100,000 years! So the general climate of being must be very different. Man's physical structure is also said to be of a far finer and more etheric quality than it is today and one imagines that the rest of the physical creation follows suit. And one wonders what might be the activities with which such an etherealized man fills his days. Certainly not the pursuit of a large investment portfolio!

What the enhanced subtlety and etherealization of a Sat yuga does to the fossil record is anybody's guess, but strangely enough it provides a means by which we may understand the punctuated equilibrium theory of evolution. This notes, you will recall, that while something must have happened to result in the extinction of numerous old species and the creation of many new ones, there is no evidence anywhere at all of one species gradually changing into another that radically differs from it.

Some evolutionists therefore surmise that the emergence of radically new species happens during very short periods of time when conditions change dramatically – over a period of one to two million years – such that the only means of survival is rapid evolution. But it all happenes so fast that no record is ever preserved.

What is preserved, however, are *strata* or layers of rock, each containing a record of several million years, during which time the fossil flora and fauna remain almost constant. Then, over a period of perhaps a million or half a million years, there is a rapid extinction followed by a rapid proliferation of new species. Between these geologically brief periods of rapid change lie eras of equilibrium, when only mild adaptation to minor environmental change takes place. No radically new species emerge at that time.

During proliferation phases, there is often a burgeoning of new species and families. Even new groups and classes can come into existence at these times. But there is no evidence of a very gradual evolution of new species from the old, by tiny random changes to their outward form; no evidence of 'lower' forms evolving into something 'higher'.

Perhaps, too, during a Sat yuga, when life is so vital and exuberant, physical life becomes so subtle and mental, with barely a skim of physical density, that bodies leave no remains dense enough to form fossils. So there is even a real gap in the fossil records of the time. But this is only speculation. What is certainly true is that when we attempt to trace the *life* history of our planet from its *inert* remains by examining the fossil record, creatures do seem to arrive suddenly and disappear quite as rapidly. So perhaps it is during a Sat yuga that there is an influx of new creatures, arising by physical and biological processes which are, no doubt, understandable at the time, but difficult for us to envisage now, weighed down with the vibrational density of a Kal yuga.

A key to some understanding of this regenerative process could lie in the ancient Hermetic axiom, 'As above, so below'. As we have seen, the tattwas first manifest as subtle essences in the realm of the Universal Mind, far beyond the physical realm, in far finer form.

And it is possible that when the inner and the outer worlds come 'closer' together during a Sat yuga, when the subtlety of their vibration is in greater synchrony, then the subtle tattvic patterns 'spill over' into the physical realm and – somehow – they come into physical manifestation. The super-species are more readily manifested in physical form. The inner is the blueprint of the outer, upon the formative dimension of the Mind. But all the same, the new patterns are formed out of the seeds of the old. Nothing is ever really new.

And just as man, at least within known history, has always been a breeder of species and an integral part of the expression of life and Mind upon this plane, so too may the spiritualized man of those times be involved in the 'breeding' or regeneration of the new planetary life forms. Exactly what processes that entails, we do not fully understand, but there must be some natural process. I am not suggesting that new species just appear miraculously one morning, glistening and fresh from the Creator's mixing pot!

SEEDS OF THE MIND

These great cosmic tides, this ebb and flow of the yugas, must be like the rise and fall of some of the world's great cities and civilizations. The energy and vitality of a culture grows, increases and spreads. Yet ultimately, that very proliferation occasions its inevitable decay. Then, like the Phoenix emerging out of the ashes of its predecessor, a new culture blooms.

The formative seeds of both yugas and civilizations are the mind patterns of the past. The souls of the old may be the souls of the new. But the minds of the old stock proliferate anew, in a new springtime, a new birth. The basic pattern and balance remain essentially the same, but the outward garments exhibit different forms.

Bodies, species, races, nationalities – these are all only garments of the Formative Mind, a part of its outworking. They are reflections and patterns thrown up upon its surface by its deeper creative processes. Whether in the birth, death and rebirth of an individual, in the cycling of the yugas, in the development of apparently new species or in the change of old ones, the formative seeds of the old are reaped as the harvest of the new. The formative seeds are impressions or memories in the energies of the Mind – individual and greater. In the Formative Mind lies the memory of nature.

Events too, and all apparently material substance – the workings of what we call nature, the physical creation we think to be so solid and real – all these are only waves and bubbles upon and within a greater ocean of Mind. It is only the splitting of light into multicoloured designs by oil moving on water; it is only the repeating patterns of a kaleidoscope formed by multiple reflections within itself of one primal pattern.

AEONS AND AEONS

The earth, say the geologists, is 4.5 billion (4,500,000,000) years old. How can one envisage such a span of time? Yet even the oldest known sedimentary rocks, dated at 3.5 million years, bear signs of life. When the thinnest of slivers are viewed under the electron microscope, the rods and spheres of ancient bacteria can sometimes be observed. Even occasional single cells with nuclei have been seen.

Niles Eldredge, curator of invertebrates at the American Museum of Natural History in New York, comments, in his book *Life Pulse*:

> Looking at these incredibly old rocks and fossils, you get the feeling that life is an intrinsic part of the Earth, not merely some latecomer, an appendage haphazardly stuck on as an afterthought of creation.

This research is recent and earlier geologists had found nothing older than the extensive remains of sea-dwelling creatures, dated at 600 or 700 million years, little more than half a billion years ago. But noting that such exceptionally ancient rocks are extremely rare and that such sediments would have been baked, crushed and ground under the most phenomenal of pressures, it would be an unwarranted expectation to find the fossils of any larger creatures. Such structures would have long since been destroyed.

But let us start at the beginning. Let us briefly tell the amazing tale of the little that is known concerning the geological history of our planet earth, this wonderful, natural spaceship. Let us, as Thomas Huxley suggested, 'Sit down before the facts as a little child', and see what will emerge.

And since everyone looks at things through the eyes of their own mind, let us be clear that we are looking at this geological and palaeontological evidence with the understanding of one who considers that the universe is continuously created and maintained from within, every moment. That life or consciousness is prior to form; that life patterns form; that inner structure patterns the outer structure and that the Life Force energizes it all; that it is a projected image arising from activity in a hidden dimension of the Mind; that what we are observing in the fossil record is therefore the scanty, dead and inert remains of life forms from which the mind and Life Force have long since departed; that the individual souls have taken birth elsewhere, carrying their mind patterns with them from body to body, continuously gathering and never shedding the deeply hidden and finely etched inward memories of myriad lives.

WATER, ICE, OCEANS AND LAND

Geologically, the present state of our planet is most unusual. We are in the midst of an ice age which began a million years or more ago. Geologists call it the *Pleistocene* era. The land masses of our planet earth stand high above the oceans with much of the water locked up in extensive polar ice caps. Nearly 30 per cent of our planet's surface is presently dry land; the rest is ocean. This may seem a small proportion, yet geological studies show that, historically, even this is high. In its 4.5 billion years, geologists say that for most of that time, the land percentages have been far lower than they are today.

Even during an ice age, however, there is a periodicity. The glaciers advance and recede over a time span of about 100,000 years, with interglacial, semi-ice age periods in between, each lasting about 10,000 years. Presently, we are enjoying such a brief remission.

When the ice began to recede only 20,000 years ago, the polar caps were larger than they are today. Glaciers covered much of northern Europe and North America, locking up great volumes of water in ice sheets often in excess of 10,000 feet thick, higher than many mountain ranges. Even today, 10 per cent of the earth's land mass and 12 per cent of its oceans are icebound, nearly a quarter of the planetary surface.

The glaciers in the centre of Greenland are over 10,000 feet deep, covering an expanse of over 650,000 square miles. Yet these are dwarfed by Antarctic glaciers, where the ice sheets cover an area of nearly 5 million square miles of land at depths, once again, of over 10,000 feet. In some Antarctic valleys, the rock base lies over 8000 feet below sea level. If the ice ever receded, these valleys would become vast inland seas, some merging with the surrounding ocean itself.

Imagine, then, the sheer weight and volume of such ice and its effects upon the earth. Geologists say that the earth's crust sinks under its weight. Imagine, then, how much water is released into the seas when the time comes for a melt.

Since the ice began to recede the oceans have been steadily rising. The British Isles were once a part of Europe; now the water which was so recently trapped in vast glaciers covers the low-lying land between ourselves and Europe.

The process is continuous and the warming of the earth will inevitably mean a rise in the level of the oceans. It has happened many times before. Sea walls will be of little help as vast continental areas of Europe, America, Asia and Australia sink once again beneath the waves.

On a regular basis, geologically speaking, much of the land is washed over and submerged by the tides and oceans. How little land remains is difficult to say, but when the 25 million cubic kilometres of water now locked up in glacial ice finally melts, then it is estimated that the oceans will rise by over 200 feet. London, Tokyo, New York and most coastal cities will disappear. There is no 'if' about it. It is quite certain. It is only a matter of time.

Many islands, especially in the Pacific and Indian Oceans which only rise 50 to a 100 feet above the sea, will also disappear. Over the course of maybe only a thousand years they will all be lost. And since the vast majority of human populations live in low-lying arable and coastal areas, mankind and indeed all land-living creatures will be subject to a vast decimation of population or, at least, to mass migration.

Man has experienced all this many times before. The myths of ancient cultures from Polynesia, Australia, New Zealand, North and South America and the Middle East all – almost without exception – talk of a deluge. The dates are usually placed in pre-history, perhaps 7000 to 10,000 years ago. Since, at that time, the glaciers were receding, giving way to our present interglacial period, the seas would have been rising. The low-lying islands and areas of the South Pacific and elsewhere would most certainly have been swamped at that time. Is this, then, the origin of the stories of the Flood? Geologically, there is no doubt that over the aeons, deluges have been a commonplace.

DRIFTING LAND THAT RAISES MOUNTAIN RANGES

The rise and fall of the oceans is not the only geological factor causing the land and sea to change their places. Vast buckled layers of rock, sometimes folded like a hairpin, together with the extensive limestone remains of ancient sea beds and marine fossils high up in the mountains, tell us that even more far-reaching planetary processes are at work.

The land is not static while the oceans simply rise and fall like bath water. The surface of our planet is in constant, active movement. Continents slide and collide, while mountain ranges are heaved up from the planetary surface. Sometimes with great rapidity, always with slow and inexorable change, our planetary exterior is being constantly recycled.

The source of energy for this continuous motion is the interior heat of the planet. Evidence of a hot interior is to be found everywhere. Volcanoes, hot springs, increased temperatures in mines and bore-holes all bear witness to the intense heat not far beneath our feet. At depths of 25 miles, the temperature can range from 500 to 1000°C. In the deepest South African gold mine, 12,500 feet (2.36 miles) below the surface, the rock temperature can reach 55°C (131°F), hot enough to cause a burn. Massive refrigeration plants churn out 800,000 tonnes of ice per day, keeping the air at a workable temperature.

Until the latter half of this century, it was believed that this heat was residual, dating back to a time when the earth was a molten blob of rock, flung out from the sun to cool slowly in outer orbit. But calculations and observations made it clear that although the molten core, some 1800 miles beneath our feet, may retain some of the original heat imparted by the sun, the outer layers would have soon cooled down. So the heat that drives this massive planetary engine of moving rock, is being continuously generated from within itself.

It seems that our planet earth is a vast heat engine. It is a giant and diffuse thermonuclear reactor in which intense heat is generated by the radioactive decay (fission) of uranium, thorium and potassium. Uranium is present in granite, a common rock, and calculations indicate that its radioactive decay in a hypothetical shell of granite 12 miles thick, encompassing the earth, would release heat energy equivalent to the total energy released by 250,000 one megaton nuclear explosions, *per year*. This is also equivalent to the heat reaching the earth's surface from its deeper interior and is about 1000 times the energy released each year in earthquakes. So the heat generated and present within the earth is quite enough to move the continents and lift mountain ranges.

It is likely, of course, that there are other active processes as well, yet to be identified, which keep the interior hot. Some scientists suggest that deep within the earth's crust the nuclear fusion of hydrogen and deuterium (a heavy isotope of hydrogen, found in heavy water) into an isotope of helium also generates vast energy as heat. The deuterium comes from sea water sucked down into the interior of the earth.

The diameter of the earth is about 8000 miles, making a distance of roughly 4000 miles from surface to centre. The notion that the interior of the earth is entirely molten is now largely discredited. These days, it is generally thought that although the earth is extremely hot inside, the liquid centre, consisting mostly of iron, begins some 1800 miles beneath the surface, extending inwards for a further 1400 miles. But the centre of this core is presently thought to be solid, covering the last 800 miles.

The evidence from seismic soundings, however, as well as from volcanic activity, also indicates that there is some considerable degree of molten material in areas not far beneath the earth's crust. It is from these more outer layers that molten rock or volcanic *magma* occasionally erupts.

But no-one has ever been there. The information is largely based upon mathematical calculation, laboratory experimentation and seismic observation, seismic measurements being obtained from the reflection of natural and artificially induced shock waves. These give us some idea of the solidity, liquidity and density beneath our feet. And though the data we possess concerning our planetary interior is very general and incomplete, it is nevertheless thought to be more or less accurate.

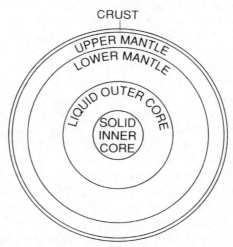

Figure 3.1   The interior of the earth according to current theory. The upper mantle consists of the asthenosphere *and the* lithosphere. See also Figure 3.2.

The central core of the earth, then (see Figure 3.1) has a central solid nucleus surrounded by liquid. Based upon calculations of its size and density, the favourite candidate for the composition of this fluid is molten iron, lightened by the admixture of about 15 per cent silicon. The earth's chemical composition concerns us little here, however, but it is worth remembering that it is this which provides the array of elements necessary for life to flourish so successfully upon its outer rim.

Outside the central core lies the *mantle*, 1800 miles thick, which constitutes the greatest volume of the earth. Thought to be a composition of the crystalline oxides and silicates of many elements, especially iron and magnesium, it extends, in places, to within 25 miles of the surface, before forming two outer layers, the *asthenosphere* and the *lithosphere*, with which we must now become more familiar.

Working from the outside-in, these layers are (see Figure 3.2):

1. The *lithosphere*, the upper layer of the earth's mantle. The lithosphere presently consists of a dozen or more slowly moving *plates*, whose outermost layers comprise the oceanic and continental *crusts*.

   The lithosphere is an integral part of the biosphere situated upon its uppermost surface. It varies in thickness from between five miles or even less under the oceans, to around 30 miles in continental areas, thickening to perhaps 45 miles under high mountains.

2. The layer lying immediately beneath the lithosphere is known as the *asthenosphere*. Because seismic waves are absorbed more readily in this region than anywhere else within the planetary interior, geophysicists feel that this layer, which in mid-ocean ridges can even reach the surface, is of a crystalline-liquid mixture, containing a small quantity of molten rock or magma. It is due to pressures and movements within the earth's surface layers that this molten rock is sometimes able to burst through to the surface, erupting as volcanoes. The magma is formed within the asthenosphere due to the heat generated therein. Volcanoes are not, as was once supposed, simply an overflow from a molten core.

Magma contains numerous mineral elements and forms the basis of all igneous rocks upon our planet. The word *igneous* means 'formed by fire' and the granites and basalt which form the basis of the continental crusts are all of igneous origin. It is the interaction between the asthenosphere and the lithosphere, with its external continental and oceanic crusts, which seems to provide the basis of the changing external geology of our planet.

One can think of the earth as a giant, spherical Christmas cake with

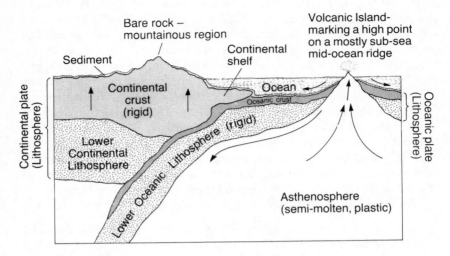

Figure 3.2 The heat engine of planet earth. The hot, semi-molten asthenosphere reaches the surface at the mid-ocean ridges, forming new oceanic crust and plate material. The oceanic plates diverge at this point. Where they meet the more substantial continental plates, they usually pass beneath, adding to the continental plate, and/or becoming semi-molten in the asthenosphere, which later rises again into the continental land masses by a variety of processes, not fully understood. As the continents are pushed up from below, they are eroded from above. The resulting minerals and rocky particles aid in the formation of soil, sand and sediment, ultimately reaching the sea. Some of the sediment rests on the shallower waters of the continental shelves and is later pushed up above the waters as the continent rises. Other sediment reaches the oceanic crust and is recycled as it passes beneath the continental crust. Moving at a rate of about 4 inches a year, as many plates are now doing, it would take only 50 to 100 million years for new oceanic crust to be recycled, destroying all fossilized remains from the deep ocean bed. Erosion of the land, recycling of the deep oceanic plates, plus the ideal nature of the habitat provided by the continental shelves, make these sediments the most prolific source of fossils.

a liquid centre and a hazel nut suspended in the very middle. A rather strange Christmas cake, I must admit. The main body of the earth is comprised of substance under phenomenal pressure due to the weight of material above – just like the weight of water at great depths. The pressures generated by the weight of hundreds of miles of solid rock above are phenomenal.

In our Christmas cake, the outer layer of marzipan, softer and more

pliable than the main body of the centre, comprises the asthenosphere, while the firm and undulating mountainous icing of varying
thickness represents the lithosphere with its crust. Now, in your
imagination, set it spinning and fill in the low-lying areas with sea
water, and you have a mental image of the earth. But with a fair
amount of imaginative licence!

The main factor to bear in mind is that the whole affair is
malleable. A geophysicist for whom I once worked used to describe
the earth to his students as a giant suet pudding. Looked at over a
period of days or years, the earth appears to be solid enough, but
studied over periods of thousands to millions of years it is only a
large, very hot, layered dumpling, continually generating its own heat
and – as a result – churning about inside itself and upon its surface.

Now the lithosphere, the more rigid icing on the softer marzipan, is
currently made up of about twelve separate plates. And they move.
Continuously. When two plates diverge – the ocean moves between
them. When one plate meets another plate they either both go up in
the air, as one tries to rise up above the other. Or one of them tries to
slip down and underneath the other. What does not happen when
they meet each other is that they stop. The planetary heat engine is
continuously active and that energy needs to be constantly expressed.
Movement in the earth's outer layers is continuous.

The result of plates meeting is either a high mountain range, such as
the Andes or the Himalayas, or a deep ocean trench – a huge sub-sea
valley. The speed of movement varies. The Himalayas, for example,
are still rising at a rate of seven millimetres per year, a process which
began when the smaller continental plate we call the Indian sub-
continent crashed into the great underbelly of the huge plate we call
Asia, 40 to 60 million years ago. And though movements are by no
means regular, it seems that the Himalayas are rising faster now than
they did then.

Again, the great Rift Valley, running south from the Red Sea
through Ethiopia and into East Africa, is widening at a rate of about
one inch per year. There are cracks in the land where the local people
say that if you wedge a stick there in the morning, it will have fallen in
by the following day. The Red Sea is actually a part of this rift, itself
expanding at the same rate as Africa slowly moves away from Arabia.
One day, East Africa will be a vast island in what we presently call the
Indian Ocean.

Similarly, the famous San Andreas fault, part of the great fault
running along the western coast of both North and South America, is
the junction between the low-lying Pacific ocean plate and the North

and South American continental plates. The two Americas are themselves separated because of a further fault running west to east along the northern coastline of South America (see Figure 3.3).

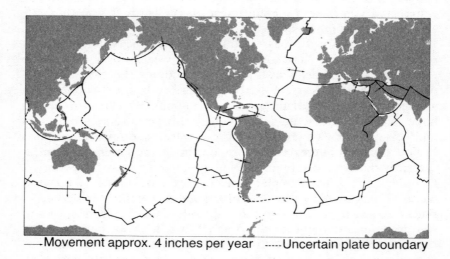

——— Movement approx. 4 inches per year   ----Uncertain plate boundary

Figure 3.3   The earth's present lithospheric plates (simplified). (After The Oceanic Crust *by J. Francheteau. Copyright 1983 by Scientific American Inc. Plate motions modified from the work of J.B. Minster and T.H. Jordan.)*

Like the continental plates, the thinner oceanic plates are constantly on the move. Where the plates move apart, a deep sea upwelling of molten magma from the asthenosphere beneath adds new material to the trailing edge. This is how new crust is formed. As the magma pours out of the rift, huge mountain ranges develop on the sea bed. Geologists call them mid-ocean ridges, the mid-Atlantic ridge rising up to 10,000 feet above the sea floor, for example. Thus is a cycle of renewal made complete. Fresh minerals are brought up to the planetary surface from deep within the earth's interior. And much of the planetary material has been recycled many times.

In places, these sub-sea mountain ranges rise above the surface, forming the oceanic islands of the world. The area where the ocean plates meet is volcanically active, of course, which explains why many oceanic islands are, or have been, volcanic.

The surface of the earth, then, is constantly on the move, re-adjusting the position of the land masses. The movement of the ocean plates results in huge crustal bulges where they diverge, displacing vast quantities of water, which spills over onto the land. At the same time, the polar caps recede and advance, adding to the flooding of the low-lying continental areas. As a consequence, much of what we now know of as continents become vast inland seas, often no more than 200 feet deep, a warm and watery haven teeming with all manner of marine life. This is the continental shelf, at the edge of which the level drops steeply down a submerged cliff to the deeper ocean floor beneath.

Going back only 150 million years, neither the Atlantic nor the Pacific oceans as we know them today existed. And 200 million years ago, all the continents were, it is supposed, grouped together into one supercontinent: *Pangaea*, the German meteorologist Alfred Wegener called it when he made the suggestion earlier this century.

But the idea was not a new one, though rejected at the time. In the latter years of the nineteenth century the Austrian geologist, Eduard Suess, made the more tentative suggestion that what are now the southern continents of Africa, South America, Australia, Antarctica and India were once joined together into a supercontinent he called *Gondwanaland*. These ideas, with certain refinements, are now thought to have been correct. Gondwanaland was the southern continent resulting from the first split in the more ancient landmass of Pangaea.

How does a continent break apart? No-one is altogether sure, but one suggestion has been this. Here and there, extensive plumes of molten rock, 250 miles in diameter, force their way up from the asthenosphere beneath. Strangely, these plumes can remain stationary for long aeons, and if a continental plate passes over such a hot spot, its rocky fabric melts, as if by some giant planetary flame cutter. Over the course of millions of years, the continent is thus cut into two, two new plates now freed to go their separate ways.

Allowing for an average movement of 4 inches a year over a period of 4.5 billion years (a pure guess – it may have been vastly more or less, but it is in accord with present rates of movement), that would have enabled plates to have moved nearly 300,000 miles. That is more than ten times around the circumference of the globe – a distance of about 25,000 miles.

Evidence in the fossil record of this continental drift is discovered in a variety of places. Ancient Palaeozoic fossil strata, older than 245 million years, from both Europe and North America contain very similar, often identical collections of fossil species indicating a probable prehistoric land connection between the two, as well as the existence of a similar environment. Likewise, the experts say that the ancient fusion of Africa, South America, Antarctica, Australia and India into Gondwanaland is demonstrated by the presence of similar fossil fauna.

So the land and the oceans have changed and are continuing to do so. And since the continents are largely formed of igneous rock, it is also supposed that, in a way not fully understood, vast quantities of magma are being continuously heaved up to the surface from the deeper areas of the asthenosphere.

From the world of the subatomic to the stars and galaxies, from the functioning of single cells to the miracle of whole organisms, nature demonstrates order and perfect design. Should we not have expected to discover such rhythms and patterns in the functioning of the earth's interior and in the maintenance of its biosphere? Three and a half billion years is a long time for life to have continued unabated in a biosphere where minute changes to any one of innumerable parameters would have long ago destroyed it all. Do we really believe that it is all maintained by chance and random mutation? Indeed, when everything is so fittingly ordered, what do we mean by chance?

THE ACCEPTANCE OF A THEORY

The science of *plate tectonics* only became acceptable during the 1960s. Before that, geologists had lived with a number of uncomfortable anomalies. Weakly magnetic iron minerals, for example, when laid down in sediments, orientate themselves to magnetic north-south. The subsequent compression and solidification of the sediment into rock then fixes these mini-magnets in their relative positions. But the magnetic orientation of rocks of the same age varies in different parts of the world. Why? Why did plotting the position of the Devonian magnetic north place it at a point in the north Pacific when measured from the American east coast, but at another location when calculated from England? Once it was conceded that the continents had been on the move relative to both each other and to the earth's axis of rotation, these anomalies became understandable.

In fact, during Middle Palaeozoic times over 350 to 400 hundred million years ago, the equator ran diagonally across America, through Mexico or Southern California, in what is now a north-easterly direction. And the south pole was only a few hundred miles north of Cape Town, then a part of the massive continent of Gondwanaland.

Plate tectonics is a relatively new appreciation of what is happening on our planet and many of the details are still obscure to us. As recently as the early 1960s it was mentioned to undergraduates only as a loony heresy, though the suggestion was first mooted at the end of the last century. Yet by the end of the 1960s, the 'new idea' had become the accepted reality.

This kind of sudden and rapid acceptance of an old theory is a threshold event. Science goes forward on an existing paradigm as far as it is able: old, habituated patterns are always preferred by the human mind. But when the old paradigm can no longer contain the new evidence, as well as the new thinking and the new consciousness of the times, then like any energy system stretched beyond the point of equilibrium, a new balance is quite suddenly established which accommodates all the new parameters. The older generation may mount a rearguard action, striving to maintain previous habits of thought. But a new generation rapidly sweeps away the debris of the past.

This is like the change of state from solid to liquid, or liquid to gas. The change is not gradual but sudden. Between states, there may be a short period of chaos, while the players are reshuffled into their new roles. And the change may have been building up for a long time. But to external eyes, the event seems sudden.

Similarly, we are experiencing such a threshold in the scientific thinking and general world-view of our present times. We are at a turning point. Increasingly, people are rejecting the old idea that 'to be a scientist' one has to believe only in molecules, subatomic particles and electromagnetism as the fundamental basis of all life, existence and experience of being.

EROSION AND THE FOSSIL RECORD

While the earth's crustal plates heave and shift, being recycled from beneath, activity upon their exterior surface is no less dynamic. On the ocean floor, the currents slowly turn the soft sedimentary rock to fine sand and silt. Countless bacteria and protozoa remove any remaining organic debris. Only the minerals remain. Hard igneous rock is powdered and pummelled until even granite is thrown up in soft, rounded chunks upon the sea shore. Bacteria, too, play their part: some species, not averse to digesting stone, release minerals for plant life to feed upon.

Much of the 'dry' land receives a regular dowsing under the sea, cutting back sedimentary accretions to the continental crust. Ancient sea beds are thrust so high that sea shells are found high up in the Himalayas and other mountain ranges. And whenever land rises above the level of the oceans, then the persistent forces of wind and rain, river and ice begin their process of erosion.

Glaciers, flowing downhill under their own weight, carve out valleys from the land, thousands of feet deep, such is the pressure of the ice. In the Alps, glacial speeds vary from a few inches to three feet per day. In Antarctica, the ice is advancing in the direction of Rio de Janeiro at a rate of nearly 30 feet per year!

At the Grand Canyon, the River Colorado has been eating away at the land for a relatively short 15 to 20 million years, yet the size of the canyon, more than a mile deep in places, varies from 4 to 18 miles wide and is 280 miles long. An immense hole in the ground laying bare the sediments of the last 600 million years or more. The sides of the exposed cliffs show clear strata of mostly sandstone, limestone and looser shale, all being the sedimentary deposits of ancient seas. At the lowest levels, these date back to Precambrian times. And the rim of the canyon, once under the ocean, is now 8000 feet above sea level.

Some mountains, like the Himalayas, are of geologically recent origin. These are the high, sharp and craggy peaked ranges. Time and erosion will break down these rough and sharp-edged contours, like suffering brings humility and understanding to a proud and egocentric heart. Old mountains are rounded, even flattened to a plateau like the Ozarks of Missouri and Arkansas, ancient stumps of prehistoric mountain ranges themselves thrust high by plate movements hundreds of millions of years ago.

With erosion of the land and continental shelves, the fossils too are broken up. Fossil formation upon the land is very much a hit and miss affair, even at the best of times. Hungry mouths, erosion and the frequent ingress of the sea wipe the slate clean. Terrestrial animals and plants have little chance, relatively speaking, of leaving behind remains which will last untouched through hundreds of millions of years.

Fossilization takes place best in sediments, but sedimentation only happens where there is water – along the water margins, estuaries and the shallow beds of lakes or oceans. And the most prolific fossil finds have always been in the sedimentary deposits of ancient seas, more especially along the shallower waters of the continental shelves. The constant re-forming of the oceanic crust leaves us with diminished hope of ever finding fossils from the deep oceans that are older than 175 million years.

Even amongst the fossil riches of the ancient Palaeozoic we find little evidence of marine plant life – of seaweeds – yet there they must have been, as an integral part of the food cycle, trapping the energy of the sun into organic molecular formations. Without such plants there could have beeen no life.

Many conventional evolutionists envisage the land of the most ancient of those times as arid and hostile. Even freshwater lakes would have had no life within them, so they say. But does this seem reasonable? Land and fresh water do not accumulate such vast fossil treasures as the ocean floors, nor do they have the processes that create such vast sedimentary deposits. Are they not mistaking a lack of evidence due to natural causes for an affirmation of the theory?

In present times, we know that the planetary ecosystem requires both land and sea to be populated for the cycle of rain and water to be complete. Do we really believe that life could exist in the seas and not upon the land? How would such an ecosystem function without forests or land-based vegetation?

The fossil record of the land and sea are both so incomplete, especially that of the much-scoured land. Even today there are many creatures whose numbers have become so few that the future fossil record will proclaim them as already extinct, preserving no memory of their existence. On the land, it is only the bones and teeth of vertebrate animals which remain, though even these are far more readily destroyed by natural processes than hard invertebrate exoskeletons and sea shells. Nutritious bone tissue makes a better meal than the mineral shell of a limpet! How ironic that the dead remains of shellfish reach more determinedly for immortality than any legacy of man!

The sedimentary shales and limestones, siltstones and sandstones get buried deep, under a tremendous crushing pressure, some perhaps even to be absorbed into the magma and asthenosphere beneath. Their solidity is only an illusion. Sedimentary rocks are comparatively soft and behave just like our planetary Christmas cake when under pressure for long periods of time. The fossil forms are so easily destroyed.

The earth's upper mantle is a churning, pressuring, baking, grinding yet balanced system with a thin layer of life forms on the top. Nature's processes are designed to recycle the remains, not to create a neat and ordered layer of fossils for man to ponder over! In time, all the fossils, even of the Palaeozoic, will go the way of the yet more ancient Precambrian rocks. But would we then be justified in declaring that life was almost absent in those times?

I contend, as do the ancient sages of far wiser cultures than our own, that life was always here in full expression. Even man would have had his part to play. This is the way in which the cosmic drama is unfolded. The mystic plan requires it.

INTERLUDE

BEFORE THESE HILLS AND VALLEYS WERE YET FORMED

The following extract from a conversation in 1971 between Maharaj Charan Singh and a disciple refers to a letter written by the great mystic, Maharaj Sawan Singh (1858–1948), to one of his disciples concerning his own spiritual preceptor, Baba Jaimal Singh (1839–1903). Considering that plate tectonics was not an academically acceptable theory until the late 1960s, the dating is of interest. The letter was written sometime during the 1920s about an incident which would have happened between 1894 and 1900.

Question: In a letter from Maharaj Sawan Singh to one of his American disciples, there is this quotation:

> At Murrie Hills (in the Himalayan foothills) my house faced Maksh Puri (a place of Hindu pilgrimage). One day when Baba Ji (Baba Jaimal Singh) was visiting me, I pointed in that direction and said, 'Look Sir, what beautiful scenery!'
> Baba Ji laughed and said, 'I have seen it,' implying that he had seen it long ago.
> I asked, 'Was your regiment ever posted there?'
> He replied, 'My child you do not understand these things. We saw this place at a time when these hills and valleys had not yet been formed.'

What did Baba Ji mean by this?

Maharaj Charan Singh: He is referring to his previous births. Now even the scientists and professors of geography tell us that all these hills were plains at one time. There may have been a sea where the Himalayas are now – scientists have found evidence for it. So Maharaj Ji was just saying how beautiful the hills were, and Baba Ji said: 'I have seen them before.' Maharaj Ji naturally thought he must have been posted there in the army.

But Baba Ji said: 'No, not in this life.' He is referring to some previous birth, when he came and saw all those places when there were no hills there.

Spiritual Heritage, Maharaj Charan Singh

4. MEMORIES IN THE MUD: THE FOSSIL STORY

SOME OLD FOSSILS AND HOW THEY GOT THERE

The majority of fossils have been — and always will be — the hard, inedible exoskeletons of marine invertebrates. Walking the shoreline of many coastal areas one comes across those places where the sea seems to take a natural delight in collecting her debris, piling the discarded shells of marine creatures into one small area. Digging down into the sand and sediment one finds a multitude of shells that may have otherwise lain buried, deeper and deeper, for millions upon millions of years.

The collecting places in the shallower waters of ancient seas — on the continental shelves or when the ocean covered what are now our continental land masses — these are the major forming ground for the sedimentary rocks of future ages.

The igneous, granitic, basal rock of the continents is ground down by wind and weather. Previous sedimentary deposits and rock formations are eroded and recycled. The sea, too, slowly pummels her rocks to fine sand and sediment. And there, on the ocean floor and on the shoreline, it collects, marine mud, sand and various deposits — part of the basic material for the rocks of future aeons.

But the cycle of sedimentary rock formation is more elegant than the simple recycling of silt to rock. It is more beautiful and simple than one could ever conceive. It is a service performed by myriads of tiny organisms. Life herself administers her own environment.

The minerals leached slowly from the rocks find their way into the sea. There they are used by algae, and a multitude of other microscopic marine organisms, as shells, skeletons and cell-wall strengtheners of many different kinds. The creatures die and their hard remains, picked clean of almost all organic material, drift slowly to the ocean floor. So dense and continuous is this deposition that scientists have called it 'marine snow'. One class of algae, the *diatoms*, form a skeletal structure out of silica. After their brief lives, the skeletons sink downwards, adding an incredible 300 million tons of silica to the future sedimentary rocks, every year. Likewise, *coccolithopores*, tiny single-celled algae or phytoplankton, construct a shell for themselves of calcium carbonate and these too are added to the ocean floor, millions of tons of fragile flakes, every year.

The process of rock formation is an integral part of nature's processes. Without these and similar marine organisms, the sea would soon become too overloaded with minerals to support life. So it is precipitated as microscopic shells and skeletal structures. The ancient rocks and mountains of the land provide minerals for the plants, which support all terrestrial life. The residue is washed into the sea. There the excess is deposited upon the bottom – rock in the formation, later to be raised up as land for the completion of the cycle. And there are a host of tiny living creatures performing similar functions for all the many minerals and substances that find their way into the sea.

The process is also self-regulating for when the concentrations of silica and calcium carbonate rise, so too do the diatom and coccolithopore populations. If the concentration falls, so do these populations. Similarly with the other organisms.

Other marine creatures die. Their soft bodies quickly become the food for a thousand hungry mouths. Even bones, being an organic cellular structure, make a good meal for millions upon millions of bacteria, of single-celled protozoa, of tiny worms – or even those larger creatures possessed of crushing jaws. Everything gets used in nature, nothing goes to waste. So under normal circumstances only those organisms with inedible exoskeletons – the shells and carapaces of armoured creatures – remain. They sink to the ocean floor and are buried in the sediment. The process of fossilization has begun.

Here and there, perhaps associated with some natural disaster when all organic life in an area was suddenly extinguished – the scalding heat of a magma flow as it reached the sea, for instance – we find the impression of some soft-bodied creature whose body was covered and its impression preserved before life returned to the area. Or we find the tracks of some ancient worm or other creature as it slithered or skuttled across the ocean floor so many millions of years ago. But mostly the sea gives us invertebrate exoskeletons and a few fish bones, just as the coast line and the sea floor do today. Our palaeontologists are beachcombers of those ancient shores, rootlers amongst those ancient sea beds. So when these creatures die or fall prey to one another, their protective shells are discarded. Food for no-one, ripe for geological recycling – for rock formation and for mineral resources.

So mostly it is the sea that has given us our fossils. Perhaps as much as 99 per cent of our fossil record is of marine creatures. Indeed, not only is it difficult to uncover evidence of land-based fossils, it is difficult to find ancient evidence of land itself. Erosion is a continuous and relentless process, soon ensuring that all exposed surfaces are ground back to water level and below. Without the constant uplifting of the planetary plates, there would soon be no land left at all. So the closer one gets to modern times, the more is one likely to find the fossils of terrestrial creatures. But this does not mean that ancient life only existed in the seas.

Sedimentary deposits are the result of land erosion. In the planetary cycle, everything passes through the sea. That is why there is such a paucity of land-based fossils. Only those terrestrial creatures which regularly visit or live near water stand much chance of being fossilized. But even then, their remains must fortuitously get buried in the sedimentary muds and then lie undisturbed for millions of years.

Forests and temperate climes are no place for fossils to collect, with the hosts of moulds, fungi, microbes, insects and other larger sca-vengers all in search of food. Nor do deserts and plains provide protection from the elements and other creatures. Finds such as the Flaming Cliffs of Outer Mongolia are startling abnormalities. Not only were complete skeletons of the small dinosaur, *protoceratops*, discovered there, but also their undisturbed nests of unhatched eggs still lying tidily within. Some sudden disaster must have overtaken them, to be covered rapidly by wind-blown desert sands, only to be exposed in our own time by the wind and rain of the Gobi desert.

But such finds only serve to remind us of the abundance of life in those past eras and of how much has been lost without a trace. Let us then, for a moment, look at these eras as the geologists and fossil experts see them (see Figure 4-1).

Geologists say that the earth has existed for 4.5 billion years. Until recently, the most ancient signs of life took us back 'only' to the Cambrian era, half a billion years ago. There are few sedimentary rocks older than this. But in those Cambrian sediments we find, as if from nowhere, a veritable explosion of *trilobites*, a diverse family of ancient marine crustaceans who left us a vast storehouse of their exoskeletons. Their nearest living relatives are the horse-shoe crabs. With them, we find the remains of a multitude of snails, clams,

Years Ago (In Millions)	Major Divisions (Eras)	Sub-Divisions (Epochs)
	CENOZOIC	Quaternary
— 1.66 —		Tertiary
— 66.4 —	MESOZOIC	Cretaceous
— 144 —		Jurassic
— 208 —		Triassic
— 245 —	PALAEOZOIC	Permian
— 286 —		Upper Carboniferous
— 320 —		Lower Carboniferous
— 360 —		Devonian
— 408 —		Silurian
— 438 —		Ordovician
— 505 —		Cambrian
— 570 —	PRECAMBRIAN	
— 4500 —		

Figure 4.1 *Eras and epochs of the past (note the absence of scale).*

brachiopods (lampshells and many others), echinoderms (e.g. sea urchins and starfish), arthropods and a host of other invertebrates.

Life would appear to have been in full swing for many a million years and palaeontologists had always assumed that more ancient fossils had been baked and crushed into remains beyond our wit to fully decipher.

There are many fossils which show signs of past geological activity. Their features may be eroded almost flat; they may have been shorn in two in some ancient catastrophic happening; they may be crushed, distorted or lacking certain parts of their bony or exoskeletal anatomy.

Sometimes, sediments are later eroded and their fossils loosened, as the land and oceans move. These are washed downstream to mingle with the remains of the current species of the times – all these then being deposited once more in some new sedimentary repository. Found by modern palaeontologists, the creatures would appear to have lived side by side, though they may in reality have been separated by hundreds of millions of years and have come from a variety of sources.

Palaeontologists are aware of these problems. Dating sedimentary rocks is by no means as easy as with igneous rocks, for they contain no radioactive elements to date according to decay rates and may contain the eroded and re-deposited elements of far more ancient relics.

Sedimentary rocks are often dated according to the age of the igneous rocks found embedded in them. But even this can be misleading for the vast pressures of crustal movements and volcanic activity can thrust molten magma into the heart of ancient sediments as easily as pushing nuts into a Christmas cake with your thumb. Or new sediments can form around more ancient igneous rocks.

Where no igneous inserts are available for analysis, their age is estimated by correlating their fossil fauna with fossils drawn from rocks whose age is thought to have been more accurately determined. But with so much unknown and constant geological movement, mistakes can so easily occur.

The beginning of earth time is said to be 4.5 billion years ago. Yet those ancient Cambrian fossils – the trilobites and their associates – come from creatures who lived only half a million years ago, almost 4 billion years later. Yet those very first fossils are close relatives of the living creatures of today. But what happened in those first 4 billion years?

The oldest granite yet recorded comes from Australia, dated at 4 billion years, a relic of Pangaea. The most ancient sedimentary rocks have been found in northern Australia, entwined with volcanic lava flow dated at 3.5 billion years. But sediment means that there was water – oceans, lakes, rivers, estuaries, rain and flood plains – 3.5 billion years ago. And water means that there was life upon the planet, upon the land and sea, for without life forms the temperature would have risen so much that the water would have evaporated. If only we could persuade those rocks to tell their story!

Beginning as sedimentary deposits beneath the waves, thrust up onto the great slip-sliding land mass of Pangaea, they travelled across the face of the earth, their boat an entire continent, their sea the softer rock beneath. Caught up in some ancient volcanic eruption, covered by the debris of millions or billions of years, washed again and again by the ocean currents as the seas receded and advanced, subjected to deep pressures, pulverized by the glaciers of innumerable ice ages, at length to find their way back onto dry land where erosion bites and chisels until such ancient rock is once again exposed . . . Who knows what incredible saga will have been enacted before such deposits are exposed once again, still partially intact, upon the surface of our planet?

Yet finely preserved, deeply etched into the fabric of these primeval rocks, are signs of life. The rods and spheres of bacteria, the fossilized relics only of the tiniest creatures now remain, the structure revealed in wafer-thin slivers seen under high-powered microscopes. No bone or exoskeleton could ever have survived such a journey. Under the enormous pressures deeper within the earth, the rock even changes its crystal structure. What chance does some ancient seashell stand of passing through unscathed?

So these Australian deposits and sedimentary rocks from a few other areas, share similar evidence of life from times between 700 million and 3.5 billion years ago.

But then, suddenly, the broken fossil record jumps from bacteria to trilobites and much more. Most of the ancient past left no record in the mud, and so many of those primeval deposits have been recycled and are no longer available for inspection. So much is buried too deep for us to ever find it.

WHAT DID THE VERY FIRST CREATURE EAT?

Thinking of those primeval rocks, one wonders what such ancient microbes found to eat? Were they a part of a thriving economy of creatures? Or were they almost on their own, living upon the fortuitous organic debris from which the first self-replicating molecules are supposed to have sprung, by chance, to life? Or did they tap their energy from the energy welling up from the volcanic mid-ocean ridges as some bacteria do today, though they are also part of an active ecosystem?

But perhaps, fortuitously, they fed on 'blue-green algae', an interesting, microscopic, filamentous seaweed, not possessed of a genuine cell structure but 'successful' enough to have survived through to present times, like their bacterial cousins. For also in the hardened sediments of 3.5 billion years ago, we find strange cabbage-shaped mounds (*stromatolites*) that continue to appear in the fossil record right up until the present time. To this day, they are found – made of particulate sediment – in Shark's Bay, off the northern shores of Australia. And these mounds are formed from daily growth layers of this so-called 'primitive' seaweed. But around them lives an active and varied ecosystem, possessed of myriad different species. The one cannot exist without the other. . . .

Seaweed, bacteria and traces of some other cellular creatures are the only fossilized remains of life before the late Precambrian era. But are we really to assume that a thriving, self-balancing ecosystem and biosphere can be comprised of little more than bacteria and algae, all alone?

And the question also has to be asked – what did the *very first* self-replicating organism eat? Or is the mechanistic theory suggesting that DNA, RNA and the whole, complex self-replicating process plus chlorophyll, or something similar, all came spontaneously into existence in some primeval thunderstorm, thereafter deriving its energy from the sun? Or did the first self-activating molecules live, like the bacteria, off other organic material that somehow had just chanced to be there? Or did they use some process to take in energy from the ocean's deep volcanic chemistry?

And did the dead bodies of all those first organisms then just lie about for further millennia awaiting the dawn of some mutant cousin who spontaneously developed the ability to gobble up the dead bodies of all his forebears? And if that second mutant species was so 'successful' at eating the dead and undecayed bodies of his ancestors, why did it not try its hand at eating its *living* relatives, thereby putting a rapid end to life on earth in the very first act of warfare?

Again, if representatives of all other species on the scale of evolution are to be found alive today, then why are none of these primeval, self-replicating molecules to be found in present times, hovering upon the borderland of life and inert substance? And what, anyway, would have terminated the life of this first, primeval self-organizing, self-replicating molecule, who had no competitors? Why should it have ever died at all? By evolving into something that competed with itself and ate itself up? The second move upon the evolutionary tree being a predator that preyed upon the first?

How could life have got started in this way? From so many points of view, it makes no sense. That life spontaneously generated itself from dust and water is a belief not so very far removed from that of mice spontaneously generating themselves in soiled linen kept in closed cupboards. Surely even the myths of some so-called primitive peoples have expressed more likely thoughts about the origin of things!

ARE OUR EXPERIENCES OF LIFE NO MORE THAN MOLECULES?

Do scientists and people generally, however materially minded they may be, *really* believe that life is nothing more than molecules? That consciousness, a sense of self and the knowledge of our existence are actually nothing more than happenstance, a cosmic coincidence, a strange freak? That thought and emotion, love and hatred, personality, psychic and mystic experience – that all these are phantasms of some molecular dance? That ideas, music, art, poetry and the appreciation of beauty are spun out of nerve cells and electricity? Many do believe this to be so.

But if this were true, that life is no more than material substance, from where do we derive our sense of values? How is it that we value justice, morality, human rights and decency? What is human weakness and human strength? From where do we derive such evaluation of human conduct: that one man is of strong spiritual or moral fibre whilst another weak? From where – since substance has no sense of discrimination – do we derive our feelings of 'good' and 'bad'? What then are wisdom, understanding, tolerance and love – if mind and consciousness are purely to be found within the molecules of the brain?

The material paradigm leaves too many fundamental questions unanswered and neglected. Is the ultimate 'goal' of 4 billion years of evolution to have a good economy, low inflation, and to make money for just three score years and ten?

If man is no more than molecules, then why is murder considered to be the ultimate crime, whilst premeditated murder – a murder planned within the mind – is held to be the worst of all? Why are our human law courts so concerned with mind and motive? How can molecules develop a sense of ethics and aesthetics? Why do crimes and misdemeanours leave a sense of guilt upon the mind? Is guilt no more than molecular patterns? But then, what are molecules and the subatomic particles comprising them? Whence do they arise? Material science has no encompassing and satisfying answers to these questions.

ANCIENT ECOSYSTEMS

We have already made passing mention of the relevance of our modern understanding of self-balancing cycles and ecosystems to a study of the fossil record – a subject rarely tackled by evolutionists. Modern ecosystems explicitly require the presence of almost all classes of life – from bacteria and plants to invertebrates and higher animals. The spectrum of living creatures represents a mutually interdependent orchestra of self-help and balance. This is the essence of James Lovelock's Gaia hypothesis.

Yet many fossils, even those dated at half a billion years, are of forms which all but an expert could mistake for present day species. So one assumes that their life histories and feeding habits were similar. How then did they maintain the environment as modern creatures do, within the very finely tuned range of conditions in which life can exist? Especially if – as evolutionists maintain – there was no life upon the land and neither fish nor vertebrates swimming in the sea. As we have commented, life in the sea is deeply and completely integrated with and dependent upon life on the land.

One thing is certain: if the invertebrates in my garden: the slugs, the snails, the caterpillars, the aphids and other bugs – had no warm-blooded vertebrate predators to keep their numbers down, they would very soon have eaten up all the available plant life. And that would be the end of that. Cold-blooded predators, operating at a lower metabolic rate, require far less food than warm-blooded ones. Ever hungry, warm-blooded predators are an essential aspect of all modern ecosystems, especially on the land.

Similarly in the sea. Without the fishes, the invertebrates would soon eat themselves out of a living. And without the mammals, birds and bigger fishes to gobble up the smaller fishes, life would soon become untenable.

Evolutionists might argue that there were species of particularly large and voracious invertebrate, eating up their lesser cousins, in the absence of higher creatures. But surely such hungry organisms could only have evolved much later than their smaller brethren, which would therefore have had ample opportunity to eat themselves out of a living before such gargantuan predators arrived upon the scene? And anyway, why have we found no remains of them?

It all seems a somewhat dubious proposition. That the fine balance and exquisite processes of nature, from the 'lowliest' bacterium to the full planetary ecosystem, have evolved by what man perceives as 'chance'. Yet of the nature and origin of that highly ordered 'chance', he can give no account.

Lovelock also points out that without the maintenance of the biosphere by living creatures, planet earth would soon possess surface temperatures well in excess of boiling water, the oxygen would be reduced to a minimum, carbon dioxide would dominate the atmosphere, and the boiling seas – if any – would be so saline that nothing could exist in them. And that is just for starters. In fact, our planet would soon resemble Mars or Venus, where scientists believe that life like ours could never exist. It is the life forms themselves which keep the earth in a condition which supports life. So how could life ever have got started, bringing so hostile an environment to heel? Clearly there is something missing in these explanations.

Furthermore, as James Lovelock has pointed out, the finesse of ecological balance extends to more than just the food cycle. The finely tuned and essential balance of minerals in sea and on the land, for instance, is maintained by the life forms themselves, as are all aspects of the environment, even the nature of gases in the atmosphere. It is marine creatures, as we have described, which keep the salinity of the sea at just the right concentration in which organic cellular systems can exist. The balance is so exquisitely fine that the concentration of minerals washed off the land would otherwise have made marine life impossible within a geologically short space of time. All the seas would rapidly have become saltier than the Dead Sea.

While some organisms maintain the planetary mineral cycle, others administer the distribution of other elements essential to life, converting them to gases which waft back over the land, falling with the rain, and helping, too, to keep the atmospheric content balanced. Gases containing essential iodine, for example, are produced in tons by the seaweeds of the ocean shores. Without them, all higher creatures would soon suffer thyroid problems, for iodine lies at the heart of thyroid hormones. Many of these gases contribute to planetary temperature control, also administered through the automatic feedback response of other creatures. Man is not the only contributor of greenhouse gases.

Even our planetary water — the oceans, lakes, rivers, ice, snow, moisture, dew and rainfall — even these are maintained by the life forms themselves, and held in optimum conditions for the continuation of life. So in the absence of life, how could such an elegant system ever have got started? How could a hostile planet have ever been tamed by chance and self-organizing molecular patterns? From whence arises this mysterious 'self-organization' of creature and cosmos?

SOME MORE OLD FOSSILS

Some of the early trilobites were nearly 2 feet long, some size for a crab or a marine woodlouse, and the group consisted of hundreds of genera, let alone individual species. They lived, most probably, like their present cousins, as well-designed scavengers or by preying upon the soft-bodied creatures of their day. Judging by the numbers of trilobite fossils, there must have been plenty of food for them — dead or alive. And that means plenty of other creatures, a thriving ecology.

In the earliest Cambrian fossil records, dating back 570 million years, we find ourselves looking at a mass of exoskeletons and, not long after, at the bony armour of even a few fish. Little else has survived.

Prior to Cambrian days, there are only a few places where the fossil record is both preserved and exposed. One such area, the Ediacaran Hills of the Australian Flinders Range, was discovered during the late 1940's. These fossils are thought to be 670 million years old and, strangely, the deposit is largely the impressions of *soft-bodied* creatures — worms, jellyfish of several varieties, soft corals or sea pens and other species. And most interestingly, the species we find there are closely related to those of modern times.

The circumstances under which they were preserved must indeed have been unique for even in the later fossil record such deposits of soft-bodied creatures are rare. Similar fossil remains, though none so prolific as the Ediacaran deposits, have been found in Newfoundland, England and South Africa, some species being as long as six feet. And in all cases the species bear little resemblance to anything found in the later Cambrian deposits of hard-shelled creatures. Such is the selective sampling of the fossilization process.

To account for these soft-bodied impressions at such an early date, evolutionists had once tried to argue that the possession of soft bodies is more 'primitive', less 'highly evolved' and therefore represents but an evolutionary step in the direction of the heavily armoured – and therefore more highly evolved – trilobites. But one could as readily have argued it the other way around if the findings had happened to be reversed.

Is the soft-bodied octopus, for example, with its large brain, its eye resembling that of the mammal and its development of jet-propulsion, less 'evolved' than a woodlouse or a crab? Or are sea anemones less evolved than shellfish? Man, too, is largely soft-bodied. Is he less evolved, then, than a trilobite?

This evolutionary manner of talking in terms of 'progress', describing certain creatures as 'primitive', 'successful', 'lower' or 'highly evolved' needs to be examined with some rigorous thought, for it presupposes that some creatures are more 'highly' evolved than others without really defining what is *meant* by 'higher' and 'lower'. But we shall return to this topic in later chapters.

It is only the paucity of fossil data that makes evolutionists draw conclusions from such isolated and non-representative finds. When there is so little evidence, every find that is made changes the theory. The fossils only tell us that there were soft-bodied creatures at that time, not that there were no hard-shelled ones. Such deposits are isolated freaks of wave and sediment, perhaps related to planetary conditions at that time. It is certainly insufficient grounds for evolutionary theorizing.

I mention this instance because it demonstrates how easy it is, in the absence of data, to find an explanation to fit the evolutionary theory. But in the last twenty years, a whole series of hard-shelled invertebrates, clearly related to modern molluscs, have been discovered in Upper Precambrian rocks pre-dating the earliest signs of the famous trilobites, and prior to the magic 575 million year date which had long been stated as the earliest signs of life on earth. So the soft-bodied creatures were not alone after all. It was just a happenstance of fossilization.

And for protection against what predators were those hard exoskeletons required? In modern seas, the larger predators are fish, squid, mammals and birds. Yet – say the evolutionists, anxious to demonstrate an evolutionary lineage – there were no fish or any such predators in those ancient seas. They could not have yet evolved. But with such fragmentary and isolated finds, surely it is too difficult to draw such wide conclusions? And since nothing is wasted in nature, there must have been predators worthy of a 2-foot long trilobite.

One of the richest finds of Late Precambrian fossils was discovered in an extensive sequence preserved amongst the Vendian sediments of

Siberia – whose famous salt mines must themselves be the relics of ancient ocean mineral precipitation and evaporation.

Here we find many hard-shelled fossils, spanning many millions of years, but amongst them all there is no evidence of any actual evolutionary progress, no gradual development towards the wealth of different species found preserved in the later Cambrian deposits. Of course, it could so easily have been purely a matter of geographic distribution, of where these sediments happened to form. Not all places possess the same flora and fauna. One finds few sharks and no coral reefs along the shores of modern England, but that does not mean they are uncommon elsewhere and will leave no traces in the fossil record. These ancient deposits are so comparatively rare that we cannot extrapolate from the evidence of just a few widely spaced sedimentary deposits, making assumptions about life in *all* the seas and on *all* the land at those times.

Again, in the California White-Inyo range of hills, part of an area where the ancient Cambrian rocks have been exposed, recent, deeper excavation has revealed an even lower section of Late Precambrian sediment, beneath the Cambrian trilobite zones. No trilobites are present in these lower strata, yet in one high wall of sandstone we find many tracks of some creature, a worm of sorts, maybe, down amongst the oldest levels. Ascending higher, the tracks become more complex. Here and there we find the tiny shells of some ancient creature, even the tracks of trilobites scampering across the ocean floor as identified in later deposits. But no trilobite exoskeletons themselves. Clearly this was not one of the ocean's collecting places.

The ocean is fickle where she casts her treasures, and the heaviest sediments and fossilized remains are formed mostly in comparatively shallow waters. These lower deposits of the Californian White-Inyo hills, showing no signs of trilobite and other hard-shelled life, were most probably a different habitat, perhaps under deeper ocean waters than at later times, thus collecting fewer hard-shelled fossils.

It is only evolutionary fervour that makes a palaeontologist assume that there were fewer hard-shelled creatures at that time, that hard shells were an 'advancement' over soft-bodies, and that the hard-shelled creatures evolved out of the soft-bodied. Humans, after all, carry no hard shells around them, at least not in their physical anatomy.

So the Precambrian Ediacaran fossils are not unique. Similar ancient rocks in England, Newfoundland, California and Siberia have also revealed comparable fossils. But the absence of missing links, essential for the conventional evolutionary theory, and the presence of only fragmentary records, characterizes the entire field of palae-ontology. We are not seeing a representative and orderly selection of species as they were in those times. We are looking at fragments of the past, preserved only when circumstances were just right.

And through it all the land and the oceans drift and heave, exchanging places, sometimes ravaged by cataclysms we find difficult to imagine. Comets, giant meteorites, volcanoes, earthquakes, plan-etary conflagrations, solar explosions emitting intense radiation, occasional alignments between the planets of our solar system causing orbital fluctuations, switching of polarity in the earth's magnetic field and shifting of the planetary axis. All these and more, beyond our ken, have been visited upon the planet. One long, continuous saga.

Yet life continued, when only small fluctuations in any one of a host of parameters would have rung out its death knell. Not only is life itself a miracle, but its continuation is even more so. We little realize how finely poised are the factors which hold our planetary biosphere in equilibrium. Without an understanding of how the apparently outer world is linked to the inner life of all creatures by the encompassing and integrating processes of the greater Mind, we could only conclude that the coincidences required for the continu-ation of life are simply far too great.

But throughout the aeons, life has blossomed. It has not struggled, it has burgeoned. It has not only survived, it has been abundant. Yet without the inner Life Force, there is nothing. The yugas have rolled on inexorably, the ebb and flow of life's tide of inward power. The move into synchrony with the subtle, then the ride into grossness once again.

Species have come and gone. Outward forms have changed. Yet was the biochemistry, physiology or behaviour of an ancient jellyfish or a trilobite any the less complex or 'evolved' than that of their relatives of today? It seems unlikely. Man and mammals, birds and reptiles – or their ancient equivalents – may even have been present throughout, for their remains are far less enduring than hard, inedible carapaces. When most of the ancient land itself has long since been eroded away, how can we expect to find fossils of their remains? Sea-born life forms may have more readily left their shells for our future puzzlement, but does that mean that life *began* in the seas, or that no fishes ever swam those ancient oceans? The fossil evidence does not prove it.

Fossilization is not a complete and accurate filing system of the past. It is not even representative of all species that have lived. It is an exceptionally patchy record, heavily biased towards the preservation of particular kinds of creature, found in certain kinds of habitat.

There will have been fluctuations in the numbers of individual species, just as there are today. Maybe there *was* a preponderance of the lower species in earlier times, but that is still the case even today. Maybe there was, and maybe not. But how can we make such an assumption from such scant records? After all, we are talking of a time hundreds of millions of years ago! Even several billion fossils is a poor record of such a long span of time.

The attempt to understand our planetary history from the fossil record is like a reconstruction of the past from a vast library of history books where each volume covers a different period. But only one volume in a billion is preserved, and then only from those that happened to have a particular style of cover. And even there, the dates are mostly missing or confused, the pages have all been torn out, most of them have been lost and the remainder have been reshuffled. The only really concrete conclusion we can make is that there *has been* an extensive history, but the exact nature of that history is very difficult to determine. However, man is curious — and we do our best, even with what little we have!

INTERLUDE

A FOSSILIZED HERD OF *IGUANODON*

In 1822, Mrs Mary Ann Mantell encountered the first known bones of the massive 16-foot, 3 ton, herbivorous dinosaur, the *Iguanodon*, lying in a pile of gravel beside a English country lane in Sussex. It was the first dinosaur known to science and since then, many bones of the long extinct creature, which was common in Jurassic and Cretaceous times, have been found in various parts of Europe and North Africa.

Initially, no complete skeleton was found and from the available evidence, scientists reconstructed the *Iguanodon* as a reptile that walked upon its four legs. In 1877, however, a remarkable deposit of *Iguanodon* bones were found down a coalmine in the Belgian town of Bernissart, near the French border. A herd of twenty or more of these dinosaurs had been swept along in a flood and deposited in what must have then been a deep ravine, together with an ample and protective encasement of mud.

Reconstructing the newly discovered skeletons, many of which were complete, scientists realized that the creature had walked upright upon its rear legs, with its stout tail most probably aiding in its balance, like a kangaroo. More recent thoughts on the *Iguanodon*, see it as a grazing animal, close-cropping the herbage – also like modern kangaroos – and probably warm-blooded and hairy as well.

THE PATTERN
EMERGES

PUNCTUATED EQUILIBRIA AND THE GREATER LIFE CYCLE

As we have said, the age of sedimentary deposits is hard to determine when embedded granite and igneous rocks are absent. The age of granite can be determined by radio-uranium dating, by the state of decay of its radioactive uranium constituent. But even when embedded granite is present, it is hard to know at what stage the rocks became entwined and thus achieve a reliable date. Accurate dating of fossil finds is therefore difficult.

When the age of a rock is hard to determine by radio-uranium dating, the fossil experts are consulted, for an identification of the particular group of fossil fauna found in the deposits. Then, by comparison with other fossil finds where it seems that the age can be more accurately determined, one can assess the age of a layer of sediment.

This method is at least reasonably accurate from the point of view of comparative age, for it is an interesting and accepted fact that sedimentary deposits spanning millions of years have a fauna which is *stratifed*. That is, *there appear to be long periods of time spanning about 5 or 10 million years when the fauna changes little*. Then, without any signs of any evolutionary graduation, their place is suddenly taken by another group of creatures, usually *similar* but by normal scientific definition *different*, and containing many new species. It is observation of this *stratification* which has given rise to the theory of *punctuated equilibria*, first suggested by Niles Eldredge and Stephen Gould. Writes Eldredge in his book *Life Pulse*:

> When Gould and I first proposed the theory of punctuated equilibria back in the early 1970s, we stressed something that had been known to Darwin and, indeed, to all palaeontologists who were contemporaries of Darwin:

once they appear, species tend not to change very much at all. They may last 5 or 10 million years – sometimes even longer – and yet, while a very few might undergo the sort of gradual, 'progressive' modification we have come to expect of evolution, most will stay pretty much as they were when they first evolved . . .

Entire assemblages of organisms remain recognizable for millions of years, with some species dropping out, . . . The assemblages remain recognizable because the component species contributing populations to those ecosystems have themselves changed little. . . .

The basic pulse of life in the Palaeozoic, then, is economic business as usual for intervals as long as 5 or even 10 million years. Ecosystems are established and tend to run on virtually unchanged until an extinction event disrupts the system. If the event is severe enough, many species will become extinct. After relatively mild extinctions, replacement ecosystems tend to resemble those they have replaced, simply because close relatives are still available to stock the habitat. More severe extinctions mean more radical change in the complexion of replacement ecosystems.

Detailed charts of geological time readily bear out this phenomenon: the names of the geological systems and the corresponding periods of time ('Ordovician', 'Silurian', 'Devonian', etc.) reflect the experiences of early geologists who saw natural divisions in life forms in the different bodies of strata.

Each system, moreover, is divided into a sequence of series, in which the faunal turnover is relatively less severe. Major extinctions are less common than milder events – a fact that enabled early geologists to divide up the time scale in the first place. This pattern of periodic disruption of ecosystems in varying degrees of intensity is the dominant signal of life's evolutionary pulse – and nowhere is it better seen than in the ecosystems of the Middle and Upper Palaeozoic.

It is evident from the fossil record that for periods of time spanning several million years, nature maintains a *status quo*. Then, clearly etched into the fossil record, there is a massive extinction of existing species, sometimes by as much 90 per cent or more, at least amongst those represented in the fossil record. This is followed by a rapid regeneration of a brand new flora and fauna – many often related to previous species, but some and occasionally many, quite new forms, whose likenesses had not been previously recorded. And in both cases, there are none of the obvious links that are predicted by the *very gradual* and natural selection of a Darwinian evolutionary process. Microevolution may be there, but not even *once* in any of the myriad strata spanning nearly 600 million years do we find evidence of one species changing into something significantly different. Even in microevolution, the changes often seem to have occurred in sudden shifts.

As Eldredge pointed out, he and Gould were not the first to spot these jumps in the fossil record. Georges Cuvier (1769-1832) and others prior to Darwin were convinced from their observations that species remained constant until hit by some catastrophic event, which resulted in their extinction. New species, they thought were then created to fill the gaps. But how that new proliferation came about, they did not know.

Darwin, however, realized that his theory of evolution by natural selection required a *gradual* change and suggested that the lack of palaeontological evidence for it was purely a temporary hiccough, related to the scant nature of the fossil record. Further careful digging amongst the ancient sediments would, he felt sure, reveal the missing links. But far from further fossil discoveries and a more detailed analysis of fossils, using electron microscopy and other modern techniques, revealing evidence of such gradual change, the reverse has been true. Species changes always seem to be sudden, at least geologically speaking, and even whole groups of radically new species appear to pop up suddenly out of the woodwork — or rather, from the stonework!

Some of this can be explained by geological circumstance — the withdrawal of the sea, some subsequent erosion of the sedimentary deposits and then, perhaps a million years later, the return of the ocean under new environmental circumstances, bringing in other species of the same epoch that were more suited to the new conditions. The resulting sediment therefore exhibits a stratification because it is not a continuous record in time and because the environmental conditions were not the same.

But this does not explain the majority of such species extinctions and renewals, especially when those changes can be charted in widely spaced fossil records from around the world. For these cyclic extinctions and renewals are both *global* and *synchronous*.

For reasons already given, the exact periodicity of this cycling phenomenon is hard to determine from the fossil record, yet it is clear enough for palaeontologists to have enlisted the aid of astronomers in the search for some periodic factor which could be causing it.

In this respect, let me quote from an article I sent to *New Scientist* and *Nature* magazines in mid-June 1988. Naturally enough (!), it was not published by them, but it did appear in the next issue of the *Scientific and Medical Network Newsletter*, an organization of academics and others who propose a deeper perception of life's processes than is allowed for in current scientific thinking.

The article was entitled *The Search for the Missing Link in the Theory of Punctuated Equilibria*.

Reading through the work of Niles Eldredge and Stephen Gould, especially the former's recent book, *Life Pulse*, it seems that there is little doubt that species have come and gone in a more or less constant cycle of extinction and renewal, each cycle lasting around 5 or 10 million years, on the presently accepted time scale. The question therefore becomes, what is the factor (or factors) causing this periodicity?

Researchers have concentrated largely upon extra-terrestrial possibilities, though Eldredge points out that extinction has not usually occurred as *precipitously* as a cosmic disaster might be expected to bring about. Geologically speaking, the extinctions would seem to be abrupt, spanning perhaps a half to a million years. After that, the introduction of new species seems to be very rapid. But a half to a million years is certainly not the time scale in which a collision with a comet (for instance) might be expected to have caused mass extinctions. This does not mean that there have been no such disasters, only that they do not constitute the underlying cause of the regular extinction/renewal cycle.

So the punctuated equilibria scenario would be more readily explained by some *ecological* factor, yet to be identified, than with a mass planetary disaster. For such a cataclysm, in spite of its widespread devastation, is actually supposed to *initiate* a sudden flourishing of life forms and extensive repopulation. Life is more likely to be hanging on by its teeth after such devastation, rather than be suddenly bursting into evolutionary activity.

If, therefore, we were to search on the positive side, surely it should be for a '*vitality and vigour factor*', something present at all times within the total planetary scenario. Something which is under our noses all the time, but which varies so slowly that we fail to notice its change, yet something exhibiting periodicity. Something, too, presumably, which cannot be immediately detected geologically – else surely someone would have spotted it by now?

The graph of such an extinction/renewal cycle might look something like this (see Figure 5.1):

At the present time, the planet is losing species at a rapid rate, a rate which appears to have been increasing over the last 100,000 years or more. So assuming that we are now on the downside of the cycle, we can say that this mysterious 'vitality and vigour factor' is presently on the decline. The current activities of man are thus only a part of the outworking of this factor in nature.

It seems probable, given the rapid proliferation of new species after a cyclic extinction, that the dynamics of the system follow those of thermodynamics. That is, the decline continues within the parameters of a certain equilibrium until the balance is no longer tenable. Then, like an old man receiving the elixir of life, the depleted store of living organisms is almost miraculously restored as the 'vitality and vigour factor' is 'released' in great abundance, stimulating the emergence of new organisms, and setting the scene for the new cycle.

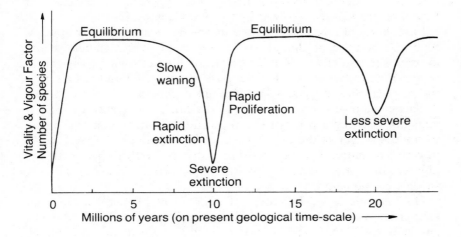

Figure 5.1 The pattern of punctuated equilibria. The severity of the extinctions and extent of the proliferations vary from cycle to cycle.

    The question is: what is this ubiquitous 'vitality and vigour factor' of which we are failing to take cognisance? Is it a part of some implicate order we have yet to observe or understand? Maybe it has something to do with the nature of life and consciousness itself? A cycle within consciousness, perhaps? We do not, after all, really know how consciousness arises.

This short article did not, at that time, suggest an understanding of what has been going on – or rather, what *is* going on, right now! For we have by no means reached the end of this long series of cycles.

    My own suggestion as to the possible nature of this missing 'vitality and vigour factor' has, of course, already been described. It is the Life Force itself, the manifested power of God – Who is the mystic Source of Life – in the creation. It is the Creative Word or Logos of Greek and Christian writings, the Primal Vibration which underlies all other vibration or movement in the creation. It is the power which keeps all subatomic particles in incessant motion and thereby in existence. It is the Divine Sound or Music of the Spheres, as Pythagoras and the Greek mystics called it. It is the Kun of the Quran, the Nad of the Hindu Vedas, the Wisdom or Torah of the Hebrew Bible. It is the primal power experienced by mystics of all ages and cultures and known by many names. It is the essence of the life or soul within all creatures. And it is the apparent waning and waxing of this primal force of life or consciousness which – I am suggesting – is the cause of the mass extinctions followed by the great renewals.

In reality, the Life Force neither waxes nor wanes. It only appears to do so because of the screen of the Mind, which increases and decreases in its density. In a Sat yuga, the life-bestowing light within pours through, while in a Kal yuga the density of Mind is such that the physical universe is cloaked in inner darkness.

This cycling of the yugas and the rhythmic occurrence of the Sat yuga are essential aspects of the physical creation. It is the means by which the power of the Life Force can flood through into this world in order to maintain it in working order and refurbish it with the physical life forms necessary for the outworking of the karmic law, the law of the Mind.

On a cosmic scale, therefore, man cannot be blamed for the mass extinction of creatures which he appears to have occasioned. Man is a part of nature, a part of this great cycling. The greed and egotism, the lack of real contact with our inner selves and consequently with our fellow men and fellow creatures, which has brought about this great modern extinction and decline of species populations, is a part of a greater cycle in nature. When the power of consciousness is obscured, man automatically loses the spiritual perception which induces him to work as a conscious participant in the outworking of the Divine or natural law. Then the life of other creatures, even of his fellow humans, becomes a matter of little meaning or value to him while he himself, being ignorant, fears his own inevitable bodily death as the worst possible fate. He then acts in a totally self-oriented manner, unaware of his real place in the order of things, thereby endangering not only his own well-being but that of other living creatures, too.

This does not mean, however, that we should not personally struggle against inordinate compulsions to create disharmonious and destructive circumstances. For as long as we have our discrimination, we should use it, and sharpen it.

Presently, we are moving towards the end of this cycle. How far it is to the actual end is unknown. How long before the next great wave of spiritual life sweeps over the physical domain with its inherent power to illuminate, enlighten and detoxify, I cannot say. Certainly, there is a tremendous growth of awareness concerning spiritual matters at the present time. But whether this is the beginning of an uplift that will gather increasing momentum until the entire planet becomes renewed, or whether it is just an eddying to and fro, a momentary correction on a generally downward trend – I do not know.

Certainly, the present combination of downward and upward world trends is like the swirling of conflicting currents when the ebb tide meets the rising tide. So perhaps we are nearing the lowest point in the cycle, with the new unveiling of the Life Force already beginning to manifest.

But wherever we are, man's general level of consciousness follows this cycle. We are only responding to a cosmic impulse. Man is only an unconscious, though willing, partner in the great ebb and flow of the Life Force. For the Life Force brings harmony, peace and inner strength. It brings understanding of what man and all creatures really are: children of God, 'Children of the Universe' as the *desiderata* says. We are universal beings – not tied to the narrow distinctions of race, caste, religion and political ideology suggested by our minds.

These punctuations, then, this replenishment of the stock of life forms available for rebirth on this plane, appears to take place at roughly 7 or 12 million year intervals. This is calculated from the periods of stasis which last for 5 or 10 million years, adding perhaps 1 or 2 million years for the extinction and renewal phases. Bearing in mind the probable inaccuracies in palaeontological dating techniques, this is remarkably in accord with the cycle of 4.32 million years, the length of one full cycle of the yugas. At least both systems count their ages by the million. We are presently in the last half a million years of this current cycle.

Now, there are said to be one thousand such cycles before the entire structure of the three Mind worlds is dissolved. The sages or yogis of India have stated in the Padam Purana that we are about half way through this even longer cycle, so they estimate the age of the earth to be a little over 2 billion years.

To arrive at our modern scientific estimates, geologists use calculations based upon the decay rates of certain radioactive isotopes – uranium and thorium isotopes for the oldest rocks, potassium and argon for the middle-aged, and carbon for the very youngest. And they suggest that the age of the earth is 4.5 billion years, the oldest rocks actually found, Precambian granite from Australia, being dated at 4 billion years.

Taking 10 million years as the length of a cycle would give roughly a 44 per cent discrepancy between the yogic and the scientific accounts, *both* in the periodicity of punctuated equilibria (10 million to 4.32 million) *as well* as in the total age of the earth (4.5 billion to 2 billion). In itself, it is a remarkable coincidence that the margin of difference in both calculations should be pretty much the same. And note that while the two modern estimates are arrived at by empirical observations and are not otherwise connected by one encompassing theory, the yogic estimates arise from mystic knowledge and are aspects of one unified description of a vast cosmic cycle.

This discrepancy, however, would readily be accounted for if the universal 'constants' and the 'laws' of the physical universe followed a cyclic pattern. Perhaps it is an aspect of the decreasing subtlety, as the increasing density of the physical universe in the Sat yuga gives way to denser eras. We do not, after all, know *how* natural laws and universal 'constants' come to be, and since everything else in this world moves in cycles, why not the value of such 'constants' too? (Universal 'constants,' by the way, include such values as the attraction due to gravity, the speed of light in a vacuum, the value of the electric charge on an electron, the value of a quantum of energy, and so on.)

Radioactive decay is due to instability in the configuration of subatomic particles comprising the slowly disintegrating atoms. At least in one description of modern physics, subatomic particles themselves are a continuous creation, a whirling, spiralling vortex of vacuum energy to which our minds and sensory perceptions are linked. We perceive them in aggregate as the phenomena and objects comprising our physical world.

The exact nature of this process of manifestation from the vacuum ocean, however, has yet to be determined in any scientific manner. But it is the same Life Force that gives us all our consciousness which in diffuse form, through the outworking of the patterns and laws within the Formative Mind, actually maintains this process of manifestation of physical substance. This has been discussed in considerable depth in my earlier book *The Secret of the Creative Vacuum*.

So just as the ebb and flow of the Life Force is seen, biologically, in the extinction and renewal of life forms, or bodies, upon the physical plane, so too must this cycle be surely reflected in the 'laws' of actual physical manifestation. That is, in the 'laws of nature' we assume to be so constant.

In fact, the rate of decay of any radioactive isotope is known only from measurement, observation and statistical calculation, not from any fundamental understanding of how physical reality is put together. The use of statistics implies that we do not really know what is going on, but are only able to observe repeating patterns. We are unable to work things out from first principles because we do not know what the first principles actually are!

So when we make assumptions of what conditions were like a million or a billion years ago, based on what has taken place during just a few years of scientific study, we are clearly liable to error. We assume that physical conditions have been constant, without our ever understanding how physical creation is taking place all around and within us, all the time. We possess little or no awareness of the vertical, inner dimension of life.

Everything in nature moves in cycles, rhythms, oscillations, vibrations and patterns. Rarely – if at all – does anything move in straight lines, as all art students are taught in their primary classes. Yet we make linear assumptions about empirical observations, which we then call 'laws of nature'. But these so-called laws are only concepts in our minds, only descriptions of our observations, while the *real* laws of nature may be of a different character altogether!

So our time-scales, calculated using linear and statistical extrapolations of present observations, are quite likely to be wrong. And, to be frank, I would place more credence on the evidence of genuine mystic observation than upon the concepts of science, though the actual time-scales involved are really of little relevance to how we live our lives right now.

ANCIENT CORAL REEFS AND THE LENGTH OF A YEAR

There is an interesting aside to this discussion, which shows how clearly defined some of the information in these ancient fossil strata really is. The credit for this ingenious piece of research goes to the expert in fossil corals, John Wells, now retired from Cornell University, New York.

Wells noted that certain kinds of coral creature lay down a daily ring of calcium carbonate on the outermost rim of their tubes or calyces. This they are instinctively bound to do and, come rain or shine, these industrious little fellows add a new ring of fresh coral, every day. Not only that but, like many marine and other life forms, the coral creatures are sensitive to both the moon and the yearly cycle of the earth's orbit around the sun. The result is that the bands of coral show both lunar and annual or solar banding, as well as the evidence of their daily activities.

Wells had devoted much of his life to a study of the more recent Mesozoic and Cenozoic corals, but living in an area where the earth's crust had been eroded down to hills of undulating Devonian rock, it was only a matter of time before he turned his attention to the varied and abundant records of Devonian corals upon his own doorstep.

What he discovered was very interesting. The number of growth rings per year was an average not of 365, but of 400. Following up Wells's intriguing results, the British palaeontologist, Colin Scrutton, studied other Devonian corals that laid down more obvious monthly rings. Here the average was 30.6 rings per month or 397.8 rings (or days) per year.

Over, then, to the astronomers, who have long contended that the earth's spin would have suffered a small but steady tidal drag, resulting from the interaction of the moon and the oceans, slowing it down as the millennia passed. They suggest a figure of 2 seconds every 100,000 years. The length of our day is determined by the speed of this spin. Assuming that the length of a year – the time taken for the earth to travel once around the sun – has remained the same (quite an assumption, when one considers all the escapades we are supposed to have had with comets, asteroids and so on), then a spin-speed reduction of this order would mean that during Devonian times 380 million years ago, a day would have lasted 22 hours, not 24, with 398 days in the year – the same length of day and year suggested by the fossil corals. And note, incidentally, that a cyclic change in the value of the gravitational constant would not necessarily change the length of a day or a year if all such 'constants' changed in tandem, such that their relative values remained the same.

There is another interesting and independent corroboration of the shorter day, hundreds of millions of years ago. The daily layers of sediment in the cabbage-shaped mounds produced by the blue-green algae also reflect the annual movement of the sun above. And cutting a long scientific story short, the mounds of 850 million years ago indicate a year of 435 days, each day lasting a little over 20 hours. With a 22 hour day, 380 million years ago, it seems that the length on an earth day increases by about 2 hours every 400 million years. This points to something most remarkable about the constancy of planetary circumstances, not to mention the volume of its oceans, over the last billion years or so and probably longer.

Anyway, there they were, hundreds of millions of years ago, those tiny coral creatures, so similar to the species we know today, making reefs around which the fishes surely swam, the worms burrowed, the jellyfish floated; and the shellfish, the sea urchins and the starfish did whatever they have always done. Where is the concept of evolutionary 'progress' in such a scenario?

EXTINCTIONS, ZONES AND STRATA

There is little doubt, then, that the regular, global extinction of species is a recurrent theme. On occasion, the extinctions seem so complete, as for example the much publicized demise of the dinosaurs and much else besides that marked the end of the Mesozoic era, 65 million years ago, or the even greater loss of species at the end of the Palaeozoic. Are there, one wonders, even greater cycles of extinction imposed upon the 'lesser' ones? Or is it simply a natural variation in severity, just as some winters are harder than others? Or perhaps the occasional close encounter with a large asteroid or comet adds to the general cosmic merriment?

There was a time when palaeontologists thought that they would be able to map out the world by means of fossil *zones*, layers of fossils so rich and individually recognizable that they could be identified worldwide. But this was a naive supposition, for fossil records are not so obliging as to present such a clear picture of life throughout the ages.

All the same, stratification is clear enough for Niles Eldredge to have written in *Life Pulse* that such zones represent:

> Evolutionarily coherent faunas, with a characteristic beginning, history and end, followed by another wave: the clock is reset, the pattern begins anew, and history is played out along similar – though never identical lines again.

The time immediately before probably the greatest extinction of all, that which terminated the Palaeozoic era, contains some interesting geological evidence. We have already mentioned the low-lying levels of the 'continental' seas during those days, and this supposition is borne out by the vast salt deposits in some areas of Late Permian sediment, formed like the Dead Sea in shallow basins with no outlet to the greater ocean.

Norman Newell, previously of the American Museum of Natural History and mentor to Niles Eldredge and many others, noted this. He was also the first to comment upon the possible relevance of the extensive chalk deposits of the Late Cretaceous, immediately prior to that ensuing mass extinction.

The significance of chalk is that it is 'pure', largely unmixed with other sedimentary materials like mud, sand and silt. Chalk is largely comprised of an incredible number of tiny platelets of calcium carbonate, produced by the calcareous algae, the coccolithopores. Deposits of *pure* chalk signify that little other sedimentation was taking place in that area and, at that time, the coccolithopores and their like-minded companions were single-handedly performing the task of sedimentation.

The lack of mud, sand and silt indicates that the rivers – at least in that area – were not bringing much debris with them to the sea. And this means that the mountains serving the rivers were low-lying and greatly eroded. They had little debris to hand over to the rivers.

The purity of the chalk deposits of the Late Cretaceous therefore suggests that, in those far-off days, the mountain ranges had all been mostly eroded into low-lying, stumpy hills. It is a strange thought when one first encounters it, but rivers, over time, are responsible for carrying the mountains back into the seas. In modern times, the Indus river alone carries away *five million tonnes* of Himalayan debris every day, which ultimately reaches the sea. Mountains are 'soon', geologically speaking, washed away.

But when the mountains are worn down, the amount of minerals, silt and non-chalky sedimentary material carried to the sea is reduced. Consequently, in Late Cretaceous days, the quantity of minerals reaching the sea would have diminished. And since plants – in the sea or elsewhere – only flourish in the presence of minerals and because almost all other marine life depends upon plants as the basis of the food chain, life in the sea would have gone into decline.

That is to say that low-lying, heavily eroded hills result in a decline of marine life due to a diminution of minerals. In the Permian, the erosion of the mountains is attested to by the considerable salt deposits. In the Cretaceous, the same is evidenced by the extensive chalk deposits. Newell found it more difficult to find evidence that the similar conditions of decline had also prevailed upon the land during those times, but it seems most likely, for the ecologies of land and sea are so closely intertwined.

Newell's hypothesis was strengthened by the evidence of the Cretaceous coccolithopores themselves. For many species of coccolithopore simply died out at the end of the Cretaceous, to be replaced by similar but different species at the start of the Tertiary. The ecosystem remains complete and every super-species has its role to play.

So long before the final blow was struck, the two greatest documented extinctions – the Palaeozoic and the Cretaceous – were well under way. In the Cretaceous, most of the dinosaurs had died out during the previous one million years, just like the mammoths and the mastodons, the sabre-toothed tigers and the ground sloths, the giant tortoise-like glyptodonts and so many others that have all been lost during the course of our present extinction phase, within the last 40,000 years.

The dinosaurs, too, that incredibly 'successful' and widely varied class of species who existed over a span of 140 million years, also show the same pattern of stratification. There were many species of dinosaur, ranging from the size of thrushes, chickens and turkeys to the huge and famous brontosaurians. Some were vegetarians and others, like *Tyrannosaurus rex*, were the most fearsome predators the earth has ever known, over 40 feet long, standing up on their hind legs higher than many houses, and weighing up to 5 tons (see Figure 5.2). But again, there are no missing links, and no evidence of gradual change. Species and great dynasties of dinosaur lived and flourished for long periods, then they became extinct and new dinosaur families and species took their places. There is little evidence even of micro-evolution.

Figure 5.2 Tyrannosaurus rex *(right), 40-foot long, standing 20-foot high and weighing in at 5 tons, is generally considered to have been the most fearsome predator ever to have stalked the earth. The 30-foot herbivorous* Triceratops *(left), weighing up to 10 tons and possessing a massive skull up to 8 feet long and 4 feet wide, with an armoured neck shield and sporting three vicious horns, two of them up to 4 feet long, was amongst a small group of creatures able to make* T. rex *turn aside. The nearest modern equivalent is the rhinoceros. Both flourished in the Late Cretaceous and were probably warm-blooded and pretty lively on their feet. (*Triceratops *drawing by Dennis Halls.* T. rex *from a model by A. Hayward, photograph by courtesy of Natural Science Photos.)*

The reasons for the great extinction at the end of the Cretaceous have been a subject of considerable debate amongst scientists over the last decade and almost all possible theories have been advanced. There is, for instance, accumulating geochemical evidence that conditions became colder at that time, resulting in the mass extinctions.

This also suggests that the planet could respond to the decline in the Life Force, particularly in a Kal yuga, by manifesting circumstances which are less conducive to vibrant and flourishing life. The tropics certainly support many more life forms than the temperate and polar regions. Perhaps this is what really triggers the onset of an ice age, as a natural part of the outworking of the Formative Mind, where the outer is a reflection of the inner. It is not surprising, therefore, that geologists readily admit that they do not understand the factors which induce glaciation and the arrival of an ice age. For even there, all-pervasive aspects of the greater Mind are at work, which are hidden from our physical eyes.

Our own behaviour and that of other species is a reflection of our inner mind. Outward behaviour is incomprehensible if we attempt to study it whilst ignoring the inner mind energies. Similarly, the cycles, rhythms, patterns, events and structures which we find in the physical universe are only understandable if we realize that they are a projection of the inner patterns of the greater Mind. 'As above, so below'. And everything in this physical world lies within the one Egg of the Mind and is thus automatically integrated, in one whole.

After the Cretaceous extinction it seems that life may have been in suspension for some considerable while, a million years some palaeontologists suggest. And strangely, hidden in many of the rocks dating from that time, there lies a thin layer of *iridium*, impregnated into red clay about one inch thick, a very stable element not usually found in such concentrations in the earth's crust, though volcanic activity indicates that it is present deeper inside the earth. But iridium is also found in high concentrations in meteorites, usually thought to be fragments from the asteroid belt lying between Jupiter and Mars.

Many scientists, assuming an extra-terrestrial cause of this extinction, look to the iridium as confirmation that the cataclysm was due to the earth's collision with a huge meteorite. Perhaps, they suggest, the impact sent up a cloud of dust, resulting in a 'nuclear winter' due to absorption of the sun's rays. The meteorite itself would also have been vapourized by the heat generated on impact, the gases subsequently condensing as fine dust, sinking slowly to the earth, explaining why the iridium is distributed over the entire planet. In the reduction of sunlight, photosynthesis would also have been greatly frustrated and with the diminution of such an essential link in the food cycle, life would have rapidly subsided.

By way of confirming evidence, Andrew Knoll, fossil plant expert from Harvard University, reports that immediately above the iridium layer there is a temporary absence of pollen, reflecting the fact – he suggests – that many plants died back to their roots after the disaster, and regrew again from there.

Additionally, there is evidence of a highly suggestive layer of soot, lying just above the iridium – testimony to a global conflagration of tremendous proportions. Studies of atmospheric samples trapped in amber from the Cretaceous period certainly suggest that the levels of oxygen were high enough to support a widespread conflagration of the planetary biomass.

Other scientists have proposed that we may be looking at earthly evidence of the explosion of a planet which once lay between Mars and Jupiter, now forming the asteroid belt. Planets can be thermonuclear reactors, generating intense internal heat like our own, and an explosion that blows such a planet to pieces is not impossible, especially if for some structural reason it was temporarily denied the energy release of volcanoes, earthquakes and mountain formation.

Others have speculated that the final blow in the extinction, responsible for the iridium, the soot and the temporary lack of pollen, may have been due to the enormous volcanic blast that would have thrown out more than one million cubic kilometres of the earth, forming the Deccan Traps of India, about 66 million years ago. The lava flow was sufficient to cover – in two weeks – an area the size of Ireland with a layer of lava at 1200°C. Some eruption! The iridium could have been thrown up from the interior of the planet in the blast. And the timing, historically, is certainly about right. Or was that volcanic eruption itself triggered by collision with the meteorite?

What actually happened we may never know. Many ideas have been proposed. Someone once counted nearly one hundred theories accounting for the final demise of the previously abundant dinosaurs and the advent of the associated iridium layer.

Let me, then, add one more speculation. Suppose that man had been present during those so-called primeval times. . . . A heretical idea, I know, for most scientists like to place the rise of man only in the last 4 million years. We will have more to say on this subject later on, but for a moment let us suppose that they are incorrect.

Suppose that man's activities had spread across vast areas of the land, and that being well into a Kal yuga, the Life Force being on the wane and man's knowledge of himself deeply submerged under layers of selfishness and obsession with the physical, he had started chopping down the trees and otherwise destroying the habitat to energize his mental and physical busy-ness. Would that not have helped to bring about the downfall of the creatures of those far off days? It has done so in the present cycle. Could not man's activities have initiated or augmented the final death throes of those distant ages? Scientists do suggest, after all, that man is at least partially responsible for the demise of many of the large mammals which have roamed Europe and America during the last 10,000 years, just as he is in Africa and Asia in more recent times.

Suppose that man – like today – had set off upon a train of materialistic development and destruction. And out of the deep and often unconscious distress such wanton disregard for the earth's natural beauty caused its human inhabitants and because, as now, he had largely lost sight of his inner spiritual heritage, imagine that he actually used his technology against his fellow man. Suppose he let loose some destructive force upon the planet, perhaps unleashing the hidden power within the atom, in some great nuclear or other conflagration – a reflection of his anger, his despair and his lack of understanding as to who and where he really was. Or suppose he simply had an accident whilst experimenting with the creation of antimatter? Could it, then, have been man who cast the final stone in *that* great extinction? Just as he is doing in the present one?

Could iridium, in some other way, be the remnants of a catastrophic human conflagration? Could it have been, perhaps, the key element in some ancient, destructive technology or the final product of some chemical or physical process? There has to be some reason why the iridium is there and its close juxtaposition to the final blow in that mass extinction strongly suggests some association that is not coincidental.

It is only a speculation. But even if some extra-terrestrial influence were involved, this too is not disconnected from events on earth. Just as a brick may fall upon the head of the luckless pessimist, just missing the more positively-minded optimist, so too is everything drawn to us by the content of our own mind. This is the way in which nature is manifested as the outward patterning of the Formative Mind, hiddenly connecting all her creatures. So if an enormous volcanic eruption or a collision with a meteorite or a comet is the best natural redress to balance conditions on the earth, then automatically this will come about. It will be formed and drawn out of the minds of all creatures. It will have been caused by and built into the karmas of all those involved. It will be a part of the natural progression of events.

But it is not the act of an angry God, nor is it Divine retribution. It is caused by the outworking of the greater Mind, itself energized by the Life Force, the creative power of the Supreme Being. Nature keeps her own balance. How she does it is a matter of great interest. Indeed, the study of these processes is what we call science, philosophy, yoga, mysticism and many other names. For this administration, this outworking of the karmic law of the Formative Mind is what man sees when he looks at the world around and within himself.

Even if some final *coup de grâce* was administered, the extinction had already been in gradual progress over the previous one million years, as with other extinctions. And this is exactly what we would expect from a gradual waning of the Life Force, though – on this occasion – it ended abruptly in some concluding, catastrophic episode.

Indeed, a similar record will be left of our present times. So few in number are some of the remaining large animals that there is little likelihood of their being preserved for palaeontological posterity. As regards their fossil record, 'extinction' will have already taken place. And it is the events of our present century which will have been the 'sudden catastrophe'.

But whether one accepts the role of the Life Force and the greater Mind, and the consequence of its ebb and flow, or whether one prefers to look to more material causes, there is no doubt that mass extinctions have always been a part of nature.

Niles Eldredge summarizes it most succinctly:

> Let us not forget that extinctions are real. Life really did take it on the chin *severely* many times – especially at the end of the Cambrian, in the upper Devonian, at the end of the Permian, the end of the Triassic, and at the end of the Cretaceous – and less severely so many other times.
>
> Geologically, I think it looks instantaneous, but realistically, it really isn't so. And these events, whatever their cause, whatever their pattern of occurrence, whatever their true time frame, really did reset the old evolutionary clock. They really did create those opportunities to rejuvenate, for the truly new to spring forth.

RADIATION, NAUTILOIDS AND AMMONOIDS

One of the most readily observable and repeating themes in the fossil record, seen even in Cambrian times, is that of *radiation*. It is a process intimately linked with the cycles of extinction and renewal.

Describing life in those ancient days, Niles Eldredge comments:

It is very much as if complex life got going and somehow, somewhere, someone decided that it wasn't quite right. But rather than starting all over again, a simple, radical reorganization was effected: new players were recruited, to be sure, and old ones dropped, but there was also a matter of emphasis – an expanded role for some, a diminished role for others – all rather reminiscent of cabinet changes at the beginning of a second presidential term.

He mentions the brachiopods, present as subdued members of early Cambrian times, yet diversifying or *radiating* into a tremendous array of genera and species in the Early Ordovician. Again, during the Ordovician and to some extent the Silurian epochs, members of the *Nautilus* genera, related to the squid and octopus, were found in abundance, some of these huge, shelled creatures reaching lengths of more than thirty feet.

In the Middle and Late Devonian, however, their ecological niche appears to have been 'taken over' by the related *ammonoids* (see Figure 5.3) who now branched out successfully and followed a healthy and happy career right through to the great extinction terminating the Cretaceous, a dynasty lasting at least 330 million years.

Figure 5.3   A large ammonite *fossil, found on Monmouth Beach, Lyme Regis in Dorset, England. (Photo by Richard Revels, courtesy of Natural Science Photos.)*

The shells of nautiloids and ammonoids served a variety of functions, including protection and buoyancy. By filling part of their shell with gases and part with water, for example, they were able to float, dealing with the problems of depth control as well as making sure they were the right way up. And while some of them were straight, others were coiled. Author and geologist, Christian O'Brien, in reading through this book in manuscript form, commented at this juncture:

> The very gradual change in the *Ammonoidea* from uncoiled species in the Palaeozoic to partly-coiled species, and then to complete open coils, and then to a closing of the coils until they coalesced in the Cretaceous Ammonites, was a process that can be studied, stage by stage, in the greatest of detail. It is claimed by palaeontologists to be the acme of arguments for the theory of evolution.

Studying the suggested ammonoid family tree (see Figure 5.4), one notes how, in the major extinctions between epochs, many species simply disappeared. Many also died out in the period immediately preceding the boundary between the Triassic and the Jurassic. As we have seen, the geological boundaries used by palaeontologists mark zones of identifiably coherent flora and fauna that are caused by extensive extinctions and renewals, not just amongst ammonoids, but amongst all species. But each epoch spans several extinction-proliferation-equilibrium cycles, where the extinction 'winters' were of varying severity. Throughout, we can observe the continuous cycles of extinction and renewal.

In the figure, the proximity of the lines indicates similarities between individual species. But note that most species arise as if out of nowhere and fade out quite as rapidly. And this appears to be the general rule. Even evidence for gradual microevolution is very hard to find. Somehow, one assumes, they must have changed, but the process does not appear to be one of slow change due to the gradual accretion of tiny modifications. Changes, even between closely related species, could be sudden, like the sudden emergence of a four-winged variant of the fruit fly. If such a change were seen in the fossil record it would be recorded as two parallel lines, close together, but with no connecting line between.

Moreover, there is no evidence of the ammonoids ever diversifying into anything other than ammonoids over their 330 million year history.

Studying the genealogy in detail, the entire family first appears, suddenly, in the Devonian epoch, a period spanning 48 million years,

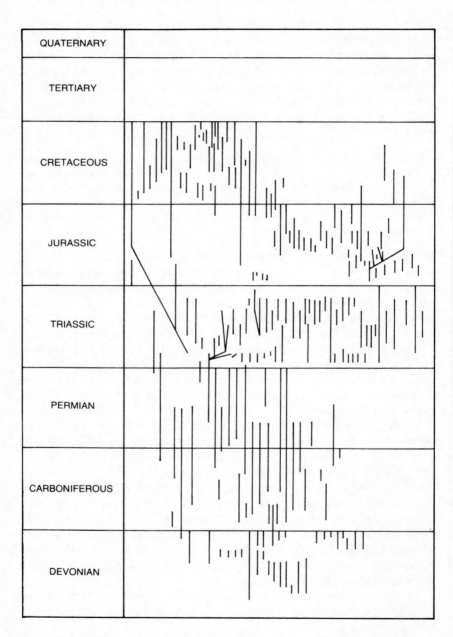

Figure 5.4   The ammonoid *family tree (after Eldredge,* Life Pulse). *For explanation, see text.*

Nearly thirty species are generated, some of which die out – or at least cease to leave fossil traces – within a comparatively short period of time. In the middle of the Devonian, there are clear signs of an extinction in which all the earlier forms, except two, disappear. And, again, at the end of the Devonian epoch, only two out of about twenty species make it through into the Carboniferous.

Similarly, at the end of the Permian and Jurassic epochs, only three or four species survive. And again, there are mid-cycle extinctions and sudden appearances relating, one presumes, to intermediate cycles of extinction and renewal. Certainly, it is clear that new forms appear shortly after old ones have disappeared. Yet there is no actual fossil evidence of the *gradual* development of one from another.

Evolutionists assume it, but cannot see it. Natural selection of tiny random changes cannot account for such sudden jumps, whereas other threshold processes within the DNA could do so. Even a consideration of DNA as somehow intimately and 'intelligently' responsive to environment in an orderly and integrated fashion, from within its own hidden pool of potentialities, makes better sense than the 'random mutation' idea.

There is simply no fossil evidence to support any really gradual evolution. The species simply appear quite suddenly. So there must surely be some formative processes at work other than blind mutation.

Neither is there evidence of early competition between the nautiloids and the ammonoids, though conventional evolutionists frequently speak of one group of creatures displacing another. Competition is again another evolutionary idea that cannot be substantiated from the evidence. An entire and diverse genus cannot 'compete' with another genus, nor even can the diversity of species in one family suddenly 'become' the wealth of species in another. To compete, you need to be an already evolved and competent species. And competition is always at a personal level. Grey squirrels, for example, have succesfully competed for a place with red squirrels because the greys eat the hazelnuts before they are ripe, while the reds are still waiting for them to ripen. So when both live in the same locality, the greys get the hazelnuts before the reds consider them fit to eat. And since hazelnuts form a far larger part of the diet of the reds than they do of the greys, the reds, being deprived of their natural food, go into decline.

Fair enough. But red and grey squirrels, though similar, do not really occupy the same ecological niche. True, in many areas the introduction of greys has resulted in the demise of the reds, but not because only one of them can occupy the same ecological niche. Man has displaced rabbits and many other creatures when he builds houses on previously open land. No doubt he is competing with the rabbits, but that does not mean that he occupies the same niche.

The evolutionary relevance is this. Squirrels, rabbits and man are well adapted to their niches, so they can readily 'compete'. But there can be no question of competition between a species who is fully adapted to an environment and one that is still trying to get its act together by tiny evolutionary changes, with nothing else to rely upon than chance. It is out of the game before it has started. One species may come and fill a niche left unoccupied by another. Or the environment and hence the niche may change to some degree, such that a new species is required to fill the new niche. But this could not take place by competition.

So it is no surprise to discover that some nautiloids existed throughout, as well as after, the Cretaceous extinction, even staging a modest comeback during the early Tertiary era, presumably filling in the ecological space after the extinction of the ammonoids. In fact, in modern times we still have a few remaining species of nautiloid, whilst there are no ammonoids. Would conventional evolutionists therefore say that – in the end – the nautiloids won? Won what? And it is interesting to think that even this species may in some future cycle once again proliferate into many cousins. The question to which conventional evolutionists have no real answer is, 'How?'

And do these few species of nautilus contain within them the potential to become all the previous as well as many future nautiloids, perhaps even the ammonoids, were circumstances to arise that could draw them out? Though reversions may occur, there is no evidence of species going back to old forms once discarded. Are our modern nautiloids the sole expressions, in present times, of the subtle super-species we earlier suggested might really constitute the true 'species'? Were all the nautiloids and ammonoids really the expression of just one – or a few – such super-species, of one or more subtle, microcosmic, tattvic energy configurations?

Looking only at the physical remains, then, it seems that there are long periods where a species remains stable, identifiable as the same species for several million years. Then, suddenly, *along with many other species*, there is an all-change. The expression of the hidden, all-encompassing Mind changes more radically than at other times and consequently, *all* species are more or less simultaneously affected. They all change together. It is an extensive, deep-rooted 'crowd' phenomenon, an aspect of Formative Mind activity.

We cannot, therefore, suggest that whatever it is that causes the changes is *species-dependent*. The phenomenon is not even geographically isolated. It happens globally, just as it is happening today.

It is seen in all the fossil strata of a particular period. Whether the continents and islands are geographically connected or whether they have been separated for millions of years, the same strata are identifiable. The phenomenon is global, cyclic and synchronous.

Clearly, we are in possession of evidence that there is a cosmic game of musical species going on, with an 'all-change' whenever the music stops! The question is: what is the nature of the music?

And even if it turns out that some aspects of DNA function are step-like in character, operating as a kind of quantum step between closely related species, that would still not explain why all species are involved at the same time and why it happens on a cyclic basis. DNA is undoubtedly involved. But the question remains: how?

Conventional Darwinian belief looks at the fossil record and assumes that there must be a smooth gradient of change. Even the concept of a 'species' should have no real meaning, for everything is supposed to be in a constant state of gradual flux. Niles Eldredge and many others, however, point out that the fossil evidence indicates that this is simply quite untrue. A species exists in a stable manner for millions of years, with only limited variation. Then, all of a sudden, it can disappear without further trace while an altogether new species, or more than one, appear upon the scene.

The new is no doubt *related* to the old – just as species within a genus are in present times – but the new form is identifiably different. And very few – if any – of the fine gradation of expected evolutionary links are ever found. They are almost always missing. Certainly, species never seem to move outside the boundaries of microevolution, and even then – more often than not – the change is step-like.

One can sympathize with the point of view which, considering material substance to be all there is, can therefore offer no other explanation than that of gradual change. And that in the absence of any perception of a hidden dimension to the situation, the driving factors are automatically described as those of chance and self-interest, i.e. natural selection. For chance cannot be considered to contain processes capable of foresight and of storing hidden potentiality for the future.

But add the ontological dimension, the dimension of being, the Formative Mind factor, the cosmic weaver, to one's appraisal of the evidence and a totally different picture emerges. Then we begin dealing, not only with physical bodies, but also with the events and the environment which surround them, as expressions of this cosmic, inward pattern-maker. Then we begin to understand that all things are hiddenly linked and integrated in a hierarchical ocean of energetic and ontological complexity beyond our ken.

Then add to this picture the possibility that there are dynamically active cycles of increasing and decreasing subtlety within the hidden aspects of this great weaver itself, with a span of several million years, and we begin to understand that there may be more to biological processes than meets our material eye. That within these mysterious living, physical frames we take so much for granted, there lie processes and responses which are hidden during the dense and crystallized days of the Kal yuga.

Then we begin to glimpse that biological processes could perhaps experience a springtime compared to which we are currently in the grips of deep mid-winter.

STRATA IN RECENT TIMES

Conventional evolutionists have always recognized – and used – the existence of these fossil strata without really appreciating their significance. They are present even from the very earliest days of the Cambrian fossil record. And it is so very fascinating that they could actually represent real evidence of the passing cycles of the yugas. They bear witness to specific phases of onward movement through time. They are not arbitrary staging posts by which scientists have divided up the fossil record, but are an indication of real historical events etched into the sediments, and conforming with the cycle of the yugas.

Looking at more modern times, the Tertiary period is of particular interest because, being so relatively 'recent' (a mere 66 million years back!), the fossil strata are even more readily identifiable.

In the Cenozoic, then, taking us through the last 66.5 million years since the great Cretaceous extinction, scientists have identified the following epochs amongst the fossil strata:

Era	Epoch	Approximate Duration
TERTIARY ERA	Palaeocene	10,000,000 – 'Archaic' mammals appeared, 66.5 million years ago
	Eocene	20,000,000 – Modern mammals appeared, e.g. horses
	Oligocene	15,000,000
	Miocene	14,000,000
	Pliocene	10,000,000 – Includes the present epoch.

Note, by the way, that the durations apportioned to these periods are approximate, for the start of the Tertiary is said to have been 66.5 million years ago, while a quick addition of the figures here comes to 69 million. Geological dating techniques are only rough estimates!

In reality, we are presently at the end of the Pliocene epoch, the last million years or so being termed the Quaternary. This period has been divided up as follows:

Era	Epoch	Approximate Duration
QUATERNARY ERA	Pleistocene	990,000 – Current ice age. Some estimates put the length at 1.6 million years
	Holocene	10,000 – Present epoch. Some recession of ice age boundaries

When the significance of the ebb and flow of the yugas is missed, this periodicity is seen to have no rhyme or reason. When one realizes that it is the waxing and waning of the Life Force itself, as the screen of the Mind rhythmically crystallizes and lightens, then the whole jigsaw suddenly fits together.

Many modern biologists, feeling unconvinced by the naivety of Darwinian interpretations of the fossil record and wishing to combine the findings of modern physics within a holistic paradigm or world view in which life or consciousness plays the supreme part, might take heart from these observations.

For the formative power of the life principle itself, as a waxing and waning as in Spring–Summer–Autumn–Winter, follows the same pattern when we pass through the yugas. And how rapidly spring can arise out of winter! How fast can rejuvenation flood through all creatures, raising the hibernators from somnolence, bringing the plants into leaf, bud and flower, making the birds sing in a way they do at no other time, even bringing the humans out into the parks, the young – and even older – eyeing each other over for possible companionship.

How deeply felt this force must be at the change-over from the depths of a Kal yuga to the brilliant burst of light and consciousness, as a new Sat yuga falls upon us! Like spring after winter, what inward pleasure and relief this springtime of consciousness must instil in us.

But returning to the Tertiary, the Palaeocene lasts 10 million years

– this, you will note is roughly in accord with the time spans allocated to the yugas in the Sanskrit Puranas, as discussed on page 65. The extinction at the end of the Palaeocene spelt the demise of many creatures. Following through the mammalian 'ancestry', we find that 'archaic' mammals are no more. Then, a brief respite followed by a sudden surge of new species – all arising apparently out of nowhere, but supposedly being the rapidly evolving remnants of those species left unscathed at the end of the old cycle.

In the case of mammals, as we enter the Eocene, the new species are of a thoroughly modern trend. Here we first meet the precursors of our modern hoofed mammals, including the horse. And note how they all appear together. But they did not all arise from one ancestor. They all seemed to get the same sort of idea at the same time, just as the successive waves of dinosaurs were reflective of their particular times.

Palaeocene *amblypods*, occupiers of the large herbivore niche – previously filled (it is assumed) by vegetarian dinosaur browsers and grazers – disappear, being replaced by species similar to today's horses, rhinos and tapirs, as well as the often gigantic *brontotheres*, now extinct. Forerunners of cattle, antelope, deer, camels, pigs and other now extinct groups also make their appearance for the first time. They are still somewhat different from the species we know today, but the similarity is unmistakable. These were the outward forms of the super-species, most suitably expressive of the mood, vibration and environment of the times.

The Eocene is allocated 20 million years on the geological calendar, which is interesting since it spans exactly two full cycles. Maybe the fossil record is being read incorrectly, or perhaps the first cycle was quite similar to the next. A mild Kal yuga 'winter' rather than an extreme one, permitting greater continuity between cycles.

The Oligocene and Miocene are apportioned 15 and 14 million years respectively – three cycles between them, perhaps, and similar comments apply to them as to the length of the Eocene. The final, most recent Pliocene era, 'ending' with the onset of the present ice age, the Pleistocene, just over a million years ago (some scientists say over a million and a half), is once again apportioned 10 million years.

Amongst the Cambrian fossils, Niles Eldredge noted similar spans between his trilobite and invertebrate extinction–radiation cycles – sometimes with more and sometimes with lesser differences between the cycles. That has been his own particular area of study. Before his and Gould's observation of punctuated equilibria few, if any, palae-ontologists had really studied the fossil record from that point of view. I imagine that the next ten to twenty years will bring some interesting and confirmatory surprises. Indeed, Robert Bakker in his fascinating book *The Dinosaur Heresies* (1986) has already confirmed the stratification in his own field of dinosaurian palaeontology.

Note also that the present ice age coincides exactly with the decline of the Life Force in the Kal yuga through which we are currently passing. We are thus on the extinction side of the present cycle. This is very clear, for species have been disappearing since the onset of the present ice age and are currently becoming extinct at an increasing rate.

Though the earlier part of this cycle saw a tremendous proliferation of new species over a few million years, the impetus tailed off, slowly giving way to extinctions in the recent Pleistocene. No radically new species have appeared during this time, except – say the modern evolutionists – man, the 'pinnacle of evolutionary achievement'. Man is supposed to have evolved during the last one or two million years at a time when all other species were on the decline. His last final leap (from Neanderthal man) is supposed to have happened only 50,000 years ago. But his 'arrival' has immediately, in geological terms, precipitated the demise of many other species, though man may not have been such a recent arrival, as we will see.

Amongst our modern mammals, there are very few, perhaps none, which predate the Miocene epochs. The Miocene and Pliocene, then, represent the last two cycles of the yugas, on the rough 10 million year scale.

Evolutionists often regard the fossil record of the Tertiary period as paramount evidence of evolution. Yet, once again, there are no really transitional species. Even the 'change' amongst horse species, from toed to hoofed and from smaller to larger, is inconclusive, for there were many species of horse present in those times, some large and some small, just as there are today. And it is easy to select those species that fit the desired sequence, whilst ignoring those that do not. Nor can one say that hooves are more evolved than toes, or vice versa. Which are the more appropriate probably depends upon environmental circumstances. One certainly cannot say that Eocene horses were *primitive* ancestors of today's species. Times have changed and so have the horses. That is all. And note, once again, that we are not denying that change has taken place. Clearly it has. We are only questioning the extent to which a species can diversify and the means by which it does so.

It is very easy to present evolutionary 'evidence' in such a manner that invalid conclusions are drawn and many textbooks proceed in this way. Even worse is the way the evolutionary 'evidence' is presented in schools, when children's minds are still deeply impressionable and unable to reject the false. If, for example, one arrayed all the species currently existing on the earth in order of their similarity, but then, hypothetically, suggested that this array should be spread across time, we could give ourselves an illusory feeling of evolution. (Note, however, that all essential missing links between families and often between species would still be missing.) But, in fact, no-one is suggesting that *modern* creatures have evolved from *each other*. The idea is that all present species have evolved from a common ancestor.

It is only the similarity in design which fools us into thinking that all creatures must have evolved from a common ancestor. But similarity in design does not indicate a common ancestor, as we have pointed out. It only shows a commonality in the formative process. It only demonstrates that all creatures are part of one cosmic pattern, that we all spring from the same inward source.

Presently, of course, we are nearing the end of a 10,000 year temperate window in the long ice age. Geologists call it the Holocene era. Can we therefore expect an imminent return of the ice? Or will that be countered by the greenhouse effect? Nobody knows. It depends, I imagine, how close we are to the next Sat yuga. We are now in the extinction phase of the present cycle. Not long from now, geologically speaking at least, the upturn will come. Perhaps it is already happening. But one thing is certain. Unless we find a way out of the world of birth, death and rebirth, we will still be here when it comes . . . and when it goes!

EVOLUTION, STYLE AND THE FORMATIVE MIND

Four-legged, terrestrial animals with bones bearing characteristics relating them to modern mammals have been found in the fossil records even of Permian times, 300 million years ago. Evolutionists call them *protomammals*. The further back in time one goes, of course, the less likelihood there is of finding fossils of any land-based creatures, due to land erosion and recycling. So we are lucky to have discovered even these ancient relics.

Palaeontologists, however, do not begin to feel comfortable about their mammalian genealogies until the early Tertiary, during the Palaeocene only 60 million years ago. For it was only then, after the great Cretaceous extinction, that the style of mammals came into being which exhibit characteristic family resemblances to the mammals of our present times. The greater the extinction, remember, the greater the possibility for consequent change of style afterwards. And although we are presently undergoing the seventh extinction cycle since the Cretaceous, the lineage resulting in our modern mammals and other creatures has not yet undergone such a massive extinction as the one which terminated the Cretaceous. Therefore, our modern mammals trace their most obvious lineage to the beginning of the Palaeocene and – in particular – from the Eocene.

Now since many of the wide and divergent group of creatures rather loosely called dinosaurs are now thought to have been warm-blooded and social, rather than cold and reptilian, and since the remains of mammal-like creatures have been found at least as far back as Permian times, it seems possible that creatures representative of the group of super-species presently called mammals have been an integral part of life on earth for an exceptionally long period of time.

Is it, actually, only a matter of style? Are the ancient Palaeozoic 'protomammals', the mammals of the Mesozoic that lived alongside the dinosaurs, and the mammals of the Tertiary, actually all representatives of the same group of super-species? Were even some of the dinosaurs also representative of this same group? Ecologically, they certainly seem to have filled the same niches.

If one compared the mammals of the Tertiary with the styles and customs of the 1920s, modern mammals would be like those of the 1980s and 1990s. And in this analogy, their Palaeozoic ancestors would be like the Romans or the Druids. The Romans, however, were just as human as we are! They were not more primitive. The point being made is that change of *style* does not imply evolutionary '*progress*'.

The Romans–1920s–1990s analogy is actually quite a good one, for although time runs continuously and smoothly, many significant outward physical changes and events are often *sudden*. There is a *sudden* outbreak of war, new civilizations and conquests can happen *suddenly*, new styles of clothing or social behaviour flourish *suddenly*, stock market crashes are *sudden* – and so on.

There is, however, always a background build-up to these outward changes. The real, more subtle connections are gradual. Note, however, that this build-up is largely in the *minds* of all concerned. War may suddenly flare up, as does anger, but a mental build up always precedes its physical manifestation. Frustration, anger, fear, greed, desire for power – all these are of the mind. But their physical outcome – war – can erupt suddenly.

Similarly, the play of life in this physical world is really a play of the minds of all involved. And this is as true of man's historical transits as it is of the great spans of time covering species extinctions and proliferations. Without minds, creatures do nothing – there is no motivation, no instinct, no activity.

With man, the mental build-up may be conscious planning for certain events: designing next year's fashions in the preceding year; making plans for the invasion of another's territory; making a shopping list; scheduling one's day or drawing up plans of any kind. Quality and character of action proceeds from quality and character of thought; this is more or less self-evident. What is not so obvious is *why* individuals have the various thoughts, plans, desires and so on, that they do. Why are we all so different, psychologically? These deeply motivating factors lie hidden within our minds, below the threshold of consciousness in most of us.

Hidden mind factors are also involved in the daily happenings of life which are apparently beyond our control, but which represent the sum total of all our minds combined – conscious and subconscious. These events are a part of the karmic outworking that is responsible for the play of life in this world. And in all of these, it is the hidden Formative Mind which is responsible for all that happens.

We do not know whence our thoughts and inner promptings, for good or bad, arise. Yet, in all our actions, our personal mind is obviously involved. An ugly crowd scene is the sum of all the minds involved, including the TV cameramen, the media reporters, the police, the 'innocent bystanders' and everyone else – even the doctors and nurses who patch up the injured, the florist who sells flowers to the relatives visiting the injured, the judge, the magistrate, the solicitors and the jury. And the primary association lies in the minds of all concerned. Without the mind's activity, nothing would happen.

To understand outward events, therefore, we have to understand the true nature of the *minds* involved. We have to know what Mind is. An analysis of the outward events and bodies is insufficient, for this great power of Mind is surely something more than molecules! We are dealing with the vast, integrated Egg of the Mind – the Formative, Universal Mind. It is this multilevel, multifaceted patterner of the primal energy which creates nature. All creatures experience this through their own personal minds. But underlying it all, linking every incarnate soul, is the greater Mind, the universal, formative engineer of all diversity.

And so it is with the fossil record. The outward changes are most definitely stratified – and yet time runs smoothly and continuously. But in addition to the vast areas of fossil history which are missing, what is really hidden from our view are the minds of those ancient creatures and the prevalent mental 'mood' or vibration of those times, and the mental build-up to each extinction cycle.

Like the 'black box' flight recorder in an aeroplane, actions, thoughts, desires and all other mental movements are recorded in the mind of the individual in 'seed,' in 'coded' or in 'essence' form. Nature, too, has a memory, just like the individual. And it is this hidden memory, the mental impressions of the past, individual and universal, which determine the form of newly emerging creatures. This is the truly 'psycho-somatic' evolution, in the widest sense of the term.

If we could only read those subtle mind patterns of the past, we would see just how and why the new forms came into being. Just as an individual soul takes a new birth after death, along with its associated destiny, and all according to the impressions etched upon the individual mind, just so would we see emerging creatures as the natural expression of the mental impressions and character of the past. The present evolves out of the mind stuff of the past. And, in the nature of things, the outward physical expression of these hidden mind patterns can be sudden.

One would expect some species to be similar to their predecessors. Some forms will come through untouched. Others will be quite different, expressive of the character of all the minds present at that time. The key to understanding it is: if you want to have a *body* like a dinosaur, then you must first have a *mind* like a dinosaur. To get a body like a dog, you must first have a mind like a dog. A soul is drawn by its karmas into that body in which it can best reap the result of all its past actions and desires. And it is an automatic process in nature to provide those forms. The hidden, administrative processes of the Mind automatically bring things about in this fashion.

6. NEW SPECIES AND THE FORMATIVE SPRINGTIME

Scientific theories are usually required to be capable, firstly, of *making predictions*, and secondly, of being *testable*. Many people have pointed out that evolutionary theory meets neither of these two criteria particularly well.

Firstly, evolutionary theory is essentially biological *history* and as such is incapable of being tested by normal scientific means. History is intrinsically open to surmise and interpretation – however well informed – not to the rigours of the scientific method. It is all concerned with what *has* happened, not what *is* happening. You cannot perform a repeatable experiment in history or evolution like you can in physics or chemistry. And since the history of living creatures so clearly involves the *minds* of those creatures, to assess the nature, vibration and general atmosphere of times long past is almost impossible in anything but the broadest outline.

The other criterion, the ability to make predictions, is interesting, for conventional evolutionary theory does predict many things, in particular that life can arise from inert mud in dead oceans and that the change from one species into another is gradual, taking place by chance mutations, selected by their fitness to survive and reproduce.

Well, no life is to be found springing spontaneously into existence nowadays and no exerimentation with lightning and supposedly primeval soups has ever been able to demonstrate anything remotely resembling even a self-replicating molecule, let alone a living creature. Why should this be so? If life began once in this way, when conditions were so inimical to its presence (for no Gaia processes could yet have started), why should it not have had *many* such beginnings? Especially now that circumstances are so conducive to life. Why only the once? Why not all the time?

And if lightning had been the magic ingredient, why should it have been more prevalent in such times than it is now? Why indeed should lightning be conducive to life, anyway? Mostly, the reverse is true. In any case, our weather is closely allied to activity in the biosphere and always has been. And no life would have meant no biosphere. So who can say what the weather would have been like, had there even been such times? The suggestion of life arising out of dust and water seems most unlikely.

The 'random mutation' theory should, on the face of it, be more readily verifiable. One can even perform experiments in selective breeding and so on, monitoring the unexpected 'mutations'. However, when 'mutations' do occur, we are unable to determine whether they were random or not, for despite considerable research, the details of genetic processes are only very sketchily understood. In fact, we understand genetic processes so little that it is impossible to really say how or whether they even *permit* random mutations. Even with selective, 'controlled' breeding we have no detailed understanding of the molecular and subatomic processes which are actually involved.

We have seen that great extinctions have occurred rhythmically in the past followed by sudden re-proliferations, but from where will the re-proliferation arise on this occasion? Are we to assume that life has really put its foot in it this time and that too many basic species have been lost for suitable radiation to take place and new species to emerge? Man's horizons stretch no further than a few decades, at most, but how is the next evolutionary step and the next great proliferation going to come about? Are there any signs of a process *already* at work to regenerate our stock of planetary life forms?

If the suggestion is correct that the major proliferation takes place when the power of the Life Force waxes strong, when the patterning power of the Formative Mind enters its own springtime, then could we expect to find traces of the process still at work, perhaps emerging, perhaps declining, but active at the present time upon the planet?

For just as man reflects the Kal yuga by becoming the hunter and the destroyer of life, so does he become a far more conscious co-worker with the Divine creative process during the Sat yuga. What then does man do during a Sat yuga? He is not going to sit around upon his etherealized backside for 100,000 years quietly contemplating the landscape! For the physical plane is still the plane of action, of doing. And such expansion of consiousness and species regeneration does not come overnight. It may take a million years or more.

So perhaps our present foray into genetic engineering presages a major understanding of a new philosophy or perception of life as it really is. This would include a detailed understanding of the formative processes of the greater Mind, and of how physical bodies are constructed from within-out as aspects of this Formative Mind. Then, no doubt, our present experimentation and understanding will be seen as a simplistic and bizarre – though essential – beginning, to which the ingredient of understanding the real creative life process itself has yet to be added. Current genetic research may be only the tip of the tip – of the tip – of the iceberg yet to come, just as other discoveries of the past have been.

Genetic engineering, after all, is really engineering of a part of the biological blueprinting system, but it is without a full understanding of how – or why – a body comes into being and how the Mind is also implicated in the process at an even more fundamentally formative level. Yet it is definitely one step on from selective breeding, a technique which has been practised for many generations.

If we agree and observe that man's understanding can advance and that what appear at one time to be radically new ideas can later become the accepted norms, then we must also acknowledge the limitations not only of our present knowledge, but also of our fundamental paradigms, the frameworks into which we fit our knowledge. For however good the observations, the conclusions will always be incorrect if our framework is awry. Therefore, it is changes to the framework within which we view things that inaugurate revolutions of perspective.

The genetic engineering of the future, if it is to progress, will need to become conversant with the manner by which the subtle energies of the mind are intimately entwined with bodily processes. Presently, the science of the subtle is still given only a fringe status. Yet the weak signals of today become the strong signals of tommorrow.

Things take time to develop. Certainly, amongst at least some sections of our planetary population, we are currently enjoying a general expansion of consciousness. Interest in spiritual matters is increasing. In the world at large, this is reflected as a concern for the rights of the individual, in human or animal; as a perception that intolerance and prejudice are incorrect though difficult to eradicate from human minds. For legislation alone does not change the content of our hearts and minds. Slavery has been abolished, though historically only very recently, but exploitation of humans by humans continues unabated. Some slaves may have even had a better life with kind and understanding masters than many 'free' people of today, trapped and enslaved by the ceaseless pressures of our modern world.

Does the human, caught up in this endless round of traffic jams, mortgages, office or factory deadlines and TV dinners, really have a better life than the 'savage' who lives beneath the trees? I do not think so. Within himself and in his attitudes, man in a suit or overalls may be far more of a savage than man in a loin cloth, in harmony with the natural world. But 'savage' or 'civilized,' this is all an expression of life as it is lived in the Kal yuga, when man is mostly unconscious and ignorant of how this dance of life is put together. The symptoms of a Kal yuga are those of inward slavery to the material world.

So the signs of an approaching Sat yuga will come from *within ourselves*. Outward life is never more than a reflection of what lies within. By degrees, our consciousness and perception increase. We place greater and greater value upon the inner side of things, for we realize the inward to be the source of life; that well-being and awareness are not to be found in the outer world, but in the deepest recesses of our own long-neglected, innermost beings.

So maybe there *is* modern evidence to support the mystical description of the cycle of the yugas, the cycle within consciousness: we are presently going through an extinction cycle, right on schedule after the Sat yuga 8 or 10 million years ago (on the scientific time scale). And man is selfish and materialistic, just as he is said to be in a Kal yuga.

And can evidence of the cosmic Springtime be observed in the expansion of consciousness presently sweeping though the peoples of our planet? Or is it only a reaction to the intense materialism on the other side of the scales? Are we really only bumping along the bottom, with plenty more yet to come before the upturn of a Sat yuga?

TESTING THE HYPOTHESIS

Evolutionary theories, being essentially history, are the most difficult of all to test. But the suggestion of the Formative Mind as a dimension of being and projected energy patterns responsible for the maintainance of bodily forms as they are now, as well as creating the changes we can observe in the fossil record, does imply certain predictions and proposals. The following, some more obviously testable than others, may be considered:

1.   Were we to be sure of our dating techniques, we would find extinction–proliferation cycles of equal lengths, globally and throughout all the available fossil record. Like winters, some of these cycles would be more severe than others. Considerable research has already been done by Eldredge and the proponents of the theory of punctuated equilibria and the results are encouraging.

2.   Because it is Formative Mind factors which provide the continuity, there will always be some similarity between one cycle and the next. But this can only be seen in the fossil remains as similarity between the species of contiguous cycles. This therefore gives rise to the illusion of materialistic evolution. But an entire dimension is missing from the observation.

3.   Existing scientific theory does not permit us to calculate the value of 'universal constants' from theoretical or first principles, or from a real knowledge of how the universe is constructed. They are measured experimentally because we do not know how they (or anything else) arises. It should not alarm or surprise us, therefore, if there turns out to be a periodicity in what we now consider to be universal constants. This includes gravity, the speed of light, the rate of radioactive decay, even the electrical charge upon the electron and proton, and the values of the other fundamental forces. The periodicity would span the same period of time as these fossil strata. Our present geological estimates of time may thus be in error by a factor of about 40 or 50 per cent, because they assume the constancy of 'universal constants'.

4.   It is suggested that the nature of material manifestation during Sat yugas is of a far more subtle quality than in a Kal yuga. There is thus a cycling of subtlety and spiritualization in the physical universe. This periodicity could be reflected in the nature of manifestation out of the vacuum state energy field, the energy of the space within which we live and which comprises the physical universe.

Some evidence of this may possibly be found in the vacuum state memory vibrations, the *akashic record* of these periods, should technology advance sufficiently to be able to read them! I have discussed this topic more fully in *The Secret of the Creative Vacuum*.

Linked to this suggestion is the idea that the vacuum state will turn out to be a sea of spatial energy in which physical matter is only patterns or effects upon its 'surface', linked into consciousness through our mind and senses.

5.   A further possibility, as a part of the regenerative process, is that existing species contain within them the capacity to change into other

allied forms in response to a change in the inner mental and outer physical 'environment'. It is also suggested that there are numerous subtle energy, microcosmic configurations made up of the subtle tattwas, underlying the physical forms of creatures. These constitute a number of 'super-species' which are manifested in many outward forms throughout time. All scientifically defined species, whether alive now or only found in the fossil record, are representatives of these super-species. But to ascertain the veracity of this assertion would require some considerable changes to our system of species classification.

6.   Sooner or later it will be discovered or realized that there is nothing wasted in the DNA; that there is no "junk DNA"; and that genetic processes are far more complex and wonderful than the sequencing of four bases on a sugar–phosphate spine.

7.   Other suggestions have also been made concerning the nature of our individual mind, the Formative Mind, life, consciousness, God – and so on. These hypotheses are all testable by entering the laboratory of one's own being and there performing the required mystic practices. But this is a personal odyssey, not a matter of academic research. And naturally, research into the nature of being requires an appropriate technique. One should not be expected to study mind, consciousness and being by an intellectual analysis of one's sensory experience of the physical universe.

The 'appropriate technique' or 'mystic practice' is a suitable form of meditation, the practice of which will also reveal that there is a hierarchy of subtle energy planes situated along the ontological dimension of Mind and Life, which can be experienced within one's own being. This also implies that the practice of meditation will make an individual more sensitive or aware of the subtle vibrations of his own being, as well as those of others and in his environment. This can be established by sincerely taking up the practice of meditation, under suitable guidance.

8.   The Formative Mind hypothesis also indicates that the body is an aspect of Mind and can only be really understood as such. This explains not only how we waggle a finger, but provides a paradigm by which all psychic, psychosomatic and psychological aspects of existence may be understood. It also gives us a glimmering of how the mind and body are interfaced and will lead us to a deeper perception of health and healing. It can be confidently predicted that absolutely no workable and complete model or description of how the brain

functions or of the brain–mind interface will be developed without an understanding that the mind is an altogether more subtle entity than the body. Neither will any coherent and unified model of the universe, and all the experiences of life, emerge which does not take the ontological dimension into account.

SUBCONSCIOUS BIAS, ANTHROPOMORPHISM AND EVOLUTION

The greater part of the language of palaeontology is riddled with words that presuppose an evolutionary process of a purely material nature. That is to say that the language used to *describe* the factual evidence is actually permeated with presuppositions concerning its *interpretation*. Not only that, but in reading it, if one is not very careful, one slips into that way of thinking and the dogma is thereby unconsciously accepted and perpetuated. As in advertising, one begins to believe a thing simply because it has been repetitively stated to be so. Many 'evolutionary' terms are widely used, but they hide some rather woolly thinking, while subliminally promoting evolutionary dogmas.

Words such as 'primitive', for instance, suggest an evolutionary principle. Evolutionists talk of 'primitive' mammals and 'primitive' reptiles, even 'primitive' man. But upon what criteria are such delineations made? Is a modern lungfish – such a highly adapted species, excellently designed for life in waters that periodically dry up for long periods – more 'primitive' than its modern 'relatives', the herring and the salmon, purely because its ancestry can be traced to Palaeozoic times? Or should one, in fact, consider it more 'advanced', more 'evolved' or more 'adapted', because it has survived so long?

Is its biochemistry, physiology or anatomy somehow inferior? No. Is it, then, less 'intelligent'? No again, I imagine, though I wonder how such tests could be performed! And anyway, what really constitutes intelligence? Does it have less ability to survive and to adapt? No again, for lungfish have stood a far longer test of changing environmental circumstances. In fact, if survival of the fittest is the keynote, then the lungfish must surely be considered amongst the fittest and the choicest of creatures in a Darwinian world.

So 'primitive' is not the word to use. Amongst the world of men, are we with our nuclear arsenals, guns and rockets less primitive than our forebears? Neanderthal man, it has been discovered, used tooth-picks and probably grew flowers, 50,000 years ago. And even earlier than that, about 100,000 years ago, dwellers in southern Africa on the borderland with Swaziland and Natal manufactured beautifully worked agate knives. At the same site (Border Cave), the body of an infant was also found who had obviously been given a ceremonial burial. It seems those ancient people believed in an afterlife and had a well-developed language, for the appreciation of aesthetics and intimations of immortality cannot be conveyed by grunts and gestures. Yet, for some strange reason, scientists do not like to think that man could even speak as recently as 50,000 years ago.

Now how does all that (and much more) marry up with the hairy, violent images we are shown at school? No palaeontologist would dare to put the flesh on any ancient creature and say *for sure* that this was how it *really* looked. So why do we do so with man? There is no evidence that Neanderthal man was any the less intelligent than we are. Neither is there any evidence as to whether he ran about naked or clothed, though even this is not a good criterion by which to judge social behaviour and intelligence. He may have led a far better life in terms of basic human values.

Children's comic books and many evolutionary textbooks alike both portray the dinosaurs as overlarge, clumsy and stupid, poorly adapted or designed for their way of life. This conditions childrens' minds at an early age to accept these naive interpretations. Yet these days, scientists have come around to describing dinosaurs as superbly adapted creatures, many of whom were probably warm-blooded. Some of them lived in herds. Some laid eggs like birds and may well have cared for them just as fondly. The ancient evolutionist dogmas of our school education and of popular misconception need to be revised and thoroughly dispelled.

Huge dinosaurian footprints, 3 feet long by 2 feet wide, holding enough water to bath a baby are preserved in the Jurassic limestone of Davenport Ranch in Texas. Robert Bakker describes the passage of a compact herd of two dozen brontosaurs, their passing imprinted in the ancient Jurassic mud, in which the larger bulls (or senior cows) took up protective positions fore and aft, while the smaller footprints of their young are found sheltering in their midst.

These were the days of the *allosaurs*, one of the most fearsome predators ever to have walked the planet. Their size was suited to the huge dimensions of their prey, the mammals perhaps escaping persecution at this time by virtue of their more diminutive dimensions. And there, impressed into the mud, flanking one of these ghostly footprint herds of herbivorous dinosaurs, one finds the huge, three-toed, bird-like tracks of an ancient predatory allosaur. Yet this seems strange, for such herding and socially protective behaviour is more reminiscent of birds and mammals than of the reptiles with which dinosaurs have historically been grouped.

Whether or not one *believes* (that is the correct word!) in conventional evolution or in some far deeper creative process involving Mind and consciousness itself, many outmoded concepts concerning evolutionary theory must be dismissed in the light of present day science. More than 99.99 per cent of all past species are now extinct. Is the current set the most 'evolved' or is it just a reflection of the times?

If man is the ultimate 'aim' of all evolutionary processes, then where next do we go? How strange, too, that we happen to be living just 2 million years after man, the pinnacle of evolution, is supposed to have evolved so very rapidly from our primate brothers! Will man then die at the next punctuation, the next extinction, only to emerge as some new class of creature? But how? Man shows little tendency of evolving into any other species.

The Darwinian dogma of natural selection, seen as a constant force at work sifting the 'good' from the 'bad,' needs considerable revision. We glibly quote 'The Survival of the Fittest', without ever really considering the underlying implications. Does the fossil record really suggest that all that has been happening for the last 4 billion years is a search for *better design*? Does it even suggest that at all? And what constitutes 'better'?

The same comments apply here as to the concept of 'primitive'. Were bacteria 3.5 billion years ago less well designed than their counterparts of today? Was a Precambrian clam, 675 million years ago, any better designed than its modern relatives. Do we ignore habitat in this concept of design? Indeed, is man a 'better' design than a clam? Design for what? What is this mysterious but unnamed goal of Darwinian evolution? How is such vision and direction maintained by chance and self-organizing molecules?

Darwin himself emphasized the 'extinction of less-improved forms'. But nowhere in the fossil record is there any evidence that species of the past were 'less-improved' or less 'evolved'. It seems far more likely that each was perfectly suited to its times.

Since Darwin's day we have come to realize far more of the amazingly complex and interwoven processes to be found in living organisms. The very subatomic fabric of physical substance is patterned and ordered to an extreme degree in the bodies of living creatures. Is evolutionary theory suggesting that the physiology and biochemistry of bygone creatures was somehow 'less-improved' than their counterparts of today? Traces of ink have been found in association with the fossils of ancient Cambrian octopuses. But did they possess a 'less-improved' physiology and anatomy for manufacturing and squirting ink than their modern cousins? It seems unlikely.

Again, life in the Palaeozoic seas is often described as *simple*, while life forms today are said to be more *complex*. But is the structure of *any* living creature simple? No-one understands even an amoeba or a bacterium well enough to know how to *begin* to actually *make* one! Was a Devonian octopus with its mammalian-like eye, so perfectly fitted for life in the water, any the less complex than a man in terms of its biochemistry, its molecular organization?

No scientist knows enough about how a life form is really put together to make such an assumption. Man and octopus both possess a cellular structure, nervous and endocrine systems, blood vessels, muscles, lymph, digestive organs and all the rest of it.

Is complexity, then, to be equated with size? The five and half foot scorpion − one of the largest arthropods ever to have lived − can hardly have been any simpler than its smaller relatives of today. What is this scale of complexity, so commonly equated with evolutionary 'success', which places man as the highest because he is the most complex? What are the critera for determining biological complexity? If man is higher and more complex because he has more cells than single-celled amoebae, then should not a shark, a whale, an elephant or many other creatures be considered higher and more complex than a man because they possess more cells? Is a bigger person higher on the scale of evolution than a smaller one? Of course not.

Taking this argument to extremes, one could suggest that − as in mathematics and physics − the *simplest* form is the most superior, the most aesthetic. In maths, complexity and inelegance are usually indicative of error. So is the virus, the bacterium or the amoeba the most 'advanced'?

Again as in maths, when all sides cancel out, so that zero equals zero, we have reached the final line of the calculation. We can go no further. So is the ultimate evolutionary 'goal', the *elimination* of life forms? Has 'evolution' been a journey into devolution, away from the 'perfection' of nothingness?

'Ungainly', 'archaic', even 'grotesque', are other words commonly used to describe animals of an earlier period. Such words imply that they are 'evolutionarily inferior'. Were they really? And does that mean that evolution has presently reached a state of perfection? 'Perfection' according to whose ideology? Does 'modern' equal 'best'? How can we assume that our current status is somehow one of perfection or even just 'better', whilst all others of the past were only striving to reach the status of today? Do we look perfect? We seem to be confusing 'difference' and 'change' with 'progress' and 'evolution.'

The use of such words would seem to be an almost unconscious attempt to impose the Darwinian thinking pattern upon creatures of the past, unable to raise a roar, a bleat, a bellow or a squeak in their defence! 'Grotesque' is representative of human prejudice and personal, emotional reaction, rather than a serious, scientific comment on evolution. Should a species be expected to become extinct simply because someone does not like the look of it? I imagine that the bones of a rhinoceros or a polar bear might seem ungainly to one who had never seen the creature in real live action. And the Irish Elk, an extinction victim of our present ice age, often accused of downfall through possessing antlers far too big for its head, was most probably a real beauty to watch in action, finding no difficulty in handling its extravagent, but beautifully balanced headgear.

It is such a fallacy to assume that only modern creatures are well adapted, while all of those of the past were only struggling to arrive where we are today. If everything is now perfect, where is it supposed that evolution will take us during the next 10 or a 100 million years?

The comment, for example, that such 'large, lumbering, downright ungainly mammals all turned out to be evolutionary dead ends' (Eldredge) is definitely reverse logic. One could, I suppose, say the same of the dodo, which would have seemed perfectly suited to its terrestrial habitat in Mauritius until the arrival of modern man and his dogs upon the scene. Surely one could say the same of man whose self-destructive conduct is seemingly so bizarre and unsuited to his continued existence? 'Man turned out to be such a selfish and destructive creature that he soon destroyed his own habitat and thus himself. Another 'evolutionary dead end'!'

Such concepts of a 'successful' species or 'goals' of evolution are essentially anthropocentric projections of our own western psychology. As are 'competition' amongst species, even the 'selfish gene', as neo-Darwinist Richard Dawkins likes to call it. How can a molecule be selfish? Does DNA possess a self? Can science tell us so assuredly of the nature of the self that it can ascribe a sense of self to molecules? This seems to be a reflection of man's ignorance of the nature of himself, a projection of his own mental confusion. Even the psychologist and the brain specialist have little or no common ground, such is man's unconsciousness of how he is inwardly constructed.

Nature is a co-operative economy. It is in man's small-minded world, ruled by his personal fears and sense of inadequacy, where competition, prejudice and intolerance reign. But this is what happens when the Life Force wanes. There is no blame associated with it all. Life goes on the way the Creator, the Supreme Life Force, intends. But it is Life which gives life – not molecules!

Then again, if one were to apply the criteria of *success* to the animal kingdom, what yardsticks would one use in making such a judgement? The prize for longevity of presence within the fossil record would undoubtedly be won by bacteria. Also, for sheer numbers, bacteria would again be the winners. Plants would come out top when judged for their employment of available natural resources. No other species taps right into sunlight as a source of physical energy. But then without bacteria, worms, moulds and fungi, plants would have no soil or humus in which to grow. There would be no creatures to break down their old leaves, stems and branches. Furthermore, insects, birds and animals are all employed by plants to pollinate and carry their seeds. Nature is a co-operative whole, despite the fact that creature eats creature. Integration is the ultimate keynote of function within the worlds of the Formative Mind.

If efficient transport and long distance travel were the 'goal' of all 'successful' life, then birds would surely win. And the archer fish – who can shoot down insects by 'spitting' a jet of water almost vertically for distances of up to fifteen feet, even adjusting for the refraction of light as it passes from air to water – they would certainly win their category in the animal olympics. But how could such a feat even have evolved? The sight, the musculature, the behaviour – all these and more are involved and most beautifully integrated. How could the myriad integrated pathways in the physiological, neurological and biochemical tapestry ever have arisen by chance? Was the first archer fish simply a bad and feeble – but persistent – shooter?

The list is endless and the point has been well made. Man is only superior in his potential spiritual and mental capacity, his ability to more fully understand the processes of life. The inner linkage of akash to his inner mental structure gives him the potential to be aware of the relationships between all things and to perceive his place in the scheme of things. He can decide to use this discrimination, developing it – and proceeding far higher – by means of meditation. It is then that one discovers many things, automatically. Realizing that while man indulges in the supermarket of opinions, it is God who has the Reality!

Darwin certainly helped release recent man from bondage to a creationist dogma that insisted upon a strange and distant God having done it all in six days, in 4004 BC, thereupon taking a holiday

on the seventh! But we have gone to the other extreme to insist that
the precious life within us is no more than dust and water, caught up
in playful self-organization, orchestrated by chance. Especially when
the physical world is actually made up of sensory experiences within
our own minds; and when the dust itself seems to be the creation of
the Life Force, also empowering the Formative Mind within us. Why
relinquish one dogma to embrace another, equally as bizarre? Why
not seek for experience of soul, of being? Life is a drop of the great
Creative Ocean of Life, of God, of Consciousness, of Love, of Bliss.
To find *that* within ourselves is the true goal of human life.

Perhaps, then, it is some distant memory of our true inward reality
which stirs us to believe in some kind of evolution. We do realize, too,
from observation that we are *higher* than the other animals; that dogs
are higher than birds, birds than reptiles, and reptiles than amoeba.
And that all these are greater beings, in some indefinable way, than
plants. But what is it we are perceiving? Is a dog really more
physically complex than a bird? Can a dog build a nest, or make
honey in a hive?

The difference, lies, we know, in intelligence. Man has a greater
intelligence than dogs or birds. At least, he has the potential for it.
And dogs demonstrate greater intelligence than birds, and birds than
insects or reptiles. So then we look at the size and complexity of the
brain and say that that must be the goal of evolution, to develop a
bigger brain, to possess greater intelligence. But what is intelligence
and what is mind? What is consciousness? We do not find them in the
brain however hard we look. We cannot even find a place where
memory is lodged, even in insects or birds. These all lie in the subtle
patterns of the creature – man or beast. The soul is the same in all.
The laws of the Mind are the same for all. But the nature or
configuration of the energies that surround the soul varies. The real
life inside is indestructible. It journeys on from body to body, its
subtle structure varying as it goes, according to the laws of the
Formative Mind.

So why the creation? Well, only He knows. And when – say the
mystics – we *become* Him, then we can understand. To find God
within oneself is the epitome of all evolution. This world and all
others are His Natural Creation, the true evolutionary goal is to find
the Weaver of the magic, the Binder of the spell. Then we will find
rest from this eternal round of birth, death and rebirth.

One has to ask, 'What is the driving force behind any economy of
creatures?' It is the life within the creatures. The vibrancy of that Life
Force actually creates that ecosystem around them. It is the essence of

'green fingers' – the quality of life and consciousness in the one who cares. It pours through the mind as a subtle current of vitality, of vital energy, increasing the vigour in the one who receives. This is true of all contacts in life – not just with gardeners. We should try it out on our fellow humans, not only on our plants!

All things come and go, except the Eternal Essence. And in this physical domain, it is the waning of the Life Force which permits decline, senescence and extinction. Then even man forgets his divine birthright and enters the foray as a destructive influence. Perhaps this low point on the graph of human consciousness signals the trough, present in all extinction cycles.

But when that new vitality comes flooding through, as the gates are opened once again to a new Sat yuga, then once more 'all losses are restor'd and sorrows end[1]'. Then the vibrancy of a fresh spring must be nothing compared to the floodgates of inner bliss, peace and love which man may then enjoy.

Yet from the highest point of view, this is still a device of the Mind, to keep us in this physical world. Therefore, even whilst enjoying peace and bliss, one should never abandon the inner quest for ultimate union with God.

NEW SPECIES, ECOSYSTEMS AND THE FORMATIVE MIND

Let us for a moment recap on a few of our themes. We have said that creatures are alive, conscious and possess a mind; that it is this mind and its inner subtle structure which determines the outer form of the creature; that over the ages, there have been myriad outer forms, some alive today, others with no living counterparts; that these forms change over at regular intervals every 10 million years or so on the present geological time-scale; and that there is no evidence of any evolution of lower to higher forms taking place at all.

What is changing, of course, are the expressions of the super-species, their subtle 'creature-blueprints,' as the cycles of the yugas pass. But the nature of *life* remains the same. And inasmuch as the environmental conditions and the general 'mood' within the Mind at the start of one cycle resemble those at the end of the previous cycle, then there is similarity between the old set and the new set of creatures. The new is formed out of the seeds of the old, sometimes

[1] *But if the while I think on thee, dear friend,*
   All losses are restor'd and sorrows end." – Shakespeare, sonnet 30.

with greater changes, sometimes with less. But all the same, whenever new creatures come into being, there seems to be a threshold – a sudden jump.

Not all environments change as much as others – it may be only the sea or the land which particularly require the greatest regeneration. Or perhaps certain areas of the globe remain relatively intact even after the decline of the Life Force during the Kal yuga, so their flora and fauna continue on in much the same style. Certain creatures seem to come through many cycles without a change or with only minor modifications, though even in these changes the jump from one form to another is often sudden.

Both physical bodies and so-called outward 'environmental' conditions are therefore the creation of the Formative Mind, projected under the influence of the 'law' of karma. But as we have said, karma is not a law which is *applied* to the Mind. It is the *inherent*, implicate law of Mind function. Karma is what happens automatically when the web of the Many is woven by the Mind across the face of the One. Oneness then gives way to relationship.

One of the difficulties associated with all descriptions is that we use the intellectual process which likes to see things in a linear fashion. We think that one thing happens *because* of something else. In fact, in the processes of nature, there is no ultimate 'because' – everything is just one integrated whole. From our limited perception we mistake relationship for causality, but in reality there is only one 'cause' – the Supreme Reality itself. And it is a Source so integrated with the existence of everything that there is really no question of causation, in a linear sense.

All ecosystems are really controlled from the level of the Formative Mind. The 'cause' lies in the realms of subtle Mind energy. Creation is only a multilevel patterning of the Mind over the Essential Being. The interplay of physical bodies is only a reflection of what is going on at a Mind level. And the law of the Mind – karma – we do not really understand. But to be responsible for the creation of such ecosystems, integrated at a multitude of levels and in so many different ways – anatomical, behavioural, instinctive and so on – the law of karma, involving the individual minds of every incarnate creature, clearly demonstrates deeply integrated aspects of Mind energy function.

The physical world is the world of shadows, of projected images. But from an image one can derive some information concerning the nature of the more inward patterns. The tapestry of intricate and multitudinous relationships in the physical ecosystem demonstrate just such inwardly integrated laws and patterns of Mind energy.

So, applying this understanding to the fossil record and the cycle of yugas, we can say, for example, that the dinosaurs first appeared upon the scene because this was the natural outcome of the combined mind energies carried over from the last cycle. They were dinosaur-*minded*. Indeed, even some of the 'protomammals' in the ages immediately preceding the advent of the dinosaurs were of a size and disposition not too dissimilar from the dinosaurs who followed. They were already moving in that direction. And after reading Robert Bakker's book, it is difficult to think that either could have been anything other than warm-blooded.

I think that it must be the biological plasticity and subtle nature of physical vibration during the Sat yuga which makes it possible for new forms to emerge and radiate so rapidly into a multiplicity of new species. They arise from some inner mental 'breeding ground' of forms, by genetic or perhaps other processes which we find difficult to understand. And energizing this, of course, lies the more inward Life Force.

The 'new' forms, spun out within the constraints of the existent tattvic configurations or super-species, are formed as a direct result of all the mental impressions of the souls involved. And since the karmic law also includes one's destiny and the events of a life, the Formative Mind simultaneously creates the environment, the ecosystem, the physical bodies, the behavioural and the instinctive patterns – everything. The Formative Mind is the more-than-holistic originator of the integrated physical world, of what we call nature.

So, just as we humans receive the kind of body and the events of life that we 'deserve' or have earned, according to the nature of our own inner mind and its impressions from the past, so too did the souls inhabiting dinosaur bodies get just what they had themselves desired and created out of their own minds! It was both the mood of the times and the mood of the individuals.

When we look at old, fossilized dinosaur bones, we are indeed looking at just that: old bones! We may not even see the bones assembled; we certainly do not see the flesh, the soft organs, the skin and the sense organs in their places, though very occasionally we may get an impression of their skin in the soft mud. And of their behaviour, we can deduce no more than the barest outlines. Did they migrate? How did they care for their young? What sounds did they make in their communications? What were their social and courtship rituals? How did they make love?

If we could observe all these aspects of an ancient creature, within the context of their times, then – I feel sure – we would see an animal, perfect for its time and place, as are all the creatures of today.

The material evolution of physical bodies from one remote ancestor can never have taken place, because that is not how either
physical bodies nor the physical universe come into being. Darwin
would surely have been incredulous if he discovered that his 'one or a
few ancestors' had been reduced to some primeval and unknown
self-organized and self-replicating molecule.

There is an inner dimension to things which makes a science based
purely upon material premises hopelessly incomplete, like trying to
describe the world in just two spatial dimensions. We cannot look at
an image upon a screen and by analysing relationships within it, think
that we know how it moves and changes. If we think that the image is
the only reality, ultimately we may be led to believe that it acts as a
complete, self-organizing whole. But we are still far removed from
understanding how it gets there!

But were we able to see the movie film in the projector and the
lamp behind it, then we would realize that there is a far greater
creative process at work, which also demands our study. And since
this movie film and the source of light are within us, a quite different
method of study is required. How do we study what lies within
ourselves? The answer is meditation. And not just any old meditation,
but as in any well conducted experiment, a spiritual practice based
upon distinct but simple techniques, with a particular goal in view.

At the start of every new cycle of yugas there is an opportunity for
renewal. The exact process of that renewal requires a full perception
of greater Mind function, and that can only be acquired, personally,
by meditational practice. It cannot be understood from a book.

Nevertheless, there is something which can be said in this respect.
The three worlds of the Mind – the physical, astral and causal – are
an integral whole. When dissolution comes after 1000 cycles of the
yugas, all three are dissolved together. You cannot dissolve just the
physical world, or just the astral, because they are intricately entwined with each other by laws which our intellect – part of our
individual or physical mind – cannot fully comprehend.

The causal world is the realm of primal 'ideas', original blueprints,
archetypes or energies in seed form. In the astral region, these
blueprints come into a more manifested form, clothed with the
substance or energy of the astral realms. In the physical world, these
astral patterns, forces, forms and bodies are projected outwards,
becoming the bodies we see all around us. The Life Force, the
Creative Word, holding it all together and vibrating through all things,
reaches down into the physical realm only after attenuation by the
Mind patternings of the causal and astral domains. And originating

within these three worlds, there is this ebb and flow of the Life Force which we experience in the physical world as the cycle of the yugas.

Looked at from this cosmic Mind point of view, we can imagine it as a periodicity in the 'conjunction' or the relationship between the causal realm and its astral and physical projections or reflections. It would be just like a reflection in an optical system coming in and out of focus as the relationship between the components changes.

It is this higher periodicity, this Mind-breathing, which causes the ebb and flow of the yugas on the physical plane. It is not actually the Life Force which ebbs and flows so much as the Mind which becomes a greater or lesser screen across the face of the ever-constant Ocean of Life. And when there is the closest 'proximity' between the causal, astral and physical realms, when the Mind is at its most subtle, we have a Sat yuga. Then we have a springtime like no other we have known. Then there is a flood of subtle vibration and Life Force into this world.

When the heavy density enshrouding the physical world is lifted, then the blueprints within the Formative Mind, expressions of the many super-species, 'fall into' or are manifested in the physical realm. I do not mean by some miraculous and sudden appearance, but somehow they find a natural means of physical expression. As I have pointed out, even now we understand practically nothing of genetic processes and the means by which an embryo is formed and becomes an adult. But it is all dictated by the combined karmas of the souls involved and fully under the control of the Formative Mind.

The process is automatic and it most probably also involves man himself. If, out of ignorance, we are responsible for the demise of life forms, then out of spiritual wisdom and harmony with the intrinsic laws of nature, we will be able to use our talents for the outworking of the divine plan and the creation of new forms.

So this, perhaps, is how the proliferation of new species comes about so suddenly and apparently out of nowhere. For the fossil record tells us nothing of the subtlety of the vibrational conditions prevailing at those times. Or if it does, we have yet to decipher it. We are looking at the remains *in our own time*, not as they were when enlivened by the soul-mind combinations of those days.

Now we may think this to be somewhat bizarre, but there are already new forms coming into being all around us, all the time, where the mind is most clearly involved. Man's inventions, for a start. The steam engine, the computer, the aeroplane, the radio and everything else have all arisen from blueprints or ideas worked out in the minds of men and women. Actually, we do nothing but it first passes through our mind. Behind all forms, animate or inanimate – lies the activity of Mind, in its many expressions.

Modern man has enough understanding of how to work with the gross patterns and forces to enable him to make exceptionally accurate machinery and electronics with his hands – guided by his materially-centred mind.

When his mind is focused upon the subtle, then he finds that he can also work with the subtle. Man is presently gaining knowledge of how to work with the subtle forces and patterns of nature – knowledge which he has had before and lost. When he begins to awaken from the deep sleep of unconsciousness, then many more things become possible for him to achieve. But then his ego is not so prominent and he behaves far more as a channel for the Divine intent, in tune with the greater plan of which he is a part.

Then he also realizes that his abilities to rearrange the energy patterns by what he calls science have a far deeper meaning and a far wider scope. Science, like all else in this physical world, is meant for man's own education, for personal growth, for his own inner evolution, to train his inward faculties. Yet nowadays, science has largely become a means of exploitation and money making. A sad affair! But given a more spiritual outlook and an expanded consciousness, man automatically behaves in a befitting manner. He no longer desecrates himself and his world.

Science is only a knowledge of how the physical plane of being – the sensory field of experience – is constructed. How deep that knowledge is and how we use it depends upon the content of our own minds. The deeper the man, then the deeper his science.

GENETIC RESPONSE TO THE ENVIRONMENT

We have said before that there appears to be good reason to assume that creatures can respond genetically to environmental changes. Let us take a simple example from present times. It is well known that, given time, species will develop an inherited immunity to toxic substances or diseases, especially those arising from bacterial, viral or other microbial infections. This is especially so in the case of creatures which breed rapidly, such as insects, rabbits or rats, and even more so in the case of the fastest of all breeders, bacteria and viruses. Such micro-organisms are well known for their ability to develop immunity to substances which previously poisoned them.

This, it has always been assumed, is due to some fortunate but chance mutation which permitted one such member to live whilst the others died. The lucky survivor then genetically transmits this good fortune to his or her offspring. Species therefore possess the capacity to change in response to circumstances.

Now, within the overall framework of Formative Mind function, we have suggested that there is no potential for chance, that everything is supremely well ordered. What we call chance – when viewing things from the physical level – is only an imperfect view of bubbles on the ocean; we cannot see the formative ocean connecting them all beneath the surface, and out of which they spring.

I would suggest, therefore, that the very presence of a toxic substance or pathological organism creates an ambience which has both outward as well as subtle components, and which in some way stimulates the required genetic response from within the subtle state. Just as coffee or alcohol (material substances) affects our mind (subtle substance) and just as our mind affects our body, just so does the subtle vibration induced by the toxin or organism stimulate the genetic system to produce the required 'mutation' at the physical level. It behaves like a self-correcting or self-balancing energy system, a living gyroscope.

Note how it is mind, ambience and circumstance which give rise to the appropriate genetic change, which – if we then ignore considerations of the subtle – appears to be no more than a fortuitous or chance affair.

Taking this just as one example, then, of the formative processes acting between mind and body, from subtle to gross, consider how much more readily such transference of patterning would take place during a period when the crystallization or strait-jacketing of physical matter were far less dense, under the vitalizing power of the Sat yuga.

Everything, then, is being constantly patterned anew. The theme is an old one, as old as the creation itself, but the refrains and variations are new. The basic patterns are the same, but some of the details are different.

So, too, with the coming of a Sat yuga and the replenishment of the store of life forms within the physical domain. But then the degree of creativity must be enhanced a millionfold. Man himself will feel that he is involved in the creation of new life forms, just as feels he has invented so much in his more recent history. One only needs to survey the landscape to know how much the mind of man has touched every corner of the planet.

Now we are setting out upon the road of genetic engineering, a process which we understand in only a very limited degree. How much more might we accomplish if we were working in concert with the natural law, as conscious co-workers?

Man in the Sat yuga is highly spiritualized and etherealized. Even now one observes that some human bodies appear to be of a dense, dull and coarse nature while others are of an altogether more subtle quality. One feels this in the atmosphere or vibration around a person, as well as in their touch, in the things they say and do, and in the way they do things.

Suppose that man came to really understand the subtle processes of himself and other creatures, that he came to understand this multi-level Mind-body system and the real role played in it by DNA and all the other aspects of our present reductionist, analytical science. Then might both his motive and his skill be immeasurably different, making his current efforts, driven by financial profit and desire for fame, seem like something out of a cheap movie. Modern researchers in genetic engineering even fight competitively over whether their latest 'creation' can be patented or over who owns the patent! To 'own' the 'rights' to a living creature! How much better it would be to work in real harmony and understanding with the natural law.

BACTERIA TAKE THE CHANCE OUT OF EVOLUTION

By one of those 'coincidences' which demonstrate the linkage of all our minds at the formative level, the above section was written on the very day before I received my weekly copy of New Scientist magazine, dated September 22nd, 1988.

Leafing idly through its pages, waiting for my morning kettle to boil, my eye leapt to a headline, 'Bacteria take the chance out of evolution'. I sat down and read on. The article began:

> Bacteria can mutate in ways that specifically enhance their survival. This discovery – by John Cairns, Julie Overbaugh and Stephan Miller at the Harvard School of Public Health in Boston – challenges one of the cherished tenets of Darwinian natural selection – that mutation is spontaneous and random.

The article went on to describe how Cairns and his colleagues had shown that the ability of bacteria to develop resistant strains is not random but is directly *stimulated* by environmental conditions, in this case the bacteriocidal viruses to which the bacteria had been experimentally subjected. Quite simply, the bacteria could respond too precisely, too rapidly and too repeatably for their adaptation to be due to chance. The work had been published in an recent edition of *Nature* (vol. 335, p142), which I had not seen.

The question therefore becomes, 'How?' And although there is undoubtedly a change at the biochemical level of genetic function, I would suggest that the fuller answer is that the process is psychosomatic. And if, by the way, you are thinking that bacteria are so small and inferior that they cannot have a mind? You might first like to answer the question: 'What size is your own mind. . . ?'

We can experience and observe the far-reaching psychosomatic effects of mind on body without ever really knowing *how* it does so. The mind influences the entire biochemistry and physiology of a creature. Why, then, should we assume that it can have no effect upon genetic processes, as well? Why this insistence that natural selection and genetic mutation *have* to be random? Why should not the amazing ability of creatures to respond to their environment also be capable of expression through genetic processes?

It seems to me that the effect of the inner mind of a creature upon its physical existence, *including* its genetic processes, is of paramount importance *as a feedback loop* in determining and manifesting environmentally appropriate genetic changes within the creature. That is, a creature can genetically adapt itself to changing environmental conditions, *not by chance but as a direct response*.

If someone were to insist that the bacteria *had* managed to adapt by natural selection of random mutations, then they must also consider that the ability of bacteria to deal with the bacteriocidal virus must have required a considerable amount of biochemical reshuffling – something more than the effect of just one gene. So how does that tolerance actually arise so rapidly and does the required biochemical chain evolve piecemeal or all at once?

If piecemeal, how do the bacteria or the evolutionary process 'know' that the biochemical changes so far produced – though *presently* useless – are links in a chain not yet completed? If we are relying upon chance, we cannot also impute a knowledge of a *goal* to the process. And if the change is complete, sudden and totally efficacious, then how do all the required genetic changes take place all at once? There is clearly some guiding, formative and more subtle process at work.

And it would be interesting to know whether non-resistant bacteria develop the *same* strategy in separate, yet identical, experiments. This would be even more unlikely to occur by chance mutation. And do they develop the resistance *faster* in successive experiments, by 'morphic resonance' – as Rupert Sheldrake's theory would predict?

BREEDING AND THE HIDDEN SUBTLETY OF THE
FORMATIVE MIND

Any breeder will tell you that a high degree of exacting artificial selection, over a multitude of generations, is required just to increase the size of a dog's ears or the depth of colour in a rose. And in the process, many other features may be lost: the fragrance of a hybrid rose may be delightful to a human, but the butterflies and insects in my garden definitely prefer the wild dog roses and the less flamboyant meadow flowers for their nectar.

Also, as soon as the artificial tension of selective breeding is released, species revert very rapidly to the wild type, as if the constraints had been removed from a spring, permitting it to re-adopt its most harmonious configuration.

In fact, many of the most significant new breeds amongst domesticated species have arisen not through long breeding efforts that added tiny changes to tiny changes, but through the *sport*, the sudden reshuffling of many genetic patterns to produce the basis of a new breed, all in one step. Thus arose the *ancon*, the 'otter' or dwarf breed of sheep, which arrived suddenly in Massachusetts in 1791, when a ram was born with short legs and a long back. Since such sheep could not leap over fences, they were found useful. And interestingly, flocks of the new breed were seen to congregate together, keeping apart from others in an enclosure, as do herds of separate species. And with only bones remaining in the fossil record, I imagine that otter sheep – if their complete fossilized remains were ever found – would be classified as a separate species – and a sudden jump noted rather than gradual change.

Clearly, the genetic processes by which new breeds arise are not fully understood. The breeder is waiting as much for the useful sport to arise by processes he does not understand, as he is attempting to create a particular new breed by selective breeding.

Nor should one forget the pressure applied at the Formative Mind level by the mental-emotional desires of the breeder. This is a part of the unconscious formative mental field surrounding his experimentation, a part of the subtle environment. And just like bacteria struggling with a new antibiotic, the new 'mutant' arises *suddenly* out of the subtle pressures applied at the level of the Formative Mind. The necessary genetic changes are thus triggered by the subtle energy fields of the mind. That is to say, the *desire* of the breeder can make things happen.

In quantum physics, it is said that certain events exist only as potentialities until the experimenter intervenes and makes an observation. That is, that the mind of the experimenter collapses the web of potentiality into one particular reality. Thus, some folk argue, does man have free will, for nothing is certain until the decision is made, however simple and unconscious it may be. That is, we create our own reality out of our own mind.

Mystic philosophy would agree with this, but would add that the freedom to make that all-important decision is already conditioned by the karmic web of our own mind energies. These have arisen from past actions – mental and physical. Thus our free will remains only as a *potential*, for the potentiality is already determined by the karmic predisposition of our own minds to make the decision we thought was an act of free will. That is: we act in a manner totally conditioned by the content of our subconscious minds.

The relevance of this to the breeder and to evolution in general is this. No outward situation arises independently of the minds of all the living creatures involved. The Mind, with its formative and habituated nature, acts as the determining 'boundary conditions' on all events. Any attempt, therefore, to understand the evolution or development of forms without first realizing the role played by the Mind is doomed to failure.

It is the same paradox presented to all of us concerning our feelings of free will. Intellectually and by observation, we may realize that our 'free will' is hemmed in on all sides by circumstances, as well as by the conditioning and predispositions of our own subconscious psychology. But in the moment, we do not see any of that and we feel that we do have free will. At best, we admit that we have *conditioned* free will.

Similarly with events which scientists and others call *chance* or *random*. We do not see the full and hidden background in a situation, the formative factors in the inner levels of Mind, which act like the images of a movie film being projected to us upon the screen of what we think is outward physical reality.

Some while ago, whilst on a trip to Switzerland, I visited a centre at Würenlos where the clairvoyant and mystic, Emma Kunz (1892-1963), had once lived. This remarkable lady, famous for her drawings and paintings, also demonstrated an ability to make plants grow in an unusual fashion. I saw there many snapshots of marigolds sporting multiple heads, but all unusually growing upon one stem (see Figure 6.1).

She had simply gone into the garden and mentally induced the young marigolds to grow in that manner. It was as simple as that.

Figure 6.1   Emma Kunz and some of her psycho-engineered marigolds. Copyright by Emma Kunz Zentrum, CH-8116 Würenlos, Switzerland.

Interestingly, however, the seeds of these marigolds grew normally, so one presumes that the changes induced were not transmitted to the DNA of the seeds.

Such gifts, at present times, appear miraculous, but in the subtle days of the Sat yuga, man more readily understands the nature of such creative processes and works with them. He realizes the role played by his own mind and the interconnection of all minds at the deeper level.

Imagine the outcome if this knowledge of subtle, psycho-bio-engineering were to work hand-in-hand with advanced genetic understanding. Then we would have a perception of blueprinting and formative processes that would make our present-day genetic engineering and breeding programmes look like kindergarten stuff.

But these perceptions will only arise in an inwardly more harmonized mind, in one who is increasingly aware of the Divine intent and can work in harmony with that. This seems to be an automatic self-protective process of nature, precluding the unready from up-setting the finer fabric of creative manifestation.

7. HENS' TEETH AND HORSES' TOES

HORSES' TOES AND GENETIC PROCESSES

Distinctive modes of transport, comments Stephen Gould in his book, *Hen's Teeth and Horse's Toes*, from which the title of this chapter is derived, are as much in favour now as ever they have been. Reminding us of Julius Caesar's favourite conveyance, he quotes the Roman historian, Suetonius. Caesar, writes Suetonius:

> ... used to ride a remarkable horse, which had feet that were almost human, the hoofs being cleft like toes. It was born in his own stables, and as the soothsayers declared that it showed its owner would be lord of the world, he reared it with great care, and was the first to mount it; it would allow no other rider.

Four-winged fruit flies, insect antennae which develop into well-structured legs, sheep which spontaneously appear in a short-legged form and horses with toes, reminiscent of their ancestors of many millions of years ago, hens' embryonic dental tissue which can be persuaded to show signs of growing teeth – all these atavisms or throwbacks are helpful indicators of genetic processes which we do not understand.

It is said that horses' hooves are really the middle toe of an original complement of four, as possessed by the ancient Eocene forebear, *hyracotherium*, a horse no bigger than a medium-sized dog. Strict evolutionists insist that some more ancient ancestor must have had the full mammalian complement of five, though no such missing link has yet been found. But in modern times, horses have just the one toe with vestiges of the second and fourth toes to be found as short splinters of bone, located high above the hoof.

So when horses are born with either or both the second and the fourth toes more fully developed, though not to any functional degree, it tells us something of the nature of the genetic process. It means that there are factors hidden within the genome or more subtle energies which can quite suddenly express themselves as major morphological changes. Conventional evolutionary theory demands that such changes are present purely as genetic memories of the past. But what is it that determines which ancestral memories are genetically retained and which discarded? Is it – once again – our old friend 'chance'? And what determines when they should suddenly reappear? In a world where so much is clearly ordered, our friend is being asked to carry a motley assortment of burdens, each of great significance, and invoked as an explanation when all else fails.

Sudden changes which relate to the evolutionary future, however, cannot by conventional theory be expected to occur, for there is no genetic pool to draw upon. New changes, by conventional theory, must needs be slow – a fish could not be expected to suddenly develop a leg, for instance, nor a reptile wings.

In fact, if memories of past forms are still retained within the DNA, with their emergence governed entirely by chance, then surely it would be more likely for creatures to 'evolve' *backwards*, into *previous* forms, than *forwards* into *new* ones? This would certainly be the line of least resistance. Why build up an entirely new design when one has so many excellent ones from the past to choose from?

Time, like space, is also a creation of the Formative Mind, being a division of the One. There is no reason, therefore, within such an expanded scenario, why the genome should not *already* contain the potential for the future, as well as memories of the past. It would all be a part of the overall integration of nature. Time, like space, is an experience arising due to limited perception of how things are put together. But in the realm of the Universal Mind, the past, the present and the future are all seen as part of one great dance.

I am suggesting therefore that the genome, as a reflected pattern of more subtle, formative energies, could contain not only a 'record' of the past but also the potential for the future – perhaps already programmed into it or with the potential for being so programmed. In fact, what we have is an elastic design which has taken many forms and can take on many new ones.

Returning to the genome, modern geneticists, struggling to understand how the genetic process really works, have discovered many remarkable facts concerning DNA and its associated biochemical and physiological allies. For a start, DNA does not resemble a string of sausages with each sausage being a 'gene' relating to some aspect of body function or form. Not even in the simple, single-chromosomed bacteria and blue-green algae is the DNA encoding so obligingly simple.

Most of the genetic engineering one hears about in the media, although undoubtedly clever, is remarkably low key, relating only to one small aspect of DNA function – that of protein manufacture. But in higher organisms, only a tiny percentage of the DNA is involved in protein manufacture. In humans, it is between 1 and 2 per cent. Moreover, the coding for many of these proteins is not to be found in just one chromosome[2], but spread across two or more.

Human globulin, for example, the protein part of our blood's haemoglobin, is comprised of two amino acid chains – and the DNA coding for the manufacture of each lies on separate chromosomes. Why? No-one knows.

And as for the other 98 or 99 per cent of human DNA, its ability to code for nose shape, hair colour and the human form in all its particulars is only *assumed* from the evidence of breeding and reproduction. For the processes remain quite obscure.

Furthermore, at least 15 to 30 per cent of both the human and the fruit fly genome (for example) contain long sequences of DNA which repeat themselves tens or hundreds of times, often widely dispersed and on different chromosomes. About 5 per cent of the human genome consists of sequences which repeat themselves hundreds of thousands or even millions of times. Why? Again, no-one knows.

So although most geneticists are happy with the Darwinian model of evolution, the exact processes by which adaptation, mutation and selection are actually supposed to take place are still almost entirely a matter of speculation. Our greatly limited understanding of the genetic process and structure thus gives no positive support to conventional evolutionary theories. DNA, like brain function and so many other biological aspects of life, is still an entire world awaiting elucidation. Even an overall and intuitively acceptable model has yet to be put forward.

This is no matter for surprise, since genetic studies almost totally ignore the findings of modern physics. For myself, one of the most satisfying descriptions of the physical universe offered by physicists is the suggestion that the primary physical reality is space itself, but as a sea of energy. Thus, all subatomic particles – and consequently the

---

[2] Chromosomes are long strings of DNA. Humans have 23 pairs of these chromosomes. In sexual reproduction, the pairs split so that the ovum and the sperm contain half a set each. At conception these half sets combine to form a genetic constitution derived half from the mother and half from the father.

atoms, molecules and all else into which they are formed – are really no more than whirling, vibrating bubbles on an ocean. They cannot be separated from the ocean within which they exist.

Now, the vast majority of material substance is actually comprised of pure space or vacuum. Apparently solid objects are actually more than 99 per cent 'empty' space or vacuum, with only a tiny proportion of that space occupied by the subatomic particles of which all matter consists. There is thus far more ocean than there are bubbles on its surface. For this reason, therefore, the energy of space is often called vacuum energy.

Molecules are dynamic configurations of subatomic particles. Molecular structures, such as DNA, can therefore be considered as subatomic configurations of vacuum state energy. Furthermore, in this theory, each subatomic particle, each whirling bubble, is actually only a surface display of processes going on within the energy of vacuum. Subatomic particles are actually only the tips of myriad icebergs. The real formative processes are actually going on unseen within the energy of space.

And just as space is a perception or experience in our minds, the spatial state of energy is itself linked into our minds in a hierarchical structure of energy blueprints and patternings whose ramifications and processes have yet to be universally acknowledged, let alone elucidated. An entire dimension is therefore missing in the study of genetic processes. This, of course, is our old friend the ontological dimension, the energy projection system of the Formative Mind.

If one can conceive of the DNA simply as a dynamic though focal point in an image upon a screen, then a different picture altogether begins to emerge. For there are many hidden organizing principles at work which we have yet to understand. This will be the province of subtle energy physics and a new science of subtle biology, not to mention subtle genetics!

Such a perception knocks conventional models of evolution on the head, for materialistic theories are only prepared to consider processes to be found within dense material energies. And then only at the level of molecules. The quantum world and the realm of subtle mind factors or energies are almost totally neglected.

So genetic correlations to form and function are by no means one-to-one. The relationships and processes are, quite simply, not understood at all. We observe only glimpses of the process.

One of these glimpses is of particular interest. The complex, hierarchically organized, genetic system contains many controllers and master switches capable of turning on or off entire areas of genetic activity. These small changes can result in major alterations to external form.

This, therefore, provides us with a possible explanation why changes between related species can be sudden. It is as relevant to material theories of evolution as to the processes I am suggesting. But from the material point of view, it only compounds the problem, for we are still left with no understanding of how these genetic processes are switched on and off. And although one can imagine a DNA pattern that was put together in the past being switched on again, one cannot switch on a major process involving a host of minor mutations which have not yet occurred. So geneticists are forced back to chance again, as the magic factor which 'explains' everything. It all seems very unsatisfactory.

Perhaps the most fundamental question is: *From where does order arise?* The answers fall into only two categories: *either* the ability to self-organize and possess properties, values and laws is a fundamental characteristic of matter and energy, *or* the answer is an ontological one in which energy is seen as a hierarchical patterning from within-out, along the dimension I have called the Formative Mind. In the light of this answer, creation is therefore only a dance or a dream spun over the face of the Primal Consciousness.

Clearly, I favour the latter point of view, because it explains pretty well everything. One is not left, philosophically, with a set of fundamental laws of nature and universal constants which have no apparent origin and which cannot explain or even describe a host of normal human, as well as scientific, experiences. Without decrying existing scientific perceptions, it simply adds another dimension to the matter, making present scientific findings relative to a limited frame of reference. Science is not incorrect, it simply needs to be perceived in a wider context.

So what atavism, sports and other large-scale structural mutations demonstrate is that the genome already contains tremendous potential for the restructuring of a creature – more wings or legs for insects, for instance, or toes for horses and so on. Even, perhaps, tails for humans, for simply the possession of a tail would not make us more like apes in our inner mental constitution, and it is that which makes us human.

But what atavism and so on do not tell us is what triggers the natural expression of these hidden characteristics, nor how the genome is actually organized and structured. Modern genetic thought, as well as physics, is so deeply infiltrated with the idea of chance as the major formative process that it severely hampers perception of what could be going on in the hidden energy-patterning dimension of Mind.

For if the mere waggling of a finger, and so much else in the body, is mediated through highly complex activity in the mind and brain of which we are unconscious, then there is absolutely no reason why genetic selection should not also be so regulated and controlled and hidden from our conscious minds.

DECIPHERING THE GENOME

Recent discussion of the international research programmes for unravelling the human genome, the so-called 'Book of Man', triggers a number of interesting lines of thought.

It seems quite clear that although we can see that there is a relationship between some particular genetic pattern and, say, the shape of one's nose, we cannot actually say that the shape of the nose is directly mapped in some linear, one-to-one fashion by a particular sequence or sequences of bases in the DNA.

I have discussed this in *The Web of Life* and Brian Goodwin of the Open University has also stressed this point in *New Scientist* and elsewhere. This is not a philosophical quibble, but has a direct bearing upon how living organisms are constructed and how they function.

Our intellectual minds tend to work in a linear, analytical fashion seeing pathways and particular relationships. But we cannot therefore assume that biological organisms are constructed in a similar fashion, to suit our thinking processes! Surely their integration is far more of an interwoven dance than we would like to think, or our minds are capable of analysing?

In support of this idea lies the fact that a very high percentage of the DNA appears to repeat itself many times. Some geneticists have even stated that 95 per cent of the DNA is 'junk', and not actually used genetically. Since we do not know how DNA is involved in the generation of form, this would seem to be premature. But what is it doing?

The DNA molecule (see Figure 7.1) consists of two polynucleotide chains arranged in the form of a double helix. Each nucleotide consists of the sugar *deoxyribose* linked to one of four *purine* and *pyrimidine* bases, with the further addition of a phosphate molecule. The four famous bases themselves, *adenine, thymine, guanine* and *cytosine* (known as A, T, G and C) are linked within the double helix by hydrogen bonds.

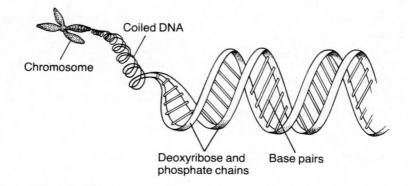

Figure 7.1   DNA consists of two long chains of sugar (deoxyribose) and phosphate groups, twisted together into a double helix, like two wires in an electric cable. Between the two chains lie the four bases: A, T, G and C. The twisted pair is also coiled up and packed tightly into a chromosome. Different species have different numbers of chromosomes, different lengths of DNA and different sequences of the bases. The sequencing of base pairs in individual members of the same species also differs. Additionally, A only pairs with T, and G with C.

In simple terms, what we have is a long molecule consisting of identical nucleotides shaped in the form of a double helix with sequences of bases spread along it. Geneticists consider the series of repeating sugar molecules as the 'junk', while it is the sequencing of the four bases along it which provide the information content, representing the 'genes' or genetic encoding. The multiple repetitions of the four bases are also classified as 'junk'. They therefore tend to think of the DNA as a string of these four kinds of sausage, three billion sausages long (in humans). And they assume that particular sequences relate to particular forms – from proteins to noses. It is this kind of linear assumption about which an increasing number of biologists feel unhappy.

To ignore the sugar and phosphate content of the DNA because it is repetitive is somewhat like ignoring the wire in the TV aerial and cable when considering the electrical signal it is carrying. The patterning of the four bases is no doubt of great importance, but an understanding of electricity requires a knowledge of how wires and conductors permit the passage of electrons. To comprehend the full picture, one cannot ignore the wire. It plays an essential, participatory role.

To write off the major part of the molecule as junk when we also acknowledge our ignorance of the full genetic system seems a somewhat hasty step.

Genetic research is also called molecular biology for the very good reason that we are studying living systems at the level of molecules. And we are somehow making the assumption that nature organizes itself in that way, too. But only a minute's thought should reveal that molecules are only a convenient staging post, a way of dividing things into manageable compartments, in both our human analytical as well as laboratory processes.

The reality is actually one of ultradynamic movement, involving atomic, subatomic and vacuum state energies. DNA (and everything else) is constantly moving and interacting with itself at incredibly high speeds. And there is no reason to believe that information is only encoded into *structure*. It is just as readily encoded in the very *movement* itself, just as the patterns and rhythms of music only exist in timing and vibration. But how to study the information and energy encoded into such a vast, complex and superlatively dynamic system? We have yet to decipher the structure, let alone understand how it moves, dances and vibrates within itself.

All of this, then, would be better described if we were to delve into the atomic and subatomic realm. At that intensely dynamic level, our A, T, G and C will not all be the 'same'. The internal subatomic activity of a particular base may vary depending upon where it lies within the sequence. Two apparently identical coins, for instance, one spinning in the air and the other spinning on a table, are essentially different in their 'information content'. Even two coins moving identically, but in different locations, contain different 'information', since their relationships to their surroundings will differ. Similarly with the so-called redundant sections of DNA which endlessly repeat their A, T, G and C sequences. Each one is actually unique if considered as something more than a simple element in a chain. Each holds a unique place in the molecule of DNA when it is considered as a whole.

So if, for example, A is different in its information content depending upon where it is in the sequence, can we really define and consider its genetic functions purely from the point of view of molecular sequencing? What I am suggesting is that ultra-high levels of internal movement within the DNA are as likely to contain genetic information as the sequencing of the four bases. This may be something infinitely more difficult for us to study, but that is our problem – not that of nature!

Similarly, it is unsatisfactory to consider the close and coiled structure of the DNA molecule as simply a good way to pack a string of sausages. It is forces within the molecule which result in the unique structure. The nature of its winding, its structure and its internal subatomic activity are too ordered for us to neglect. This, too, is likely to contain genetic information. But, how does one approach an understanding of the electromagnetic forces and patterns which will emerge from and result in this dynamic subatomic dance we are calling DNA?

The subatomic realm is not at all understood by modern physics. There is not even a fully adequate description or model of an electron or the simple hydrogen atom, let alone complex spiral molecules. So just like our spinning coins, two As – if we could appreciate their dynamic subatomic forces, characteristics and motion – would actually be different from each other. Especially when configured or arranged differently, not only in the sequence, but also within the deeply ordered, structured and organized molecule of DNA.

The constituents of matter can be described by reference to a limited number of subatomic particles, yet the order and structure of the whole physical universe is not thereby understood. We can describe the basic parts but cannot comprehend the whole. Actually, we do not really comprehend even the parts.

Similarly, the structure of DNA can be described by reference to just the four bases. But, like the physical universe, just look at the variety in which these basic 'building blocks' can be arranged! See how many species there are and have been! There can be so many complex configurations derived from these basic patterns. There must certainly be fundamental aspects to all this which we have not yet appeciated.

It is when things start altering in response to a change in their relationships that descriptions become almost impossible. The variations become too many to cope with and even mathematics and computer modelling fail. The logic continually goes into infinite regresses, with changing relationships chasing changing relationships. Yet although we may admit to our inability to describe this infinite complexity, it is *this* which comprises the genome. Can we ever hope, therefore, to really understand genetic processes? Like trying to fully understand the brain, there is just so much going on, integrated in such an amazing fashion, that one wonders just where to start.

What we desperately need is some coherent model by which to *begin* our understanding. I have suggested an energy model, one of projected, multilevel energy blueprints along an ontological dimension. This is all right as an overall picture, but to look at the functioning of the genome, we want details. So far, no-one has anything more than an inkling of what is going on.

The point I am making is that unravelling the sequence of the four sausages on the string may tell us very little of what we are seeking to find. We also need to know the nature of *all* the subatomic forces and activity which are involved in the structure of a whole chromosome. A list of the towns and villages along the A1 trunk road from London to Edinburgh does not indicate to us the way the A1 fits into the total map of England, nor indeed does it provide us with a real description of the road.

Knowing that when you start with a human ovum and a human sperm you ultimately end up with a human adult tells us *nothing* of the detailed processes that are actually involved. And these are almost as much of a mystery to scientists as ever they were. So looking at DNA in this way, it is clear that the 'junk DNA' is playing an essential and integral role in the total genetic system.

If, therefore, one develops a picture of the DNA as 'an integrated energy system' or 'field' possessing points of reference to a whole body, then one begins to lose one's linear, Lego-style model of genetic and biological function. But since biological enquiry is not yet conducted at the subatomic level, it also leads us to an admission of extreme ignorance as to the deeper way in which biological entities are organized.

Geneticists have made the decision that the secret of the genetic mechanism lies entirely in the sequencing of A, T, G and C because this is the 'easiest' aspect of DNA for us to unravel. But what about the subatomic and electromagnetic forces which have created the beautiful three-dimensional structure of DNA? Will not these forces also be a part of the total picture? And what of the strange quantum world we find so difficult to understand and the intensely dynamic energy of the vacuum? Can we assume that they are not 'involved'? It seems most unlikely that they are not.

The attempt to 'read' the Book of Man, therefore, fascinating though it is, may only inform us of one aspect of the manner in which the genetic structure is put together. And it may turn out to tell us almost nothing of the greater, more integrated processes which work at a more fundamental level.

After all, has the complete mapping of the base sequences in the fruit fly genome told us how to make a fruit fly? Or even how a fruit fly is really put together and how all its myriad biochemical processes actually function in such an integrated way? We are still as far away as ever from answers to the fundamental questions. We seem to need an entirely new way of looking at the problem.

It might be far more appropriate, for example, to look on the genetic process as an 'energetic' microcosm of the whole body. Thus, each cell carries its own microcosm to the whole body. What we would then be looking for would be points of resonance and relationship, which may be more of a holographic nature than linear and one-to-one.

In fact, the apparently meaningless repeating sequences may prove to be the essence of an amazing process of integration at a subatomic or even deeper level. And within this picture, it also makes sense for the DNA in the cells of my big toe to know how to make pancreatic insulin or nerve transmitters for my brain. For the repetition of the same DNA within each cell, wherever it is in the body, is also seen by most geneticists as a waste of resources or at least as a matter of no consequence.

Yet, within a microcosm–macrocosm 'energy-field' conception of body function, it is clear that multiple resonances between the DNA of cellular nuclei could act as essential cohering factors in whole body integration. Just as individual soldiers in an army may have specific tasks to perform and are expected to concentrate upon those, yet they will function much better in the performance of these tasks if in the back of their minds they have a total picture of what everyone else is doing.

Similarly, the repetition of the same DNA in each cell of the body is far more likely to be a part of a whole body integration system, which we presently do not understand in detail, than to be the chance fortunes of an evolutionary process.

I am intrigued by these repeating patterns and sequences in our bodily system and feel that they really should be telling us something of great importance. We are a long way from cracking the code of life!

DNA AS A VIBRANT LIGHT ENERGY SYSTEM

Experimental work by the German scientist Fritz-Albert Popp adds a brilliant vision, supporting this speculation. Popp has worked for many years on the ultraweak photon emission of living tissues, photons being another way of describing electromagnetic energy, such as light. He and others have noted that living cells emit light – including at least infrared, visible and ultraviolet frequencies – whereas dead ones generally do not. Moreover, Popp maintains that this light is coherent – laser-like – and seems to be part of an organizing wholeness within living organisms.

The Japanese scientist, Humio Inaba of Tohoku University, who heads a 'biophotonics' research programme, has also commented that though he is unsure of its exact significance, ultraweak photon emission is 'clearly associated with a variety of vital activities and biological processes'.

Based upon sound experimentation, Popp has shown that DNA is one, perhaps a major source, of this photon emission. He used a particular dye which, when added to living cells, is absorbed into the DNA molecule, first inducing an unravelling of the DNA. Then, as more dye is added, the DNA coils up once again into its complex, folded helix.

Measuring the photon emission of cells during this unravelling and recoiling cycle, Popp noted that photon emission first *increased* as the DNA unravelled, subsequently *decreasing* as it folded up again. We will return to this observation shortly.

Further experimentation also indicated that the energy level and distribution of electrons in their atomic 'shells' is *extremely high in living tissues*, quite unlike the energetic balance to be found in inert matter or dead tissues. In an atom, electrons can be in either low or high energy shells but unless there are other influential factors, they drop down into lower energy shells, like the relaxing of a stretched rubber band. Being part of a living organism is clearly one such 'influential factor' for in living tissues, the shells or energy levels occupied by the electrons are radically different from dead or inert matter.

The implications of this are quite fascinating. Firstly, it suggests that living systems are highly toned up, energetically speaking, like a tight wire or a stretched rubber band, full of potential energy. But these living systems are also ultra-dynamic. Popp calculated that in his cucumber seedlings there were something like 100,000 inter-molecular reactions per cell per second. And these are all coherently integrated into one functional cell, itself a part of a whole functional organism – itself embedded in an integrated and whole cosmos!

It should also be noted that when an electron drops down into a lower energy shell, the difference in energy is given off as a photon. This gives us the relationship between the tanked-up state of electrons and coherent photon emission, both of which are found only in living systems.

Popp's work on the coherent nature of photons substantiates the research of other biologists who maintain that a living cell is in a state of *maximum order*. However, because of its high energy condition, it also possesses *maximum potential* – maximum sensitivity to changing circumstances. Just as a tight wire or a stretched rubber band is more responsive than a floppy wire or a limp rubber band, so too do living systems appear to exist at a dynamic energy level and capacity for response that is far above that of inert matter.

Popp points out that this high degree of responsiveness is characteristic of mind and consciousness. Only mind and consciousness possess such exquisite, immediate and intimate sensitivity to both the inner and the outer environment.

If one thinks of inert matter as being in a stable equilibrium, possessed of comparatively minimum movement and internal energy dynamics, then living systems are far away at the other end of the spectrum. They are far from stillness and equilibrium. Yet they are also far from chaotic. They are in a state of maximum order.

The combination of these two attributes – maximum order and maximum potential – is entirely characteristic of living systems and reflects their ability to respond instantaneously and appropriately to a continuous stream of stimuli both from within themselves and from outside. Intensely dynamic but ordered energy, both as motion and as potential, is essential for any system to exhibit these two qualities.

Unlike our motor car, living tissues never start from cold, the internal motor is always running for as long as life remains. The car that is warm, revved up and running, moves off faster and with greater finesse than one which is switched off and cold. In living creatures, this principle is exhibited to the ultimate degree.

With the high levels of energy stored as potential in both molecular structures as well as in the high-tension electron shells, there is never any lack of energy to deal with new tasks – both physiological and in the whole organism. Is this, for example, one of the reasons why the eating of fresh fruits and vegetables seems to give one more energy and vitality than the consumption of cooked and dead foods? The molecular structures really do contain more energy, of a physical nature, when the food eaten is still alive or at least is not totally denatured.

This is a diversion worth exploring at some other time, for there are many practical ramifications. For example, 'fresh' fruits and vegetables which have been irradiated with X-rays or gamma rays have effectively been killed. The electrons in their high energy shells will therefore have collapsed, releasing their potential energy into the environment as photons. Consequently, although their *molecular content* may be similar, their *energy content* will be significantly decreased.

But how does Popp's work relate to DNA, its genetic function and to evolution? DNA only emits photons when functioning within living tissues, that is when its energy levels are high. But that photon emission is *increased* when the molecule is unravelled. What is going on?

Popp suggests that the DNA is intensely and energetically active, transmitting photon messages *within* itself. Only a few photons are sent out, perhaps to help organize the processes going on within the cell and to communicate with neighbouring cells. Photon emission and absorption *within* the DNA is intense, all the time, *but when the DNA unravels these photons escape and can be measured.*

What a beautiful and vibrant image emerges. DNA is a super-active, highly ordered complex of light and whirling subatomic particles. It 'talks' to itself – it communicates within itself – by means of light. And this super-dynamic dance itself contains or represents information. It is coded into the ordered energy dance and motion. Its patternings are held like the relationships in music. Its vibrations are a microcosmic symphony of life. Is this the way that DNA carries the information that is responsible for outer form?

Now a fascinating and very different picture of DNA is coming into view. A large per cent of DNA, say classically-trained geneticists, is 'useless material, performing no genetic function'. But in the scenario that comes to mind from Popp's work, the A, T, G and C sequencing is only one tiny aspect of how DNA performs its dynamic role as cellular administrator and organizer. The DNA is an amazingly vibrant and vital energy complex with a multitude of shifting electromagnetic aspects, patterns and rhythms. It is *this* which represents the power of DNA.

Furthermore, if these electromagnetic energies and subatomic activities are themselves only the tip of the iceberg relating to activity and formative patterning taking place within the fabric of vacuum or space itself, then we have an image of intense, but hidden, vacuum state activity manifesting outwardly as whole, ordered and integrated processes whose primal organization lies way beyond our present ken.

Additionally, if mind and consciousness are integrally linked with this continuum of space, then we can immediately see how all living creatures are integral and coherent aspects of mind and consciousness, with 'matter' being only an external aspect or ultra-dynamic crystallization of Mind.

And how does this new perception relate to the Darwinian theory of natural selection of *random* mutations? If not only DNA but all physiological processes (as some biologists maintain) are in a state of maximum order and responsiveness, then where is the potential for *random* mutation? For DNA seems to behave in a fully integrated and ordered fashion.

Whether we accept an inward patterning of Mind or think that we are dealing purely with physical substance as the only reality, the Victorian and ultra-mechanistic, linear, reductionist philosophy of natural selection of random mutations, as the primary factors responsible for changing of the species over the aeons, does not marry up with the ultra-dynamic, coherent and integrated picture of DNA – and indeed all physiological processes – which is emerging from modern research.

Whether one thinks that physical substance has self-organizing potential from which emerge mind and consciousness, or whether one feels that consciousness and mind give rise to the illusion of what we call physical substance, there seems little doubt that existence is a coherent, organized and self-existent whole. Where, then, is the potential for randomness and chaos? In either case, Darwinian natural selection of chance mutations cannot be seriously considered as a real possibility.

In either philosophy, the perceptions of an ordered whole mean that natural selection and random mutations are only superficial observations of a deeper and more fundamental, ultra-dynamic order and wholeness. As the implications of the work of scientists like Popp become more widely appreciated, perceptions of factors underlying biological change over the aeons will automatically be forced to change. Mechanistic explanations and descriptions simply do not accurately relate to the world of living processes presently being revealed.

Whatever is responsible for the order, coherence, integration and incessant activity or motion must be the primary force in the universe. It is from this source that all ordered patterns and rhythms proceed. To my understanding this is the power of the Life Force, the Creative Word, overlaid by the Formative Mind, in a hierarchy of creative projection from within-out. It is God, continuously manifesting Himself in His creation.

8. CLASSES OF CREATURE

The problem with the fossil record is that it takes in a myriad creatures spanning more than half a billion years in an incomplete sequence which was never laid down in an orderly fashion. The evidence is, at best, fragmentary and to survey this data in just a few short pages, in a cogent fashion and without omitting relevant or interesting detail, is more or less impossible.

The story, therefore, has been told almost as a pastiche, in order to build up a general picture. We have looked at the geological cycles, extinction cycles, radiation of new species and so on. In this chapter, we look at particular groups of species one at a time and though this involves a little repetition of what has gone before, it is a rather interesting picture which emerges.

BACTERIA, ALGAE AND PROTOZOA

Bacteria are present as microfossils in ancient rocks dated at over 3.5 billion years. Rocks that old are rare due to the constant recycling. They are also exceptionally hard. But in some ancient rocks from Canada, South Africa and Zimbabwe, when cut into slices so thin they are translucent, traces of the rods and spheres of ancient bacteria can sometimes be seen when viewed under an electron microscope. The individual species of bacteria are unidentifiable, but there is no reason to suggest that present day bacteria are any more 'advanced' than their cousins from so long ago.

Also, there is absolutely no suggestion or evidence that any evolution has ever taken place. The essential form of these tiny creatures seems to have been much the same then as it is now. There is no evidence of the bacteria having evolved from or into anything else at all. There is no evidence in the fossil record of creatures intermediate between bacteria and algae, nor between bacteria and other single-celled creatures, nor between bacteria and anything else. Bacteria have always been bacteria.

Also in rocks dated at 3.5 billion years, we find the first signs of microscopic plant life: the characteristic daily growth layers formed by blue-green algae that are still living today, and still making similar formations off the north Australian coast. Note, however, that there is no other fossil evidence of their existence, nor of the eco-system that must have surrounded them. All that has long since disappeared.

It is in rocks dated at about 1.3 billion years that the first evidence of protozoa and perhaps more complex creatures is found. Here, we find occasional evidence of distinct nuclei in some of the microfossils found by sectioning the ancient rock. But to whom these ancient cells belonged, it is difficult to know. Conventional evolutionists assume them to have been protozoa, like amoebae, but from the available evidence this is only surmise.

It has already been emphasized how important it is to realize that the survival – and exposure – of such ancient rocks is extremely rare. Because of the recycling, far more rocks from the last 500 million years have survived than from the previous 3 billion years. Even if they do still exist, they are more likely to be buried deep in the earth's crust than their more modern counterparts. So the closer one comes to present times, then the more numerous are the rocks. This is what one would expect, but it presents a greatly distorted view of the past. It is like trying to reconstruct the whole of a person's life from only last year's diary, plus a few pages torn at random from previous years, with fewer and fewer preserved as the years recede.

So from a handful of finds, it is quite impossible to presume the history of life over 3 billion years. The fact that almost all we have are remnants of bacteria and some daily growth layers caused by seaweeds on the ocean floor does not mean that that is all there was. It simply means that that is all we have found.

And to my mind, algae and bacteria presume the existence of a host of other creatures, too. The same species could not exist on their own in modern times. There are many ecological reasons for this, some of which have been discussed. Without the organisms that keep the mineral concentration constant, for example, the seas would have rapidly become too saline for seaweeds and bacteria to have lived. To me, seaweed – however microscopic – says, a diverse ecosystem of many species'.

INVERTEBRATES

Other than these vestiges of the past, the first signs of life in the fossil record are found amongst the sediments of the Precambrian era, deposited some 600 to 700 million years ago.

Interestingly, these early fossils are all soft-bodied, but are known from little more than twenty five sites around the world. They are generally known as Ediacaran, after the classic find in the Ediacaran Hills of the Australian Flinders Ranges. Surprisingly, these fossil remains consist of the numerous impressions of soft-bodied creatures – worms, jellyfish, sea-pens, cephalopods (octopuses, squids, nautilus) and so on.

Later Cambrian deposits mostly contain the hard exoskeletons of other marine creatures, suggesting to some palaeontologists that hard-shelled creatures were a later development. But providing some historical continuity, in the mid-Cambrian Burgess shale deposits, found near the small British Columbian town of Field, a mixture of soft-bodied and hard-shelled fossils have been found. And some of these are clearly related to the earlier Ediacaran fauna. Yet though there is a gap in the fossil record of many millions of years between the soft-bodied Ediacarans and the hard-shelled Cambrians, life was clearly continuous and the gap only demonstrates yet again the scantiness of the ancient record.

With frequent changes in the particular species and families, more or less the same kind of invertebrates live today as lived in those more ancient times. And once again, there is no sign that invertebrates ever evolved into any other forms – fishes, reptiles or anything else. 'Missing links' between vertebrates and invertebrates have never been found, nor have any definite links between sea-dwelling invertebrates and their terrestrial counterparts. In fact, there are no links even between the various classes and families of invertebrate. Ancient clams, corals, octopuses, squids, jelly-fish, sea anemones, tube worms and all the rest, have no doubt changed over the ages into their modern counterparts, though some have even stayed the same. But there is no fossil evidence of any intermediate forms showing that they have ever developed into any different kind of creature. This is not a matter of interpretation of the data, the evidence is simply absent.

Amongst the land-dwelling invertebrates, the earliest known species are Silurian, dated at 414 million years, found in the Ludlow Bone Bed in Shropshire, England, in 1990. The fossils comprise only three specimens – two centipedes and an arachnid (like spiders and scorpions). Their legs were clearly designed for high-speed movement on land and they were also predators. This, and the fact that the fossils of land plants were also discovered in the same rocks, indicates that they were a part of a thriving and well-established ecosystem. For the existence of predators means that there must have been something to eat. In fact, in all modern ecosystems, predators are almost always in the minority. They have to be or there would soon be nothing left to eat!

The Ludlow Bone Bed also contains fossils of water-dwellers and seems to have once been a beach or mudflats, occasionally flooded by a river. Once again, we see how the fossil record is heavily biased in favour of preserving water creatures. Land-dwellers, especially from the distant past, stand increasingly little chance of being found in fossilized form. Their best hope of posterity was to fall into the mud or to die in a flood. Not the usual fate for the great majority of them.

Prior to this find, insects and other land-dwellers had not been discovered before the Early Devonian. So just one find of three fossils has reset the clock by 20 million years. A period of 20 million years represented by only one find of three creatures! This is the nature of the fossil record, especially of the land. It is not much to go on in relating the history of life on earth, leaving plenty of room for error and interpretation. (See footnote on p. 212.)

FISH

Fish species comprise more than half the vertebrate population, both alive today and in the fossil record. In present times, as in the past, the class includes many variants, well suited for their different habitats and lifestyles.

Relics of the earliest fishes, consisting mostly of bones and bone fragments, first appear in mid-Ordovician times, soon after the first occurrence of the hard-shelled Cambrian creatures, but their few remains tell us little of their lifestyles.

In those earliest records, it is more frequently the larger pieces of bone which have endured, and those which were tough enough to have survived the long journey. But by later Devonian times a full complement of fish are preserved including the sharks and some of the most ferocious-looking predators which have ever swum the seas – the *arthrodires* – growing up to twenty or thirty feet in length and sporting a most aggressive set of ripping teeth. There must certainly have been no lack of large-sized prey, to be worthy of such gnashers!

But the majority of this prey was never preserved in the fossil record and now is lost from view.

Fishes appear to have been a more widely diverse class of creature in Devonian times than they are today. Representatives of all our modern species are to be found, some in far greater variety than at present times, but there are also other groups that have long since disappeared.

But like the invertebrates and the bacteria, fish only seem to demonstrate modification to changing environments, not evolution into something higher or lower. They must have been as well equipped to deal with the circumstances of those ancient days, as modern fish are to the environments of present times. Certainly, no gradation of intermediate forms between fish and amphibians, or fish and reptiles, have ever been found. And apart from the exercise of the imagination, there is nothing to suggest that the one could ever have evolved into the other.

Palaeontologists of the past have called the Devonian era the 'Age of Fishes', an attempt to imprint evolutionary dogma upon the fossil record of the past. But it was a naive presentation and few scientists use the term nowadays, though such ideas are still taught in primary schools.

Amongst the living fishy relics of the past, the coelacanths are interesting and worth a mention. The first members of this family appeared suddenly (a familiar theme), in mid-Devonian times. Although the one remaining modern species is a deep sea dweller, the fossils found today are presumably representative of those species who swam the shallower seas of long ago. For the remains of creatures dwelling in the deep sea have almost all been lost due to recycling of the ocean beds.

Many other fishes changed their style as the aeons passed but the coelacanths lived on, little changed throughout the millions of passing years until their disappearance from the fossil record in the great Cretaceous extinction, 66 million years ago. And that might have been that.

But then, in 1938, a strange-looking, large-scaled fish was dredged up by a fisherman off the South African coast, near the mouth of the Chalumna River. Realizing that he had probably found something unusual, he kept the fish. It must have seemed an anachronism, like a Roman soldier standing quietly outside Buckingham Palace in the 1990s, but subsequently it was correctly identified by a Miss Courtenay-Latimer from pictures she had seen in a book.

Since then, roughly 170 specimens have been reported though, interestingly, no more have been discovered off the South African coast. They have all, without exception, been caught by local fisherman off the Comoro Islands further to the north-east, off the northernmost tip of Madagascar. And at four feet long, their size is twice that of the last known fossil specimen, found immediately prior to the Cretaceous extinction.

Coelacanths have changed little during the 400 million years of their existence. There was a time when scientists thought that their muscular, paddle-like fins might provide some clue to the existence of amphibians. Perhaps, they reasoned, the fins permitted the fish to walk along the sea-bottom and had later been adapted to walk upon the land.

But in 1986 the German biologist, Hans Fricke, mounted an expedition to the Comoros, tracking the coelacanths to their deep sea lair using a specially designed two-man submarine. He discovered that the fins were a superb piece of natural engineering, enabling the coelacanth to swim in all directions, including backwards and upside-down.

Coelacanths are not the only odd fish to have survived from the Devonian past. The peculiar lungfish, presently found in South America, Africa and Australia, were also present in numerous forms, appearing to reach their zenith during the Late Devonian, soon after their sudden appearance in the mid-Devonian. Modern lungfish are superbly adapted to living in freshwater localitiies which seasonally dry up, for they are able to hole up inn the desiccated mud, awaiting the next rains. But the Devonian lungfish appear to have lived in the sea, though some may have been freshwater dwellers like our modern species.

The coelacanths, lungfish and all the other creatures which have survived almost unchanged since their inception, raise an interesting question. If change is due to environmental pressures, why do some creatures change and others not? Why not all or none? One might think that some species are more adaptable to different environments whilst others are not. So the less-specialized ones live on more or less unchanged whilst the greater specialists require greater modification to continue their existence. But actually this is not borne out by the evidence.

Moreover, when a new form of a species emerges this does not necessarily herald the decline of the old. Both forms often continue happily along together, occupying the same territory. Clearly, there is no survival of the fittest going on between them. The new one, perhaps, finds an unoccupied ecological niche to fill and moves into it, but there is no competition between the two. One could say that there was competition between members of the original species and that one part of the species found a better way to survive. Maybe. But natural selection of small random changes does not account for the *sudden* jump required – and often seen in the fossil record – for the creature to have significantly changed its style.

So clearly there are other hidden factors at work determining change. The minds of all these ancient creatures must also be considered. When the impressions of the mind require expression as certain forms, those forms will come into being. And the environment, too, is also a part of the outworking of the greater Mind to which all individual minds are linked. The entire affair of creation rolls forward as the integrated expression of the hidden Mind.

PLANTS AND TREES

Fossils of terrestrial life forms, as we have seen, are found only when ages of erosion and crustal movements have not destroyed them and then only when their remains were cast up and buried on the shorelines or travelled downriver to silted estuaries, or when the living creatures were overtaken by flood or had the misfortune to fall into the mud. Land-based creatures and plants have always had far less opportunity to be enshrined in sediment than the fishes and invertebrates who lived their lives so much closer to these deposits.

The first terrestrial fossils are found in mid-Silurian times, together with the impressions of land plants. Plants and trees, whether living or dead, are excellent food for innumerable creatures. They are the base of the planetary food chain, being the only life forms capable of trapping the sun's energy. But whether on land or in the sea, special circumstances are required for their remains to be identifiably preserved.

The primary requirement, as with all fossilization, is protection. In this case, protection is needed from oxidation, exposure to the weather and the ravages of bacteria, moulds, fungi and the millions of creepy-crawlies that thrive on vegetation – dead or alive. Naturally enough, only a few localities meet these criteria, and though a very few fossils are sometimes preserved in the thick leaf mats on the floors of ancient forests, the commonest source of all plant and tree fossils is coal.

Geologists classify coal as a carboniferous sedimentary rock. Formed only in swamps, marshes and other waterlogged ground, the process of coal formation begins when abundant and continuous plant growth falls onto waterlogged soil and is protected from oxidation by the continuous accumulation of further layers. At the same time, some of those twigs, branches, roots, leaves, fruit and seeds also become preserved for fossilization.

The vegetable matter accumulates, turning into peat, a porous brown mass of organic material. As layer succeeds layer, the peat becomes packed down with increasing density, being slowly metamorphosed into various grades of soft coal. With further compacting and deeper burial, the heat of the lower levels within the earth's crust slowly transforms the soft coal into a hard shiny coal known as anthracite. In the chemical reactions underlying these changes, various gases containing carbon, hydrogen and oxygen are liberated, with the result that the finest grade anthracite is reduced to well over 90 per cent carbon.

While pieces of fossilized driftwood are first discovered in Late Ordovician times, the greatest percentage of all coal deposits known in present times dates from the Carboniferous epoch, hence its name. Clearly, this was an age in which vast areas of the land were low-lying and boggy, correlating well with other evidence that the hills of the later Permian era were old, eroded and low-lying.

AMPHIBIANS, REPTILES AND MAMMALS

The sediments, swamps and flood plains of the late Palaeozoic have also provided us with the fossils of an increasing number of crocodiles, reptiles and amphibia. They were all creatures that lived in and around the water and were thus more likely to leave their remains for posterity.

The oldest, well-preserved find of amphibian fossils comes from the lake-beds of eastern Greenland, dated at about 360 million years, taking us back to the Late Devonian and Early Carboniferous. Anne Warren of La Trobe University in Melbourne, however, has described tracks of a four-legged terrestrial creature dated 40 million years earlier, in the Late Silurian. So for 40 million years, there is an almost complete gap in the fossil record of life on the land. We have made this point before. . . .

One further salient feature of these amphibians. They were carnivorous – and many of them were big. So unless they caught fish – a difficult task for a creature not obviously adapted for fast swimming

– there must have been a plentiful supply of other terrestrial forms. Fossil remains of life on the land are scarce. But whenever evidence is discovered, it always seems to lead us to the conclusion that there was a a full-blown, self-supporting land ecology.

So from Carboniferous times onward we find the old bones of amphibians. And along with them we find the fossilized bones of reptiles and *therapsids* or protomammals – creatures that evolutionists consider as the 'early forerunners' of present day mammals.

The world's oldest fossil reptile is a lizard, found in 1988 in a small quarry at Bathgate, near Edinburgh in Scotland and dated at 338 million years, in the Lower Carboniferous. With its vast areas of swampy ground, this period was probably one of the best the world has known for the preservation of land-based creatures. It is not surprising, therefore, that we find more fossils of terrestrial animals in these periods than before.

Looking at the protomammals, there is no reason to suppose from an examination of their bones, that they were any the more or less 'primitive' than mammals are today. They are different, certainly, but studies of their bone texture and likely living habits also suggests very strongly that many of them, if not all, were warm-blooded and furry. In the 1970's, Robert Bakker in America and Armand De Ricqles in Paris, quite unknown to each other, simultaneously reached these conclusions, both of them first publishing their results at more or less the same time.

The case for the warm-bloodedness of both protomammals and dinosaurs is so convincing that one wonders why no-one had thought of it before. In fact, they had. The first monographs written on the subject, also based upon bone texture, were written in the 1930s, but had been ignored. The reason, of course, was the evolutionary dogma that dinosaurs and protomammals were cold, ungainly and un-intelligent reptiles. They had to be to fit the neat 'historical' picture that they were the forerunners of the age of mammals. But before the dinosaurs, the warm-blooded protomammals flourished.

Robert Bakker's classic work, *The Dinosaur Heresies*, first published in 1986, lays out the multitude of arguments in a way that is more or less irrefutable. Their legs, for instance, were oriented vertically beneath them so that they could run like a dog, a rhinoceros or a bear rather than waddle, with splayed legs, like a crocodile or a lizard. And such a high-speed gait requires a high-speed metabolism – and that means warm-bloodedness. He writes:

Consistent with a warm-blooded metabolism, the Kanzanian therapsids [the first known, Late Palaeozoic protomammals] would have developed a more sophisticated design in the mechanics of their limbs. . . . The knee joint indicated the Kanzanians were designed for fast, bouncy gaits – the crests for supporting the extensive muscles of the knee were massively developed. When those muscles contracted on a one-ton protomammal of the Kanzanian, the great beast would surely have bounded forward into a lively run. . . .

Bakker also points out how these forerunners to our modern mammals appeared suddenly, radiating rapidly into a multitude of species:

Within a few million years, Kanzanian protomammals had taken over all the carnivorous roles – large, medium and small – nearly all the herbivorous roles, and produced dozens of small, insect-eating species as well. Never before had the ecosystem witnessed such a spectacular proliferation of new species from a single family. . . .

Right from the beginning, the Kanzanian protomammals stuffed whole clusters of species into each role. The best preserved of these are found in the rich beds of the Karoo and display a richness far greater than anything recorded before. Protomammals produced four different families of predators, with eight or ten different species, to prowl through the floodplains and forests of the Karoo. Biggest of them were the dome-headed anteosaurs, the size of polar bears, with thick, bony buttresses over their eyes for head-butting in the mating season. Anteosaurs were armed with a great row of long teeth that meshed together to clamp down on a prey. Predators from other families, the size of wolves and jaguars, displayed a wide variety of lethal devices for dealing with their prey. Plant-eaters were numerous, too. Five families and a score of species munched their way through the greenery of the ancient Karoo. . . .

In Kanzanian times, the Karoo experienced cool winters because it was closer to the South Pole than it is now. To remain active all the year round, the smaller animals might well have needed some kind of insulation. Orthodox palaeontology insists that hair is a uniquely mammalian invention, the adaptive badge of our own Class Mammalia. Several dissenters have however suggested that perhaps hair did evolve long before the first true mammal appeared in the late Triassic. . . .

Maybe our picture of the Kanzanians should include shaggy protomammals stalking their prey through a winter snowstorm, hot breath steaming from their nostrils.

But after a reign of 5 to 10 million years, says Bakker, nearly all of them suffered from a mass extinction, leaving only a few surviving groups, which again radiated into another group of protomammals. Successive waves then came and went, through the great Permian extinction, and with flourishing success, well into the time of the dinosaurs. And by the Late Triassic, species had emerged which were the forerunners of our modern mammals.

So the protomammals were an exceptionally 'successful' group. Large numbers of them appeared suddenly, filling all the available terrestrial niches. What their precursors were, nobody knows – the fossil record is lost. But certainly there are no missing links between them and reptiles. Perhaps their progenitors – the earlier representatives of their super-species – were smaller and more slightly built or for various environmental or geological reasons left no fossils behind.

There were herbivores, insectivores, and carnivores. And they came in all sizes – from those the size of polar bears to many much smaller varieties no bigger than a shrew. They may have cared for their young just like their similars do today. They may have even suckled their young and been as intelligent as modern mammals. Some may have made affectionate pets!

Vertebrate remains are composed almost entirely of teeth, bones and bone fragments, teeth and skulls being the commonest because they are generally the toughest. But bone structure does not tell us very much concerning the nature of the soft organs and tissues. So it is mostly assumptions based upon comparisons with present day skeletal structures that suggest that one particular creature was a reptile and another one a mammal.

Dinosaurs, incidentally, resembled neither, though they were vertebrates, of course. In fact, in many respects, the skeletal structure of one group of dinosaurs – those possessed of a bipedal stance and a bird-like pelvic girdle – most resembles that of birds.

The features distinguishing vertebrate skulls are often little more than the number of holes on the side. Modern reptiles have either no holes (e.g. turtles) or two holes (e.g. snakes, lizards, crocodiles). Birds also have two holes, as did the dinosaurs. But mammals have just one hole – and so did the Palaeozoic protomammals! And some of these Palaeozoic vertebrates also possessed three little bones in their middle ear – another similarity with the mammals of today and indicative of a finely-tuned sense of hearing.

So they were not 'mammal-like reptiles,' as the more conventional evolutionists like to call them, but must have been more closely related to the mammals of today. What we would like to know is whether they had the intelligence of dogs and bears or of toads and crocodiles. Warm-bloodedness strongly indicates the former. The term 'protomammals', therefore, is misleading if one takes it to mean creatures who were less intelligent and less 'evolved' than their modern counterparts.

If one looks at a creature only from the point of view of its being a complex material system of self-organizing molecules, then there is little else to discuss but its outward form and structure. But if one feels that it is whatever lies within a creature which really distinguishes it from its fellows then the discussion is immediately widened.

What was the intelligence of the creature, for example? What was its subtle mental and tattvic configuration? What were its behavioural patterns and instincts? What was its level of consciousness? These are far more interesting questions to ask, some answers to which would tell us what the spectrum of life was like in those days, on the scale of consciousness – not on a scale of holes in the head, or whether a creature swam or ran! Even living in the water does not make you unintelligent, as whales and dolphins readily testify.

I am not suggesting that the mammals of today possess skeletons which are as much like the Palaeozoic protomammals as more recent mammals. Certainly, they do not and there is no reason why they should. But this is just a changing with the times. I do suggest, however, that there is no reason to suppose that those ancient creatures occupied any less a place on the scale of consciousness than their modern day equivalents.

The reality is that it is not always so easy to identify even modern mammals just from remnants of their skeletons. Mistakes are easily made if we only have a piece of skull or vertebra to analyze. If we consider that what actually makes a creature higher or lower is its place on the scale of consciousness and its subtle energy configuration, it is easy to see that the actual degree of intelligence of some Palaeozoic protomammal is beyond our ability to assess with any certainty.

One of the skeletal distinctions between *modern* mammals and *modern* reptiles is that mammals possess three separate bones in their inner ear, reflecting a more complex auditory system, whilst reptiles possess a far simpler structure. But we can make very little use of this kind of information in our assessment of where protomammals stood on the ladder of consciousness, or how many tattwas were active in their subtle make-up.

There are many creatures, even amongst the invertebrates, which have highly complex sensory structures, as we have seen. This does not stop them being invertebrates. Unless we know in detail how the inner, subtle microcosmic pattern results in a particular outer form, we cannot really assess the level of consciousness or the nature of a creature's mental configuration from just a few bones which happened to get washed up in some ancient sedimentary deposit.

In the world of conventional evolutionary theory, all comparisons between bones and present day species are based upon *a priori* assumptions concerning evolution. Evolution is *assumed* to have happened, therefore the fossil record is interpreted in that light. And if we study the fossil record with only a material idea of evolution in our minds, then that is all we will see. If we have thoughts concerning a higher reality and an inward dimension to life, plus a perception that the physical universe is actually a projection of our conjoined minds, then we will begin to perceive a different picture.

Emphasizing the part played by one's preconceptions, Niles Eldredge comments in *Life Pulse*, perhaps not realizing the import of what he is saying:

> Only with some notion firmly in mind – that life has evolved, that complex life seems to have arisen relatively suddenly, after an incredibly long period when life remained very simple – does it make any sense to climb these rocks and collect all these fossils.

Given the nature of the fossil record, there may be no other way of doing it. But this means of study is clearly open to error. Anyhow, that is the way things have been done and all the existing evidence has been collected, catalogued and discussed with the conventional idea in mind. So to find really convincing evidence for a new interpretation, we need to look again, and to find new fossil data, also, as well as re-evaluating the old. A task of almost overwhelming magnitude.

Up to the present time, almost all the available fossil evidence has come to us through the minds of scientists who were already fully committed to a belief in evolution. Practically all the data collected is thus likely to be coloured and – consciously or subconsciously – selected by the minds of the 'objective' scientists themselves.

FROM SEA TO LAND?

From the mystic point of view, the physical universe is only a plane of consciousness, a level of perception, a realm of being within the creation of the Great Being. All creatures are microcosms of this Supreme Being. Some of these microcosms are more complete than others but they are all, in essence, drops of being or souls, surrounded by mind and body.

In this scenario, the physical universe and its creatures are intimately entwined. The one cannot exist without the other, for they are both simultaneous creations of the greater Mind. Moreover, just as there are three dimensions to space and five primary states of material substance – not some other numbers – so too can one expect that there will be a finite number of subtle microcosmic patterns or super-species.

But these subtle patterns or super-species seem to have an almost endlessly fluid number of *outward* physical expressions, though inwardly the elements – the tattwas – of which they are comprised are finite and hence the number of interactive patterns formed by them is also finite.

This does not mean, of course, that the overall balance of species has always been the same. The economy of nature may take on many shapes and colours in the course of time. In our present century, for example, we have seen an explosion in the number of humans at the cost of many other creatures. At other times, there may have been a preponderance of creatures lower on the scale of consciousness, perhaps for long periods of time. Even now, in terms of numbers, bacteria and micro-organisms are the most populous and probably always have been. I am only suggesting that the full complement of creatures has always been present. The relative numbers and distribution is another matter.

The conventional interpretation of the Palaeozoic fossil record, however, is that it was during the early part of this era that the land was almost simultaneously invaded by plants, invertebrates and vertebrates. And that the evolution of mammals and ultimately man then began in earnest.

I disagree with this interpretation and many of the reasons have already been given. First amongst them is that the meagre and exceptionally patchy terrestrial fossil record has been interpreted to fit the theory. Secondly, the earliest ecological scenario presented – of teeming and burgeoning life in the sea while the land remained barren – seems most unlikely and unsatisfying. If the land was so barren, how did terrestrial life ever get started? What was the inducement to move onto the land? Thirdly, no fossil evidence has ever been found of species intermediate between land and sea dwelling creatures. A few more words on these three topics are necessary to complete the discussion.

The absence of terrestrial fossils in the early Palaeozoic is normally taken to mean that such forms did not exist at that time. This fits with the evolutionary theory that sea creatures came out upon the land during this period and the matter is usually taken no further. But there are also other interpretations of the same evidence.

It is generally supposed that towards the end of the Permian epoch, which terminated the Palaeozoic era, the oceans were mostly withdrawn from the major continental land masses and had been so for some considerable time. Left open to the weathering of millions of years, the continents had been eroded down to low-lying landscapes, the stumps of ancient hills and mountains, devoid of almost all major mountainous features. Consequently, the land would also have lost many fossil traces of its previous terrestrial life forms. Many ancient sediments of pre-Palaeozoic times would have also been eroded and the fossil record lost. Those creatures actually living at that time – like the Kanzanian protomammals – would have stood a much better chance of fossilization than their more ancient forebears.

Before the 1960s, no-one had seriously considered that land could have been lost beneath the oceans due to crustal movements or have been recycled into the asthenosphere beneath. Consequently, given the enthusiasm surrounding the evolutionary theory, plus the paucity of data, it was very easy for evolutionists to assume that life was altogether absent from the land. They simply made an incorrect interpretation.

There is another clue to the mystery of where the fossils of the early land creatures went. The fossil record of the ancient seas indicates that some of the regular cyclic extinctions were very severe. Two of these we have already encountered at the ends of the Palaeozoic and Cretaceous. Five more major Palaeozoic extinctions, however, all within a space of 150 million years, are also relevant. One was at the end of the Devonian and another terminated the Silurian. In the Ordovician, there were three, the last one being as great as the Permian and Cretaceous extinctions. In addition, it is likely that the cut-off point at the start of the Cambrian was also preceded by a grand extinction.

Now it is after the great Devonian extinction that we first encounter coal and really begin to find larger numbers of fossilized land creatures. One assumes, therefore, that since we have evidence that a terrestrial ecosystem was already in full swing at least 40 million years earlier, in the Silurian, that the geological conditions in the Carboniferous had changed sufficiently for terrestrial fossils to stand more likelihood of preservation.

Vast environmental and geological changes must have accompanied these cyclic extinctions. So could such changes have been responsible for the erosion, crushing or general recycling of much of the previously existing evidence of terrestrial fossils in an even greater way than in the Mesozoic or Cenozoic eras?

Immediately before the Cambrian era, almost all the marine record simply disappears. Yet there are a few sites where abundant earlier fossils are found. Marine life was therefore flourishing in Precambrian times, but the record has been mostly lost due to geological circumstances. Similarly, the terrestrial record has a cut off point in the mid-Palaeozoic, yet there are a few earlier terrestrial fossil finds. So to find cut-off points in the fossil record does not mean that there was no such life in earlier times.

If ancient Cambrian deposits are rare on earth *now*, then it is reasonable to suppose that 500 million year old deposits would have similarly been rare even in Palaeozoic times. And if they were rare then, those fossil strata would now be either long gone, buried too deep to access, melted back into the underlying magma or be found only in baked, crushed, highly pressurized and fragmented form.

So to find no fossil strata that are much older than 600 or 700 million years does not mean that life in all its forms was not flourishing during those times in much the same overall fashion as it does today, and as it has done during the last 500 million years. Nor is the absence of any terrestrial fossils in the earliest record indicative that such life did not exist. It is more a statement concerning the nature of geological activity and fossilization than evidence for a material kind of evolution.

The second objection to the idea that life began in the seas, then moved to the land is the ecological one. Life in our modern seas is entirely dependent upon life on land, and vice versa. We have already described some of the detailed ecological interactions between life on land and sea. In the absence of life on the land, life in the sea – even supposing it could have existed – would need to have been radically different. But there is no evidence that it was. In fact, the contrary is true, for the fossil record tells us that pretty much the same community of creatures was present then as now. How, then, could there have been an oceanic ecosystem without the support of life on land? The planetary ecosystem would have been one-legged and could not have survived.

There is also another ecological factor to be borne in mind. A continuous supply of nitrates, phosphates and other minerals are required by marine plants and organisms. These are supplied as water runs off the land into the seas by way of rivers and streams. Neatly demonstrating this is the fact that in present times, the most abundant areas of marine life exist at the estuaries and outlets of major rivers or in areas where ocean currents provide an upwelling, carrying essential nutrients from lower to higher waters. It is such areas that comprise the world's largest fisheries.

The water that brings these essential minerals to the sea falls on the land as rain and snow. Without this continuous supply of water, no new minerals would ever reach the sea. But a land without trees and plants would severely disrupt the patterns of rainfall and erosion. Soil would never come into existence, since it results from the activity of plants and innumerable other creatures. All loose material would soon be washed into the sea, leaving only bare rocks. So the flow of minerals would be greatly diminished. Without a land-based ecology, the planet would soon be scoured down to bare rock and sand. The nitrogen cycle, from which nitrates are derived, food for plants and the base material for the building of all proteins, would be utterly disrupted. And God only knows what would happen to the nitrogen balance in the atmosphere.

Rainfall itself would almost certainly be greatly reduced, for dry rock and sand do not encourage rain in the way a tropical rainforest does. This is why man-created deserts can be so self-maintaining and difficult to reclaim. But when forests have been successfully re-established in previously arid areas, then clouds more readily form, rain falls and the ecosystem begins to flourish and expand. And then, too, the streams and rivers flow, once again carrying nutrients to the open seas.

So without terrestrial vegetation, the pattern of rain and snowfall would be disrupted. And without rain falling on a green landscape, life in the seas would come to a halt. But plants and trees exist only as a part of an ecosystem. Without bacteria, moulds, fungi, invertebrates and higher creatures, the whole system cannot function. For a start, no vegetation would ever decay and plants would soon run out of soil minerals, also choking themselves to death in the undecayed debris of their own remains.

Then, if there are insects and other creatures that eat the vegetation, there must also be larger creatures to eat the insects and keep *their* numbers under control, else the vegetation would soon be eaten up. Birds, for example, eat small insects by the tonne. But those larger creatures must also be controlled, and so we have the many carnivorous species. The planetary biosphere is such a complete system. Half a cycle would not function.

The third objection to the Darwinian concept that life crawled, jumped and rooted its way out of the sea onto the land is that there is no evidence for it in the fossil record. Even though long sequences of similar species, such as the ammonoids or horses, have been preserved as they changed through time, the missing links between different kinds of creature are all missing. Furthermore, the suggested evolutionary changes would have required probably the greatest number of coincidental, extraordinarily far-reaching and almost simultaneous mutations ever ascribed to the mechanism.

It is all very well to compare the bones of fishes and amphibians and – identifying the most similar ones – to then declare that amphibians must have evolved from them. Since they are both vertebrates, there are bound to be some species with skeletons more closely resembling each other than others. But there are still tremendous differences between these skeletons and none of the theoretical intermediate forms required by Darwinism have ever been found. Moreover, the differences between the skeletons of fish and amphibia are nothing compared to the differences in their anatomy, physiology, biochemistry and behaviour.

Additionally, the reproductive system of amphibia, involving such extensive metamorphosis from tadpole to adult forms, is quite unprecedented amongst fishes. Yet there, in the ancient Carboniferous sediments we find the fossilized tadpoles of ancient amphibia. For as long as we have known amphibia, they have had tadpoles. There have been no intermediate forms.

Having hopped out onto the land, amphibians were then supposed to have become reptiles – creatures entirely of the land, whose young no longer used the metamorphic route but emerged from eggs as miniature versions of their parent. But yet again, there are no missing links.

Amphibia also lack scales, something found in both fishes and many reptiles. Are we to believe, then, that fish first lost their scales when they became amphibia, later regaining them, though of a different kind, to become reptiles, along with a multitude of associated internal organ and tissue changes and behavioural modifications?

Little satisfied with their advances, the reptiles are then supposed to have turned into mammals and birds, not to mention – I suppose – the dinosaurs. But the changes required between cold-blooded and warm-blooded physiology – as well as behaviour – are immense. Like our earlier example of the evolution of a spider, how could all these integrated changes have come into being almost simultaneously, yet by chance?

Were there once creatures which were neither warm nor cold-blooded? And all gradations in-between? Did the myriad physiological processes associated with the possession of a furry skin come into being all at once? Or were there once part-furry and part-scaly creatures, making partial use of both technologies? How could such evolutionary indecision have survived? There is certainly no sign of any of these in the fossil record and none exist in modern times.

Even supposing that these changes could have taken place by the most prolific and lucky set of chance mutations, the required coincidences are nothing compared to those required to get all the other creatures onto the land. For life is supposed to have made it onto the land – not just once – but on multiple, parallel and simultaneous occasions.

The orthodox suppose that plants probably went first, to find a living on barren land. But plants require bacteria, moulds, fungi, earthworms and a whole soil ecosystem of diminutive creatures. And those small creatures also need the plants. So which went first? How can the one have made it onto a dry, parched land, devoid of life, in the absence of the others?

Plants, bacteria, protozoa, worms, arthropods in at least three versions, snails and all the other groups of creature and organism, large and microscopic, that previously existed only beneath the waves are supposed to have *independently* and more or less *simultaneously* formed a beach-head and gone up onto dry land. The problems for each are equally as great as for the fish–amphibian jump. And when one considers that they must have also learnt – by chance mutation – to have intermeshed with each other into a thriving ecosystem, the chances become more than remote.

Yet even that is not the end of the lucky coincidences, for there are many forms of invertebrate found only upon the land – insects, for example. And again, no intermediate forms are ever found. Here, palaeontology invokes the paucity of the fossil record on its behalf, noting that such creatures are extremely unlikely to be fossilized.

It should be noted that the suggestion put forward by conventional evolution concerning the innovatory colonization of the land by successive and simultaneous waves of creatures from the sea, is *very* different from the populating of a new area of land by existing land species. Though even this is difficult enough for them as we see in some deserts, badlands and areas of recent volcanic activity. Here, *existing*, well-adapted species and well-integrated ecosystems are searching for a foothold. But that a host of different kinds of creature all simultaneously took to living on utterly barren land and immediately evolved the required mutually-supportive ecosystem seems most unlikely. And which went first, when all depend upon each other for survival? What would have been the inducement in a world driven only by tiny chance mutations to go up on the land?

BIRDS

Birds are something of a problem for both evolutionists and creationists alike. One of the major difficulties is simply that, possessing
such light-weight bones, their fossilized remains – even at the best of
times – are few and far between. Birds die in their millions every year.
Yet apart from those lying on the road or the ones the cat brings in,
one sees very few dead birds, let alone fossilized ones. Nature has too
many hungry mouths to waste such tasty morsels.

The birds who inhabit my garden will leave no fossils. Few birds
fall into mud and even those which do are soon consumed by worms,
fishes, bacteria and the many agents of decay. Their slender bones, so
perfect and lightweight for an aerial existence carry little substance
which can survive the millennia.

The issue of the birds' arrival upon the scene is often passed over in
evolutionary texts, due to lack of fossil evidence, though the famous
Archaeopteryx has been the subject of much speculation from both
sides of the camp. There seems no reason why feathered forms should
always have been present upon the earth. It is representatives of that
group of super-species – of the three-tattwa'd mind configurations to
which the birds belong – which will always have been present, a
spectrum of niches filled almost certainly by at least some of the
dinosaur species during the ages immediately preceding and living
concurrently with the earliest fossil birds.

But somehow, I find it hard to imagine an ecosystem containing so
many insects but no birds or light-weight airborne insectivores to
keep their numbers down. Plant fossils of Mesozoic and Palaeozoic
times often exhibit evidence of having been nibbled and without birds
or their similars to control them, the insects would surely have soon
eaten themselves – and everyone else – out of a living. And if many of
the insects flew, then surely there must have been many airborne
creatures capable of catching them? Surely, such an excellent variety
of niches would not have been left unoccupied for hundreds of
millions of years? Flight is more or less essential to get rapidly from
tree to tree in search of bugs and caterpillars. And the exceptionally
high metabolic rate of the host of small insectivorous birds makes
them ideal as high speed, exceptionally mobile controllers of the
insect population.

The discovery of the earliest fossil bird was recently made in
Chinese lake sediments by a 10-year-old boy. Dated at 135 million
years, 15 million years after *Archaeopteryx*, and about the size of a
sparrow, it was clearly a tree-living and tree-perching bird, capable of

true flapping flight. However, the little creature had the small remnants of claws and fingers in its wings. And it may have had teeth. Prior to this find, the earliest known birds had been found in Spain and Mongolia, about 10 million years younger. And before that, the next oldest bird is after a gap of about 50 million years, in the Late Cretaceous. And these birds certainly had teeth, as did *Archaeopteryx*. (Note again how enormous periods of time can elapse between fossil finds. Quite inadequate for the certain reconstruction of history.)

There is also some evidence that there were birds back in the Triassic, over 200 million years ago, hotly denied by some scientists and supported by others. But the vast spans of time with only a handful of finds indicates that more or less anything could have been going on. To really know, one would have to return to the Late Jurassic, 150 million years ago, to find out by direct experience!

Only six partial specimens of *Archaeopteryx* have ever been discovered, five of them from the Solnhofen limestone of southern Germany. The sixth was found in 1988 amongst the collection of an amateur geologist who had mistaken it for the remains of a small bird-like dinosaur, *Compsognathus* (see Figure 8.1), which only underlines the point that you see what you expect to see.

Figure 8.1 Compsognathus, *a bird-like dinosaur, the size of a large chicken and a contemporary of* Archaeopteryx. *Both were probably warm-blooded. (From a model by A. Hayward, photograph by Natural Science Photos.)*

Teeth, a long feathered tail and feathered limbs at first sight make *Archaeopteryx* an evolutionist's dream-creature, but whether it was a reptile, a dinosaurian relative or a bird is really of little consequence to the present thesis. For what its level of consciousness was is not possible to say! Though not itself classifiable as a dinosaur, it was certainly around at the same time, a part of the atmosphere and mood of those times.

The evolutionary interest of *Archaeopteryx* lies in the fact that it is the earliest occurrence in the fossil record of feathers, though this does not mean that feathers were previously absent. They are not the most readily fossilized biological remains. The supposed evolutionary stages linking scales to feathers are noticeably absent. How could a dinosaur ever develop feathers by tiny random mutations? Of what use would be the transitional stages of feathery scales, serving neither the function of feathers nor of scales? Feathers, like hair on mammals, are lightweight insulation for a warm-blooded creature, as well as being superbly designed flying structures. But being warm-blooded is a major step, as is the possession of a beak, with or without teeth.

The production of feathers, the behavioural patterns required for their maintenance, cleanliness and grooming, the yearly moult as opposed to the change of skin preferred by some reptiles (such as snakes) or simply sustained growth (as we find in crocodiles), not to mention the extraordinary dexterity of avian flight and individual feather control, the musculature, the mentally originated behavioural patterns and the biochemistry – all these would require many *millions* of mutations to attain their present state had chance or random evolution been the origin of their existence.

Birds, after all, are warm-blooded creatures, capable of maintaining a constant body temperature. This itself requires considerable physiological and biochemical adaptation. There are far more differences between reptiles and birds or even dinosaurs and birds than just the presence of feathers and the gift of flight.

There is no reason why entire classes of creature, as we perceive them, should not come and go, as the yugas roll by. There may even have been many such classes of which no record remains, especially amongst soft-bodied invertebrates and the smaller land creatures. But we do not need to postulate a material and chance evolution to account for their arrival and their demise. They simply had their day, reflecting the formative conditions and karmic atmosphere of the time. Then they passed away, their place being taken by new species at the next great Springtime.

The dinosaurs were only one example. *Archaeopteryx* and maybe a wealth of similar feathered and flying creatures may even have abounded, perhaps throughout the world. But it does not mean that they were a transitional form between a dinosaur and a bird in a conventional evolutionary sense, any more than a dog is transition between a rabbit and a wolf.

Monotremes – egg-laying, toothless mammals are another such class represented now only by the duck-billed platypus and the echidnas, found in Australia and New Guinea. New Guinea is an island in the West Pacific, north of Australia, part of the Indonesian group of islands and previously connected to the Australian continent. But no-one seriously suggests that the highly specialized duck-billed platypus is representative of the missing link between reptiles and mammals. It is far too much of an individual species in its own right. It may even trace its lineage to some groups of dinosaur, many of whom were egg-laying, warm-blooded and cared for their young.

So despite all the extinctions and despite all the renewals, we have yet to see any evidence of Darwinian-style, gradual evolution taking place in the fossil record. The actual 'change' from one species to another always appears to elude us. Species and classes appear to be quite definable, there is no smooth gradient between them. It is possible to arrange a few sequences of progressive step-like changes towards modern forms, but the steps seem to occur suddenly at each great renewal, not gradually, in-between times. 'Sudden' is still a relative term, however, for the renewal period, like the extinction phase, may last a million or two years, perhaps even longer, but with a slowly declining vigour as the Sat yuga gives way to progressively less subtle times.

8,400,000 SPECIES: THE WHEEL OF EIGHTY-FOUR LAKHS

Indian mystics over the centuries have consistently stated that there are eight million, four hundred thousand species, present more or less continuously throughout the whole period of creation. They call it the 84 lakhs of species, a lakh being one hundred thousand. This, they say, is made up as follows:

Trees and plants etc.	3,000,000
Insects (probably includes terrestrial invertebrates)	2,700,000
Birds	1,400,000
Marine and aquatic creatures	900,000
Higher animals, man, ghosts, nature spirits & celestial beings	400,000

Now before we hasten to criticize these divisions for a lack of biological detail, let us see what is actually meant. First of all, mystics do not come to this world to involve us more deeply in thinking about it. They certainly do not come to teach us biology in the sense that we mean it, scientifically.

Mystics very briefly mention the nature of these species so that they may point out to us that life in this world preys upon life and as such, there can never be lasting peace or happiness here. We also naturally wonder about the species which surround us and as curious humans we do like to have some sort of an answer from them as to how things are put together. So they describe just the barest outline, within the context of their times and their culture. Hindu culture generally has been little interested in an itemized classification of other living creatures and the above list is probably as detailed as they needed.

In one way or another, mystics direct our attention to the fact that most living creatures exist in a greatly reduced and circumscribed state of consciousness. They say that man alone is able to understand the true nature of himself and of this physical world, and how to escape from it. And they instruct their disciples or initiates on exactly *how* to meditate upon the Life Stream inside and how to follow it to the Supreme Being within, the great Source and Ocean of Life. They do not come to give us a science lesson, at least not of a material nature. They teach mystic knowledge and their practice and philosophy is often called mystic science, spiritual science, or the science of the soul.

As previously mentioned, they point out that the physical forms of all creatures are composed of the five tattwas, the essential substance or energy of the three Mind worlds. The subject of the tattwas, which in their physical manifestation have both subtle and gross aspects, has been discussed at length in the *The Web of Life* and was also discussed in *Natural Creation and the Formative Mind*.

What we need to understand in the present context is that the degree to which the subtle essence of these tattwas is linked in to the mind structure of a creature determines its potential for awareness of different aspects of the physical creation. That is, the tattvic patterning of a creature determines not only its mental patterns, its instincts, its behaviour, its anatomy and physiology and its outward form, but also *its degree of consciousness*.

It is this that we observe as the intelligence of a creature, just as – amongst humans – we instinctively know that it is those with the greatest awareness who possess the greatest intuitive understanding of human nature and of life. We call it wisdom and acknowledge its existence, though we do not always understand its source.

Intellectual attainment is not necessarily supported by spiritual awareness or perception. Frequently it is not. It therefore has a strong tendency to become egocentric, dogmatic and intolerant of alternative points of view. The Sufi mystic, Rumi, writes, 'Conventional knowledge is only self advertisement', and a good friend of mine once wrote, 'There is more vanity per square inch in the world of the scientific, artistic, and theological intelligentsia than in any other area of the physical universe'. True wisdom, however, always comes with a spiritual perception of life.

Broadly speaking, then, creatures are divided, esoterically, by their particular mental configuration, by their subtle tattvic constitution. This is what really constitutes a 'species' – not an analysis of its anatomy and physiology.

We can understand this to some degree from experience of our fellow humans. We know that what makes an individual unique is his or her mind. However detailed a physical examination and dissection one may make of a person, we can never find any of those mental qualities at a physical level. It is something which we cannot grasp materially which makes us all so different. And it is from that subtle, mental level that the sense of self comes and it is to that which we really relate in all our dealings with people, whether we are aware of it or not. When a person dies, that subtle element has departed and we wish to have no further dealings with them. Their dead body even becomes an embarrassment to us and we wish to dispose of it as soon as possible.

Similarly amongst the other species inhabiting this physical creation. Their primary differences lie in the arrangement of their subtle tattvic essences. And the more complete the integration of the tattwas into this blueprint, then the higher the species is on the scale of consciousness. The more complete its equipment for communicating with the creation, then the higher is its level of consciousness. That is what consciousness actually is. And the highest level of consciousness is 'communication' or union with God Himself.

Mystics therefore say that the same 8,400,000 species have always been present upon this planet. There are, so to say, 8,400,000 different subtle tattvic configurations or super-species. Now according to the times and the circumstances, these species can clearly take on outward forms that differ widely, far more than two similar species of elephant, for instance. But the position on this ladder of consciousness is always determined by the completeness of the tattvic pattern within; by how complete an instrument panel or microcosm surrounds a soul.

This inner pattern is then *reflected* in the outer form, but the outer form itself does not constitute the essential difference. So if we use only the outer form to distinguish where a creature lies on this subtle scale, we can be wrong or at least confused. It is better to study the reality rather than the reflection. And if we use only the fossilized remains of outer forms, then we can most assuredly get ourselves thoroughly confused and concern ourselves with irrelevant details.

Generally speaking, the species as we know them today are divided up as follows:

Vegetable kingdom	Water only
Insects and invertebrates	Fire and earth, fire and air or fire and water
Fish	Fire and water
Reptiles	Fire and earth
Birds	Fire, water and air
Mammals	Fire, water, air and earth
Man	Fire, water, air, earth and akash

Now the English translations of the names of these tattwas relate only to their dense physical states and are therefore likely to cause misunderstanding, for the physical expression of the tattwas is only one of the many modes in which they express themselves. Anyway, we have to call them something and for a better comprehension of what is meant, I would refer you to *Natural Creation and the Formative Mind* and *The Web of Life*.

If you have a gut reaction against the overall division of matter into these five states, then that is not unusual. Yet no scientist would deny that matter takes on the solid, liquid, airy and plasmic states. Many, too, agree that the vacuum state is the primary formative energy field out of which the others are dynamically and continuously derived. And it is an interesting line of thought to consider how a universe would be put together if there were, say, only three or four such states – or maybe six or seven. Or no differentiations at all.

With space, vacuum or akash as the ubiquitous and primal energy field, solids, liquids and gases make three separate 'pools' of inert substance while the energy of fire drives the transmutations of one state to another. One less, or one more, would make a strange universe. Or if there were no thresholds and no sudden changes of state, our planetary biosphere would be nothing more than a homogeneous goo, a cosmic porridge: the Universal Stickiness. No, five tattwas is just right – it is another of those cosmic coincidences that are a part of Formative Mind expression, demonstrating the fittingness of things. But note how the number of active tattwas in a creature's make-up determines the degree of intelligence each possesses. This is expressed, for example, by the degree to which there is a potential for *learning* built in to the creature. That is, the flexibility the creature has within the constraints of its instincts and innate behavioural patterns.

So, looking dispassionately at the fossil record we can see that species filling these slots have been present all along, especially if we bear in mind the scanty nature of this record. There have always been one, two, three and four tattwa'd creatures. A species does not need to look modern to have had a particular inward tattvic structure! 'Archaic', 'primitive' or 'modern' mean nothing in relationship to the position of each creature on the scale of consciousness, according to the completeness of its mental microcosm.

Only man *appears* to be absent from most of this record, but I feel that in all probability this is only an artefact brought about both by his nature and habits, as well as by geological circumstances. We will discuss this matter shortly.

COUNTING AND CLASSIFYING THE SPECIES

From a mystic point of view, there are said to be 8,400,000 kinds of species. Yet, defined from a scientific angle, present estimates of currently living species vary widely between 3 and over 30 million. And when one considers how many cycles of extinction and proliferation have come and gone, then the number of species which have ever existed must be amongst the billions and trillions.

This again brings home to us that what is meant, mystically, by a species, must be a particular tattvic configuration, a super-species which contains many different external possibilities of form, depending upon environmental circumstances and the formative mental atmosphere of the times.

Perhaps all trilobites, classified by scientific criteria as members of the *group Trilobita*, are really reducible, from a subtle point of view, to one or just a few super-species. Maybe a super-species, esoterically, is more akin to a *genus* on the scientific scale of things. A genus covers most species of fox, for example, throughout the world, while all foxes belonging to the dog *family*.

But in that case, a genus would often be the expression of a particular super-species during just one particular cycle. For it is in the early phases of a cycle that new genera characteristically appear.

And after major extinctions whole new families and groups also commonly arise. But although species change and radiate rapidly during such proliferation phases, genera do usually remain stable, at least for the recurrent 5 to 10 million year periods.

Thus, modern representatives of the trilobite super-species might be horse-shoe crabs, creatures which appeared in the Late Palaeozoic, shortly before the trilobites disappeared, even though, scientifically, horse-shoe crabs are not even classified as members of the group *Trilobita*.

It is also a characteristic of species change that one or two groups of creature radiate to fill the same old ecological niches while other groups die out. The tenrecs of Madagascar or the marsupials are good examples of this in modern times, something common to all proliferation phases and all categories of creature. It is an aspect of 'parallel evolution'. But what then is the relationship of tenrecs or marsupials to their 'coincidental' counterparts elsewhere in the world? Are hedgehog tenrecs and other hedgehogs, for example, both expressions of the same super-species? And if so, by what means, for from a totally physical viewpoint they appear to have developed separately and coincidentally. Likewise, with marsupial and mammalian wolves and so many other creatures. It seems to mean that there is no single straight line lineage by which one can chart the history of a super-species; that the same super-species can run several lines of development in different parts of the world, apparently separate, outwardly, but hiddenly connected through the more subtle energies and patterns of the greater Mind.

The greatest difficulty in tracing the fossil lineage of a super-species from its many outward expressions is that – for practical reasons – scientific classifications of the species rely almost entirely upon *physical* and *anatomical* differences. And in the case of fossils, this is further limited by the availability for study of only skeletons and other hard parts. Super-species, on the other hand, are differentiated by their *subtle and mental* characteristics. The scientific scheme of classification is therefore at odds, to some degree, with our understanding of the subtle and mental side of things and needs extension. But how does one begin to classify creatures – especially those known only from a few bones in the fossil record – according to their mentality?

Furthermore, it is not clear whether the super-species actually possess definitive, though subtle, boundaries or whether they are simply merged into one continuum which expresses all the potential levels of consciousness and from which all physical species come into existence.

So, as we have seen before, there are many mysteries surrounding the generation of new species, whatever one's point of view may be. And, situated as we presently are, in the midst of an extinction phase, it is difficult to know what causes the decline to be reversed and just what goes on in a proliferation phase.

Interestingly, changes amongst the higher animals, especially those which were probably warm-blooded, seem to have been more *extensive* and more *rapid* than amongst cold-blooded creatures. So perhaps there is a key to the mystery here, as well. For it appears that the more complete the microcosm and the more flexible the mental characteristics of the creature and its underlying super-species, then the more its external form can differ over time. That is, the flexibility and the capacity to change or adapt originate at the mental level and are reflected at the genetic or 'evolutionary' level, too.

This would certainly explain the extensive changes undergone by mammals, protomammals, dinosaurs and birds over their recorded history. For while there are many fishes, reptiles and invertebrates (all two-tattwa'd creatures) that are quite recognizable after 400 or 500 million years, the lineage of the higher animals is far more difficult to trace, since the changes to their external forms have been far greater.

The figure provided by mystics of 2,700,000 species (or super-species) of insects (which probably includes all terrestrial creepy-crawlies) is an interesting one, for after the vegetable kingdom it is the largest single group of creatures. And it correlates to scientific estimates of the number of species in a way which sheds further light on the nature of a super-species.

The Scottish biologist, J. B. S. Haldane (1892-1964), when asked what inferences regarding the Creator could be drawn from his research, replied, 'An inordinate fondness for beetles'. For approximately one in every four species is a beetle! Now, 2,700,000 species is 32 per cent of 8,400,000 and with scientific estimates putting beetles at roughly 25 per cent, the figure would appear to be about right. For the difference of 7 per cent presumably covers all other terrestrial invertebrates.

Terry Erwin of the Smithsonian Institute in Washington DC has published some very tentative estimates on the number of species of tropical arthropod (the largest phylum of invertebrates, including insects, spiders and crustaceans). Based only upon studies of the forest canopy in Panama, he estimated that there were about 30 million species of arthropod in the world and less than a million of all other species, though these figures employed a considerable degree of guesswork.

Taxonomists estimate that they are familiar with perhaps only 10 per cent of all species presently alive upon the planet. When studies are made of both the forest canopy and marine sediment, for example, often more than 90 per cent of the species are new to science. Even amongst vertebrates, which scientists estimate may make up only two per cent of all known species, about twenty new species are added to the taxonomists' lists every year.

Nobody even knows how many species have actually *been* described! Estimates vary from between 1 million to 1.8 million. Moreover, a species can vary greatly and variants at either end of a range may well have been described as two separate species, whilst two very similar species may be known under only one name.

The position occupied by dinosaurs is a fascinating one, not least because of their amazing size, diversity and duration of existence. It would not surprise me if many of them *had* been warm-blooded and – as well as laying eggs – had looked after their youngsters with the same high degree of care found amongst the birds. Some of them may have also given birth to live young and perhaps have even suckled them. Perhaps others were more like the last remaining modern monotremes who lay eggs and then suckle their young. Evolutionists observe many examples of what is called parallel evolution. Why should not suckling one's young have been practised by some varieties of dinosaur, too? We have to get out of the habit of thinking of them as ungainly, dim-witted reptiles. Some groups of them may have been quite the reverse.

Certainly, modern palaeontological opinion now places dinosaurs on a level with all the other well-adapted or well-designed creatures which have come and gone on the planetary stage as times have changed. The idea that dinosaurs died because they were so big, clumsy and slow-witted is an outmoded fallacy. Many modern palaeontologists have reassessed their impression of where the dinosaurs have stood upon the 'evolutionary scale', though actually, the term has little meaning. It reflects only an intuitive awareness that there is a gradation of *something* amongst creatures. So dinosaurs have definitely received a re-rating in recent years and any lingering childhood images or subliminal impressions relating them to the clumsy monsters of the movie-makers should be dispelled from one's mind.

But there will always have been life forms comprised of three tattwas, though whether dinosaurs were two or three-tattwa'd creatures, I cannot say. Perhaps they really consisted of a number of classes – some two tattwa'd like the reptiles, others three-tattwa'd, more like birds, others four-tattwa'd like our modern mammals and most probably like 'archaic' mammals and protomammals, too.

A decisive indicator would be whether or not they really were warm-blooded. That in itself would probably be enough to classify them as three tattwa'd, on an intelligence parallel with that of birds. Intuitively, a warm-blooded brain seems more suited to express a higher intelligence and level of consciousness than a cold one.

And the metabolic complexity of being warm-blooded and thus to some degree more adaptive and independent of environmental temperatures seems to require the more complex interweaving of three rather than just two tattwas. Certainly some dinosaur brains, relative to body size, were of comparable dimensions to those of birds. So when you ask a palaeontologist where the dinosaurs have gone and he points to a sparrow on a tree, he may be right.

Then again, the state of development of the young dinosaurs when they emerged from the eggs would tell us a great deal. Reptiles such as snakes, turtles and crocodiles, for example, appear fully formed, independent and ready for the fray, however tiny they might be, though some reptiles do care very beautifully for their young. Baby crocodiles, for example, live close to mother, running for cover to hide in her mouth, so gently held, whenever danger approaches. But most young birds, of course, are quite helpless. Even chicks and ducklings who, like the young of many herbivores, enter life ready and willing to walk, still have a long way to go before they become independent of their parents.

Perhaps it needs three or more tattwas in your make-up to be endowed with the ability to really care for your young. And the question of why the young of higher species should be so dependent upon their parents for so long after birth is also an interesting one which is discussed shortly.

Pursuing this line of thought, marsupials would seem to be four tattwa'd creatures, though I am unsure what to make of the monotremes. Whether they are three or four-tattwa'd I would not like to say. I have never had a chance to get to know one at close quarters to gain some experience of their intelligence, consciousness and capacity to learn.

RAISING A FAMILY

The essence of life is one and the same within all creatures. All patterns, subtle or gross, bodily or inert, are formed by the greater

Mind, the Formative Mind. But living creatures never totally forget their essential oneness. Always, we find the desire to communicate, to express, to care, to take responsibility – in all creatures. These are external characteristics of life – even the spider cares for its young and the butterfly deposits her eggs with great care and precision. Even in the world of inert matter, of material substance, all things move and work within a greater harmony. The divine music of creation rings through all things binding them together in one totality.

The soul, hemmed in on all sides by the mind, still finds space for its expression as the Life Force itself. The less the constraints of the mind, the more can the oneness of all life find expression. It is for this reason that, generally speaking, the higher the species upon the scale of consciousness, then the fewer are the number of offspring born and the greater is the care and love bestowed by the parents.

Human parents may raise only a small number of offspring, but in general they are cared for with deep affection and attachment. Our consciousness of life is such that the loss of a child is never forgotten. The constant loss of numerous children would bring intolerable grief to normal human parents. Life could not continue in such a fashion. Our children, too, take many years to mature. In fact, the process of inner growth never stops, if we keep afresh our interest in life.

Other mammals exhibit a variety of time-spans during which the young are dependent upon the parents. Many give birth to offspring once a year or even, like rabbits and some other rodents, many times in a year. And afterwards, the family unit does not always stay together, though communities of social animals certainly keep close ties with each other. But humans never forget their children and their parents, not to mention their many other relatives and friends as well.

Even birds show signs of frantic grief when their young are lost. How could they live, if like insects or fish, they gave birth to thousands of offspring, most of whom perished? Even their grief would be intolerable to them.

Birds may attempt to rear one or more broods in a year but they are of limited numbers. And amongst all species, the more vulnerable a species is to predators, then the more offspring are produced. Small mammals and small birds, far more readily taken as prey, are usually more prolific than larger predatorial species like the eagle or the tiger. This is part of nature's economy.

Amongst the two tattwa'd creatures – reptiles, fish and amphibia – the number of offspring is vastly increased, for their young are considered tasty morsels by innumerable other creatures, while many species of insect and invertebrate, including viruses and bacteria, are capable of an extraordinary degree of proliferation.

And moving to the lowest rung on the ladder of consciousness, a plant or tree may sport tens or even thousands of flower and seed heads, setting countless seeds in just one season.

The balance is exquisite. Generally speaking, contribution to the great food larder is found in descending order amongst plants, invertebrates, fishes, amphibia, reptiles, birds, mammals and man. No species takes man as their natural food. The lion, the tiger, the elephant and the rhinoceros have no natural predators but man. Yet man kills everything in the most rapaciously omnivorous appetite upon the planet. One of man's definitions of life is that you can eat it!

From the karmic point of view, more weight is incurred on the mind by the killing of higher creatures and so a balance is once again maintained. For nature provides her largest larder from her least conscious forms, where the least karmic burden is incurred and the least suffering endured.

THE COMPLETE ECOSYSTEM OF CONSCIOUSNESS

Generally speaking, then, it seems that in the natural economy, the higher the creature is on the scale of consciousness, then the greater is its awareness of care and affection; that the more active tattwas a creature has in its make-up, then the less offspring it produces and the more care is bestowed upon them by the parents. This seems to make good sense, demonstrating yet again the completeness of the natural ecosystem. Not only are all aspects of life expressed physically, but all levels of consciousness are simultaneously present as well.

There is a Divine plan in this. All mystics have said that the Supreme Being is not only an ocean of consciousness and being, but He is also an ocean of love and bliss. His purpose in creation, they say, is to play the game of love with Himself, through His creatures. However, they have all been endowed with different levels of consciousness, different capacities to play this game. Only man, being a complete microcosm of the creation, is capable of playing the essence of this game with the greatest consciousness. Only man has the potential to seek and find God within himself and to attain consummation of the Divine game of love by merging back into the Creator Himself.

But man is also given the potential for evil, for turning away from God and from his Divine heritage. Man can also play the *enfant terrible* or the prodigal son. More than any other creature, man can act for good or ill. He alone appears to have free choice whilst all other creatures are constrained to a greater or lesser extent by their instincts.

If this creation is the Game of God, in which He is present in each and every soul and every smallest particle, then we can say that He is the Keeper of the Game. And it is a complete Game: all potential vehicles must be simultaneously present, so that His Being, Consciousness or Life can be expressed in all potential ways.

At the level of the Universal Mind this is expressed as Primal Nature, the essence, blueprint or seed form of all the complexity to be created at the lower levels. In Sanskrit, the ancient yogis called this *Prakriti*. In the physical realm, this Primal Nature is expressed, reflected or projected as what we call nature. And nature is nothing less than our complete planetary ecosystem. This, perhaps, is also implied by the expression, the 'wheel' of 8,400,000 species, for a wheel is complete – like a complete ecosystem. But actually it is only an expression of consciousness at all its possible levels.

Man is the supreme expression of this great Game of the Creator. Man has to be present because, potentially, he is the fullest expression of God. In man, everything has come together. All parts of the creation and the Creator are to be found within him. He is the perfect and complete microcosm. He is made in God's image – this is what the term really means. Man's highest role is therefore to tread the path within himself, back to God. His highest path or purpose is God-realization.

And just as God is the Keeper of the entire Game of the Creation, man is the lesser keeper of the game, at the physical level. He has a role to play in this world: man is also a game-keeper. And one of his responsibilities is the maintenance of his sphere of activity and influence in the best possible way.

During the Sat yuga, man behaves correctly, as the instrument of the Divine will in His creation. But as the Kal yuga deepens, he becomes increasingly selfish, irresponsible and self-willed. The game-keeper turns poacher. And there can be no worse poacher than man for – unconsciously – he has the knowledge and power of the game-keeper. By virtue of his akashic element he possesses the potential to understand the workings of the creation. So only man, amongst all the creatures, has the power to wreak havoc in the creation.

Without karma and reincarnation, nothing in this world would make any sense. The various species, the various tattvic configurations, the various levels of consciousness, are provided so that souls can reap the harvest of their previous actions, thoughts and desires. So that they can go where their mind needs to take them. The greater Mind always finds a way for the tendencies of the individual minds to be expressed. And those tendencies can span the entire spectrum of consciousness, from the lowest to the highest. Consequently, all levels of consciousness will always be present in the physical creation – and that means a full complement of species.

The real evolution is of the soul returning to God. But on its way it can go up or down. In the economy of life, there needs to be all levels of consciousness available for the souls, because each have earned themselves their place. Because of the energies or content of their minds, they are only fitted for that particular place, for that particular birth. So the appropriate vehicle or body must be present. It will automatically be made available.

But no birth lasts forever. Whether for a few minutes or a few years, for a hundred or for five hundred years, one birth is only a very brief passage on the cosmic clock. The soul and mind constantly move on. The soul is like Ulysses, the eternal wanderer in search of home. But, mystically speaking, the Creator's purpose in all of this apparent suffering is to refine the soul, to pass the gold through fire, so that when it reaches human form and discovers in itself the desire to find its source, the game of Divine love can at length be consummated.

If we complain that it all seems unfair on the part of God to put us through so much suffering and pain, the reply given by the mystics is to first come to the level of God and see things from His point of view, before making any final judgement on the matter. Then, they say, the soul discovers that this world has no more reality than a dream, that even time is an illusion, that past, present and future are a part of one Eternal Present. And when one awakens from a dream, then the suffering experienced in that dream fades away as a mirage that never possessed any substance. But all the dream creatures, all the roles that the mind may want to play or be karmically forced to play must be present for the full and apparently free expression of consciousness.

EXPRESSION OF THE ONE LIFE

No creature would willingly give up its life to be food for another, and yet this appears to be a grand theme running throughout nature. Conventional evolutionary theory and a projection of man's selfishness would suppose that the aim for each creature would be to become invulnerable to another's attack, but this we do not observe. All creatures die in the end, even falling prey to the tiniest of life forms – bacteria and viruses.

On the face of it, and interpreting evolutionary theory in the literal manner in which it is presented, one would have expected that plants would long ago have dispensed with all those living creatures which were of no use to them, by the simple expedient of developing toxic substances to be stored in their leaves and seeds. Perhaps they could simply have emitted poisonous gases when any creature tried to eat them that had no service to offer in return.

This would have effectively eliminated almost all vegetarian creatures. Plants do already protect themselves in this way, to some degree, so why has this not evolved into a complete protection system? Having successfully tapped into the sun as a primary source of energy, why do they then share this with other creatures in the amazing system biologists normally call the food chain.

By evolving 'correctly' plants could have ruled the world by bestowing their solar bounty only upon those other creatures which they needed for survival – mostly bacteria, moulds and fungi, and perhaps a few earthworms and their ilk – relying entirely upon the wind for pollination and seed distribution. If one objects that plants could not live without the entire ecosystem of other creatures, so that everything should be maintained in balance, I would agree. But that is not the scenario presented to us by evolutionary theory.

Such possibilities are too bizarre to consider further. It is clear that there is more to nature than competition for survival. Competition and selfishness is more reflective of man's approach to his own resources. He does not like to share his excess, let alone his life, with others. But this is not a common theme in nature.

Many humans live in terror of death, the certain reaper, as do other creatures: life is precious to all. But why? What is life that it should so vigorously defend itself against all comers? A man's greatest act of heroism is to save the lives of other humans, while putting his own life at risk. It is totally natural. But whence this compelling urge? We do not know the nature of death, yet dread it. We never wish to discuss its nature, personally. Its colours are always portrayed as grey and black. Yet it is always death which is reported in the news. Why not that other miracle, birth? Is there something deeply and unconsciously hidden inside ourselves that we *do* know about death, which appears in our conscious minds as this strange love–hate relationship with the subject?

The fact is that there is more to life than physical substance. All life is One, in its deepest essence. When covered over by the web of the Mind, the Oneness expresses itself as interaction and relationship. Consequently, creatures do not want isolation and self-existence; they need to be a part of the greater family of life. And it may seem odd, but at a physical level this means that we even eat each other's bodies.

Could one imagine a scenario where all creatures were not reliant upon each other for a living? Where all forms 'ate' inert dust and raw minerals for a living, every creature chlorophyll-green, absorbing light from the sun as their source of driving energy. Each quite unreliant upon the other, like a row of upright fence posts. Such a thing is unimaginable. Life and nature are not made like that. The web of the Formative Mind is so intricately, so intimately and so fittingly woven, even in the details of who eats whom!

Language, communication, play, hunting, being hunted, social ritual, sex, eating each other, protection, fear, affection – all these and many more are the *expression* of life, the One divided by the Mind into the Many.

Hence we find that all expression of life is backed by individual mind function. The bird and the bee, plant and animal – man and all creatures – express their life or consciousness through their own minds. All their expressions are based upon interaction and relationship. All minds are linked in a formative substratum, because underlying life is the Oneness of consciousness. Therefore the expression of life is a whole, a web of integrated interaction and relationship. So even selfishness can only exist as an interaction. There has to be something about which to be selfish and some other living creature from whom to be isolated!

IN SUMMARY

It seems evident, then, from the extant fossil record, that from the Mid to Late Palaeozoic period onwards, our planet has possessed a full complement of species covering the one, two, three and four tattwa'd, subtle microcosmic configurations or super-species. The major staging posts on the scale of consciousness have been present all through, although the outer forms have changed as time has passed. Before that, the record becomes increasingly unreliable and soon breaks off entirely, leaving records only of bacteria and sea-weed.

All the same, life appears to have been an integral part of our planet for as long as we can determine. And the hypothesis presented herein fits the facts just as well – indeed far better – than conventional theories of material evolution.

But what, then, of man? Has he been here all through or is he a recent addition to the show? Well, this I have mentioned previously in passing. It is now time to tackle the matter head-on!

Footnote to page 178

While this book was being typeset, a report of an even earlier terrestrial invertebrate find was published in the *New Scientist* (August 17 1991). Ken McNamara, a palaeontologist from the Western Australian Museum has found the clear impression of a 420 million year old *euthycarcinoid* in the sedimentary sandstone of ancient river mudflats at Murchison River Gorge, in Western Australia. Nearby tracks and burrows are also thought to belong to the euthycarcinoid, which – being carnivorous – would have been on the look-out for smaller creatures.

Previously, the oldest euthycarcinoids, which bear some resemblances to insects, were from French and American rocks, dated at 310 million years, 110 million years younger. The euthycarcinoids seem to have died out in a mass extinction, about 210 million years ago.

INTERLUDE

EVOLUTION: THE MONKEY'S VIEWPOINT

Three monkeys sat in a coconut tree
Discussing things as they're said to be.
Said one to the others, 'Now listen you two,
There's a certain rumour that can't be true!
That man descended from our noble race.
The very idea! 'tis a dire disgrace.

No monkey ever deserted his wife;
Starved her baby and ruined her life.
'And you've never known a mother monk
To leave her baby with others to bunk,
Or pass them on from one to another,
Till they hardly know who is their mother.

'And another thing! You will never see,
A monk build a fence round a coconut tree
And let the coconuts go to waste,
Forbidding all other monks a taste.
Why, if I put a fence around this tree,
Starvation would force you to steal from me.

'Here's another thing a monk won't do:
Go out at night and get in a stew,
Or use a gun or club or knife
To take some other monkey's life.

Yes! Man descended, the ornery cuss,
But, brothers, he didn't descend from us!'

Anon

9.   ANOMALIES

Until the time that Darwin introduced his theory in 1859, the scientific literature contained reports of human fossils and other anomalous human artefacts which would nowadays be considered out of place. Even in more modern times, discoveries have been made of human footprints in ancient muds and artefacts embedded in coal or limestone. The examples given in this chapter are just a few representative samples of such anomalies. With the exception of quotations, the stories have been retold and summarized.

The commonest way of dealing with palaeontological anomalies is either to explain them away, ignore them or to declare them frauds. Some anomalies have no doubt been fraudulent, but this explanation does not account for all strange finds. There are several reasons why many anomalous finds are unlikely to be fake.

To begin with, many of them have been found by good and honest people, who have gained little more for their reporting of the discovery than ridicule and accusations of fraud. Very few of them have become rich or famous from the find, while some of them have actually lost their jobs.

Additionally, many of the discoveries have been made in the presence of witnesses, during quarrying operations, often at considerable depth. For a fraudster to have arranged that the find be encased in rock and hidden at great depth in a quarry being mined with the aid of heavy machinery, that that particular piece of rock happened to come into someone's hand, and that an apparently solid lump of rock or coal happened to be split open in the presence of witnesses, stretches credulity beyond bounds. That one of the discoverers happened to be a conjuror is also unlikely, for those who knew the person and his skills would have automatically suspected him.

METALLIC OBJECTS IN ROCK AND COAL

The following is a translation of a letter (in French) sent to Messieurs Pauwels and Bergier, *Editions Planete*, Paris:

September 30th 1968, Caen, France

We would like to bring to your attention the following facts, and hope you will give our discovery some consideration. As speleologists [scientific study of caves] and investigators, we have studied for several years the Pays d'Auge region of Calvados. During the year 1968, we discovered some metallic nodules in a hollow in an Aptian chalk bed in a quarry being worked in Saint-Jean de Livet.

These metallic nodules have reddish-brown colour, a form [cross-section] absolutely identical (semi-ovoid), but are of different sizes [length]. A central section had a form [cross-section] corresponding to the exterior form.

These nodules at first seemed to be fossils, but having examined them carefully we became conscious of their entirely metallic nature. Experiments at the forge showed that the carbon content was higher than castings of today. We were led to consider the hypothesis that they were meteorites, but five pieces were found of the same nature, which leads us to reject this hypothesis. There remains only an intelligent intervention in the Secondary Era (the end of the Cretaceous) of beings who could cast such objects. These objects, then, prove the presence of intelligent life on earth long before the limits given today by prehistoric archaeology.

P.S. The Geomorphology Laboratory of the University of Caen is now studying these objects which we have sent them (without great hopes).

Source: Anonymous; *INFO Journal*, 1:22–23, 1969
Reprinted in: *Ancient Man*, William R. Corliss

In 1851, Hiram de Witt of Springfield, Massachusetts, accidentally dropped a fist-sized lump of gold-bearing quartz which he had brought back with him from a trip to California. The rock was broken by the fall, revealing within it a 2-inch, cut-iron nail, slightly rusted. He said, 'It was entirely straight and had a perfect head'.

Source: *The Times*, London, 24 December 1851

At Dorchester, Massachusetts, in 1851, a bell-shaped vessel, 4.5 inches high, was broken into two during blasting operations, having previously lain embedded in the solid rock. The bell was made of an unidentified metal and finely inlaid with silver in floral designs. A photograph of the vessel was printed.

Source: *Scientific American*, 5 June 1852

★ ★ ★

In 1891, Mrs S. W. Culp of Morrisville, Illinois, while breaking coal to bring into the house, found a section of chain whose either ends were firmly embedded in two pieces of coal which had recently formed just one solid piece.

Source: *The Morrisonville Times*, 11 June 1891

★ ★ ★

Back in the 1870s or early 1880s, a rancher from Colorado, USA, found a thimble in a piece of coal. Mr J. Q. Adams, in his report to the *American Antiquarian*, described it as being made of iron, marked somewhat like modern thimbles, with a slight shoulder at the base. Due to its being handled so much, some parts of it had crumbled away, with the remainder being so flaky that it could have been easily disintegrated by picking at it.

The coal came from the Marshal coal bed which at that time was owned and mined by one man. A long horizontal passage, 150 feet long, had been cut into the side of a hill, following the seam of coal. At its furthermost point, the depth below the surface was about 300 feet, from where the coal containing the thimble had been taken. Much of the coal from this mine is young, and too 'green' to burn well. A Professor Haydn classed the coal as lignitic, originating from the Cretaceous and Tertiary periods.

The rancher, Mr Adams' friend, had collected the coal and returned home. Putting some coal on the stove, he noticed that it was not burning well and so broke open the larger chunks. In one of these chunks he found the thimble, embedded in a small cavity, full of sand and coal and not greatly distorted.

Source: J. Q. Adams; *American Antiquarian*, 5:331–332, 1883
Reprinted in: *Ancient Man*, William R. Corliss

★ ★ ★

In 1937, Mrs Myrna R. Burdick and her mother found a metal spoon in soft Pennsylvania coal. A lump of ash had remained after the coal had been burnt, which, when disturbed, fell apart revealing the spoon. The Smithsonian Institute examined it, but, of course, did not believe that it could have been found in coal.

Source: Harry V. Wiant; *Creation Research Society Quarterly*, 13:74, 1976
Reprinted in: *Ancient Man*, William R. Corliss

FOOTPRINTS OF ANCIENT MAN

Footprints and tracks can sometimes be more liable to fossilization than actual remains. The reason is simple: you cannot eat a footprint. Tracks are found throughout the fossil record, even in the most ancient fossil deposits, 675 million years old. For a track to be fossilized, the first requirement is a softish medium – clay or sticky mud is ideal, or sediments on the sea floor. The impressions are made by some passing creature and are then covered over by a layer of a different grain size or by an altogether different material, maybe sand or silt from a flood. This difference forms a natural boundary at the level of the footprint which, when the material is later buried deep and compressed into rock or slate, manifests as a natural fault at which the rock is liable to fracture when hit with a geologist's hammer. Footprints are similarly preserved in volcanic ash that soon after has been covered over by lava.

In 1852, the detailed impression of a boy's foot was found embedded in clay stone on the east bank of the Connecticut River, a little to the south of Hadley, Massachusetts. Preserved alongside it were the tracks of four-footed animals, snails and birds, including what appeared to be those of a crow. The impression of the markings on the bottom of the crow's feet were so detailed that the pattern of its skin could be observed. Further, the pattern of raindrops that had fallen on the soft clay could also be seen, 'and were not entirely obliterated by the foot of the boy. All the striae and lines upon the sole of the foot appear distinctly. . . .'

The bed of clay stone had lain under twenty feet of alluvial sand which had been washed away by the stream. Its estimated age was not given.

Source: *The American Journal of Science and Arts*, May 1855

Undisputed dinosaur tracks exist on the flat rock bed of the Paluxy River near Glen Rose in Texas. Alongside them, however, are a smaller number of human footprints. During the American depression of the 1920s, some of the residents used sledge hammers and chisels to carve out huge chunks of the rock containing these footprints and, by their own admission, were not averse to carving out some new tracks, too, evolving a method of artificially ageing them using acid.

This has usually been enough to satisfy the orthodoxy that the human footprints required no further investigation. However, Jim Ryals and his wife were amongst the track sellers of the 1920s and he described to investigators how to distinguish real footprints from the imitation, indicating that the footprint manufacturers were quite aware of the difference between real prints and the fake.

> First [in the real prints], the pressure of the foot usually pushed up a ridge of mud around the outside of the track. Second, if the track is broken open or sawed, pressure lines [from the weight of the original body] can be found beneath the surface. Furthermore . . . when the [real] tracks were chiselled out of the riverbed, the workman was usually very careful to do his chiselling a good distance from the track for fear of damaging it. This resulted in a rather wide circle of the limestone surrounding the footprint.

Presumably, a maker of fake footprints would have taken a smallish piece of rock into his workshop, there chiselling out their modern imitation. This exploitation of the tourist industry might have been the end of the controversy had not geologist John Green and Jack Walper, Professor of Geology from Texas Christian University, re-opened the discussion in 1976 with some laborious field research. By means of pumps and diversions, they managed to empty parts of the river from areas where the water usually flowed, revealing both dinosaur and human prints.

Significantly, all of them had the tell-tale encircling ridge where the pressure of the footprint had pushed up the original mud. To have perpetrated a fake, the fraudsters would not only have needed to work under water. They would have had to chisel away a large area of rock all around the prints in order to have produced the effect of the raised rim.

The size of these submerged prints was about 18 inches long by 5 to 7 inches wide, indicating a person or persons of 9 or 10 feet in height. If these prints are all that they seem to be then not only did the trees and animals come big in Mesozoic times, but so did the humans! It was the style of the times.

Sources: *Man, Dinosaur and History*, Frederick P. Beierle
Bible-Science Newsletter, 15 April 1971
Pursuit, Fall 1976

★   ★   ★

What may be the oldest possibly human fossil footprint was found in June 1968 by amateur fossil collector, William J. Meister. He, his wife and two daughters had gone on a fossil-hunting expedition to Antelope Springs, 43 miles to the west of Delta, Utah, accompanied by Mr and Mrs Francis Shape and their two daughters. This is hardly a party to take along if you were considering the perpetration of a fraud.

They had already found several trilobite fossils when Meister split open a 2-inch slab of rock with his hammer, revealing what appeared to be a trilobite, partially covered by a human footprint. More surprisingly, the foot appeared to be wearing a sandal. Its dimensions were about 10.25 inches long and 3.5 inches wide, with the heel more deeply impressed than the sole, as would have been the case with a human footprint.

Meister did his best to find a university geologist to look at it. But since trilobites became extinct about 280 million years ago, no one was willing. So Meister went to the local newspaper and before long the story hit the national press.

On 20 July 1968, Dr Clifford Burdick, a consultant geologist from Tucson, Arizona, on a trip to the Antelope Springs site, also found an imprint of a child's foot in a bed of shale. Due to the great age of the shale, expert opinions differed as to the origin of the footprint. However, according to the report:

> The rock chanced to fracture along the front of the toes before the fossil footprint was found. On cross section, the fabric of the rock stands out in fine laminations, or bedding planes [successive layers of sediment]. Where the toes pressed into the soft material, the laminations were bowed downward from the horizontal, indicating a weight that had been pressed into the mud.

In August of the same year, Mr Dean Bitter, who worked for the Salt Lake City Public Schools system, found two further foot impressions, both wearing some kind of footwear.

Sources: *Bible-Science Newsletter*, August–September, 1969
Creation Research Society Quarterly, December 1968

In 1927, Alfred Knapp found the impression of a leather shoe in Triassic limestone, over 200 million years old, at Fisher Canyon, Pershing County, Nevada. Microphotographs revealed that the shoe had been hand-stitched with a finer thread than was customarily used by the shoemakers of 1927.

Source: *Mysteries of Time and Space*, Brad Steiger

★   ★   ★

Probably one of the most controversial sets of footprints is that of the 'Laetoli family' found at Laetoli in Tanzania, beneath a layer of volcanic ash in the 1970s. The reason for the controversy (rather than the usual disbelief) is that they were discovered by the famous Kenyan anthropologist, Mary Leakey. The discoveries of Louis and Mary Leakey and later of their son Richard are famous and considered respectable by the scientific fraternity.

This particular find, however, is dated at 3.75 million years – far too old for any of the modern theories of human evolution. The footprints are those of three barefoot individuals, walking over a distance of 90 feet. Recent studies by Dr Russell Tuttle and colleagues at the University of Chicago, comparing the footprints with walking patterns of seventy Machiguenga people from high in the Peruvian Andes, who habitually go barefoot, exactly matched those found below the ancient volcanic ash. Foot lengths and strides were matched with the Machiguenga and based on this comparison, one of the 'family' was a child, while the other two were larger – one 4 feet high and the other 4 feet 8 inches. Various solutions to the group suggest themselves: three children, or a mother, father and child – and so on.

Mary Leakey was an ardent evolutionist, but her find remains the centre of an acrimonious controversy because, according to the modern theory, man is not supposed to have stepped out until 1 or 2 million years ago. 3.5 million years is simply too old!

Source: *Journal of Archaeological Science* 17: 347–362

★   ★   ★

ANCIENT HUMAN SKELETONS

In a 1873 edition of the *Anthropological Institute Journal*, Frank Calvert writes:

I have had the good fortune to discover, in the vicinity of the Dardanelles, conclusive proofs of the existence of man during the Miocene period of the Tertiary age. From the face of a cliff composed of strata of that period, at a geological depth of eight hundred feet, I have myself extracted a fragment of the joint of a bone of either a *dinotherium* or a mastodon, on the convex side of which is deeply incised the unmistakable figure of a horned quadruped, with arched neck, lozenge-shaped chest, long body, straight fore-legs, and broad feet. There are also traces of seven or eight other figures which, together with the hind quarters of the first, are nearly obliterated. The whole design encircles the exterior portion of the fragment, which measures nine inches in diameter and five inches in thickness. I have also found in different parts of same cliff, not far from the site of the engraved bone, a flint flake and some bones of animals, fractured longitudinally, obviously by the hand of man for the purpose of extracting the marrow, according to the practice of all primitive races.

The writer then goes on to describe the strata in which the relics were found as Miocene in date, due to the fossil species discovered there. A dating which had been confirmed by various authorities, whom he names. He finally adds:

It is not more than forty or fifty years since the possibility of man's having come into being at an earlier period than the received term of six thousand years was first discussed; and it is only quite recently that geologists, upon the evidence furnished by the Quaternary drift, are agreed to assign him an antiquity of about one hundred thousand years. Some suspected traces of his existence have indeed been noticed in the Pliocene and Miocene formations, but not sufficiently marked to be conclusive.

Source: Frank Calvert, *Anthropological Institute Journal,*
3:127-129, 1873
Reprinted in: *Ancient Man,* William R. Corliss

In 1866, an almost completely mineralized human skull of modern type was found 130 feet below ground in the gold-bearing gravels of the Sierra Nevada in California. J. D. Whitney, head of the California Geological Survey, identified the stratum in which the skull was found as Pliocene, dating it at about 2 million years or more. The skull has become known as the Calaveras skull.

There was considerable evidence of human industry in the same stratum and in 1880, in an extensive report, Whitney listed dozens of stone mortars and other human artefacts. Although Whitney had been a regular contributor to the *American Journal of Science,* his controversial 30-page report could only find publication in the relatively obscure *Memorandum of the Museum of Harvard College*. There is a reprint of a lithograph of the skull in *In the Minds of Men*. Incidentally, Whitney was a believer in Darwinian evolution.

Sources: *Memorandum of the Museum of Harvard College*, 1880
　　　　Reprinted in: *In the Minds of Men*, Ian T. Taylor, 1984

★　★　★

A human skull, completely mineralized to iron and manganese oxides and hydrates was found in a 100 million year old coal bed near Freiberg (East Germany) and described in detail by Karsten, in 1842.

To decide whether the skull was actually a geological anachronism that had somehow found its way into the coal at a much later period, one must consider the conditions under which coal is formed. We have described the considerable pressure and heat required for the formation of coal. The South Wales coalfields in Britain, for example, were buried under younger sediments to depths of between 10,000 and 15,000 feet, before the coal was formed.

The pressure generated by the weight of average sediments is about 1 pound per square inch for each foot of burial. This is what compresses them into hard limestone or sandstone, for instance. At depths of 10,000 feet, therefore, the pressure is nearly 5 tons per square inch. So if one supposes that the Freiburg skull would have borne the pressure on 30 square inches of its surface, then the overall pressure on it would have been 150 tons. More than enough for a severe headache!

Bones, being hollow and porous structures are soon disintegrated when buried in coal or mineral sediments, as are many other fossils. The only way they can survive such pressure is by being totally encased – within and without – in the sediment. And then they only stand a chance of avoiding collapse, if the pressure on the inside somehow remains equal to that on the outside. So a skull is soon crushed inwards and disintegrated under the tremendous pressures. And even small plates of bone, since they are cellular and not totally solid structures, are soon crushed and destroyed. Solid shells and exoskeletons that present only two surface areas always remain the best candidates for fossilization.

All the same, there must be some sequence of geological circumstances that could have resulted in the survival of one lone skull of a man who fell – or was buried – in a bog 100 million years ago.

Though whether the Freiburg skull was genuine is no longer possible to tell, for it has long since disappeared. But the incident does highlight how difficult it is for the bones of terrestrial animals to survive. Even the bones of a community of human beings lost in a volcanic disaster and buried under ash, or those smothered in a mud slide, would have stood little better chance of survival and discovery.

Source: *Geology of Coal*, Otto Stutzer, 1940
Reprinted in: *In the Mind of Men*, Ian T. Taylor, 1984

★   ★   ★

A human skeleton, complete except for the head and feet, was found embedded in an exceptionally hard Miocene limestone in the French Caribbean island of Guadaloupe in 1812. Although the bones were dislocated and twisted, they were all in their correct places and fully articulate. The skeleton was that of a woman about 5 feet 2 inches and was fully described by Konig in 1814 in the prestigious *Philosophical Transactions of the Royal Society*, illustrated with an excellent engraving (see Figure 9.1). The specimen was on display at the British Museum for more than 50 years.

Figure 9.1   Photographic reproduction of the engraving made of the female skeleton from Guadaloupe, found in Miocene limestone estimated to be 28 million years old. Published in Philosophical Transactions of the Royal Society, 1814. *Reproduced by permission of the Syndics of Cambridge University Library.*

A second specimen was found in the same limestone at about the same time and described in *Recherches* by the French scientist Cuvier in 1812. The age of the limestone was estimated to be greater than 28 million years.

Source: Konig, *Philosophical Transactions of the Royal Society*,
London, 1814

★   ★   ★

The above are only a few of the anomalous finds on record. While there may be a perfectly natural explanation for some of them, that fits the modern theory, not all can be so easily discounted. I have placed them in a separate chapter because such evidence is by no means essential to the suggestions I have been putting forward. However, they do enable one to realize that when evidence contradicting established opinion is found, it is rarely given serious consideration or receives the professional attention it merits.

10. MAN THE FOSSIL

Despite the paucity of data in the fossil record, we find indications that all classes of life form – when they are considered as expressions of consciousness and as crystallizations of subtle, inner patterns – have existed together since at least Palaeozoic times. The only exception seems to have been man.

But I am suggesting that man, too, has been here all along. Why? Well, from the mystic point of view, we have already noted that it is only in man's form that the quintessence of the Creator's game of love can be played out. In a sense, it is only because of man that the entire physical creation exists. Does that sound overly anthropocentric or too much like religious dogma?

The followers of many religions believe it blindly, stating that man alone of all species is created in God's image. But the mystic meaning of this statement has been mostly lost, either in a literal belief in an anthropoid God or in theological and intellectual hair-splitting. All the same, this mystic reality has been independently taught by all the great mystics of the world, whatever their time or culture. And it is upon their teachings that man has commonly founded his religions. The essence of their teachings, however, is an inner experience of the mystic reality. This is the hidden or secret teaching that cannot be expressed in words because it is an ineffable experience altogether beyond words. Without access to this experience, man misunderstands the teachings of the mystics, narrowing them down into the confines of ritual and dogma. Yet it is from this mystic reality, dimly perceived and largely misunderstood, that the conventional creationists have taken their stance.

Being made in God's image simply means that the essence of the soul is God, and that man is the only form who is constructed in such a way that he can realize this. Souls in other forms must first come up to man's estate before they can really begin the path to God-realization. And since the purpose of creation is for God to play the game of love in all its degrees, including its consummation, so man will always be present in the physical universe.

Nevertheless, the received scientific opinion is that man has appeared upon the scene only in the last 2 to 4 million years. This time-span fits the Darwinian theory and modern man's opinion of himself as the highest kind of human who has ever existed, our modern civilization being portrayed as the acme of man's evolution. Even Neanderthal man of 50,000 years ago, a mere wink of the geological eye, is portrayed as something inferior to ourselves.

Ancient man, in the scenario I present, would have had much the same nature as he has today, inwardly being made up of all the five tattwas. His outward form may have varied somewhat, but not the essential nature of the inner man. Just as ancient invertebrates, fishes, reptiles and higher animals would have had similar levels of consciousness and intelligence to their modern counterparts, so too would ancient man.

Man, therefore, would have buried, cremated or otherwise *disposed* of his dead. The solution is so simple that it could easily be overlooked or discarded. If man has always been inwardly constructed in more or less the same manner as he is today, then we would hardly expect to find traces of his existence. Are there, for example, any ancient human remains in the area where you live? At the most, such remains go back two or three thousand years, in burial grounds. Only in extremely rare instances do they extend back beyond that.

Very few remains of man are ever found, even of recent times, because our nature is such that when the Life Force departs, we usually dispose of our fellow humans in some becoming and decorous manner. Burying, cremation, casting upon the waters and other means are all processes which very rapidly result in the elimination of all traces of an individual's existence. This is either out of respect for the dead or out of the fear and sense of inexplicable loss which the remaining relatives experience. Or it is simply a matter of hygiene. Man's bone structure, too, is light and readily consumed by other creatures, large or small. This is why our teeth and skull take longer to disappear. They are the strongest and most enduring parts of our physical anatomy. Additionally, the skull is the part least readily confused with the bones of other creatures.

The remains of man are scant indeed, dating back – temporarily disregarding the anomalies – to between 2 and 4 million years, at the most. This does not even take us back to the last Sat yuga. Only in the driest regions of Africa have really aged remains been found, and these, geologically, are classifiable as belonging to the present era. The ice ages and temperate climates of the less arid zones ensure that the normal processes of life dispose of all edible pieces as time goes by. The earliest relics of human habitation in Britain, for example, date back only half a million years, and these remains are flints, not bones or teeth. Discoveries of these ancient stone tools have been made at Boxgrove in Sussex and in Norfolk gravel pits.

Millions upon millions of humans die every year, but none of their bones will ever be found in the fossil record, even just a million years from now, let alone 10 or a 100 million years hence. If we are assuming that man has always been a man, then we have to throroughly root out and discard all conditioned and preconceived notions that ancient man exhibited primitive behaviour, leaving his friends and relatives to rot and moulder where they fell. This, quite simply, is not his nature. All cultures have developed a tidy means for disposing of their dead. Where, then, is the opportunity for fossilization? Only, perhaps, in certain accidents or murder are bodies left to take their chances where they fall. Even then, very few ever find some place where their remains are not rapidly consumed by the local wildlife, great or small.

Generally, then, the possibility of man leaving any fossilized remains is highly remote. And the chances of our finding them, millions of years later, is remoter still. Sometimes, perhaps, a body was laid in a cave as a burial chamber, or a solitary human may have died alone in a cave, with no one to dispose of his remains. But even then the chances are distant that any bone will survive.

For much of the time, there may well have been far fewer humans than there are today, further diluting the possibility of our ever discovering remains. Furthermore, man – being intelligent – does not usually fall into sedimentary deposits where his bones may be preserved.

So if we consider that man had always disposed of his dead in ways similar to present times, then this alone would account completely for his absence from the fossil record. It is only cases of misadventure or perhaps in murder or warfare, when man is left to lie and decay in the very place where he died. And very few humans are left to lie like that. In Africa and China, the climate has helped preserve some ancient bones for a slightly longer period, but in temperate zones such remains are rapidly recycled.

This scenario fits the facts of the fossil record just as well, perhaps better, than the evolutionary explanation. More especially because of the lack of *any* evidence that one kind of creature has ever turned into any other creature that is radically different. And certainly no missing link has ever been found, connecting ape and man. Piltdown Man, the only missing link ever found, turned out to be a deliberate attempt at fraud or a practical joke that went too far.

Many folk may find it difficult to accept that man has been present all along and, indeed, that the whole panorama of life has been in existence right from the beginning. Old thought habits, learnt in childhood and reinforced by universities, TV documentaries and the media, die hard.

SOME GENERAL THOUGHTS ON ANCESTRY

What, then, is the fossil history that we have of man? The answer is: not much. But let us look at it, all the same, and see if it supports or opposes our ideas.

Man is classified as a primate. Primates are placental mammals characterized by flexible hands and feet, opposable first digits making a finger and thumb, good eyesight and, in the higher apes, a well-developed brain. They first appear in the fossil record quite early on compared to the advent of other modern-looking mammals – back in the Cretaceous, still in the days of the dinosaurs. That is even before the more modern versions of mammal had put in an appearance.

This, of course, is somewhat embarrassing to evolution-minded palaeontologists, who mostly appear to avoid the issue altogether. For if man's supposed ancestors have been around for over 65 million years and if man is supposed to have taken only 2 to 4 million years to appear upon the scene, then why did he not evolve so many millions of years ago? What took him so long? Especially when the remainder of modern mammals all appear to have their more recognizable counterparts commencing in the Eocene, 20 or 30 million years later.

And again, if all kinds of ape and monkey are present amongst the species today, then why are there no gradations between ape and man? Most radiations of species in the fossil record that can actually be traced show that ancestors are rarely replaced by the more recent forms, but all go on co-existing happily together. A glance at the ammonoid family tree (Figure 5.2 page 122) will confirm that. So why are there none of the intermediate ape–human species still present on the planet? And why are there none even in the fossil record?

Man is so radically different in his inner potential to any other species. Physically speaking, he is not even so very well adapted. By normal biological standards, he is a generalist with a big head – that is, a big brain. But if brains were everything, man would already appear to be on the decline, for our Neanderthal predecessors had a larger average brain capacity than ourselves, only 35,000 or 50,000 years ago.

Neanderthal peoples were not the hairy, grotesque ape-men of our school education. They were strong, vigorous, healthy and intelligent enough to survive in ice age Europe from at least 100,000 years ago until the race seems to have declined 35,000 years back. Their lives, perhaps, had similarities to those of the Eskimos of North America, or the tribes living on the high tundras of Mongolia, both still living under glacial circumstances. Archaeological finds at Neanderthal sites indicate that they used toothpicks, probably kept gardens and certainly had some highly-skilled flint-knappers in their society.

Man's features, including his skull and skeletal structure, vary considerably even amongst our modern races. This itself is of interest for whilst almost all mammals have only relatively small variations in size and other features, the human species possesses an amazing capacity for diversity.

African pigmies are little more than 4.5 feet high, while people of many other races characteristically attain heights of well over 6 feet. The Chinese, Japanese and southern Indians are usually small-structured, while the Sikhs of northern India are often broad-shouldered, tall and well-built people.

Eye sockets, cheekbones, the forehead, the general shape of the skull, the jaws and the teeth – all these vary considerably from one human to another and all varieties can look intelligent, becoming and beautiful. But the eye-brow ridges of the mid-Pleistocene man of Europe, Asia and Africa, dubbed *Homo erectus*, are often used in artistic impressions to portray him as stupid and brutish. The same is true of Neanderthal man. But such ridges are still found in the people of at least one Indian community, the Munda from the Nappur Hills, where they quite definitely enhance the potential beauty of their race.

Our modern race of humans, who appear in a variety of shapes, sizes and colours, are all thought to be descendants of the Cro-Magnon race, classified – because their skulls and skeletons are shaped like ours – as *Homo sapiens*, Man the Wise, an interesting self-given, epithet. The name Cro-Magnon, incidentally, is that of the cave in the Dordogne area of southern France where the first remains were found in 1868. Neanderthal man is named after the Neander valley, near the German city of Dusseldorf, where the first of his bones were found in a cave, by quarrymen, in 1857.

Whether man really lived entirely in caves during those days is open to dispute. Stone dwellings carved out of the rock or taking advantage of other natural features of the terrain may well have been in use. We too use mostly rock, earth and wood to build our homes. It is certainly more likely that the remains of ancient man would be found in a dry cave than out upon the open land, but one cannot therefore assume that he lived only in caves. He may have built igloos, cottages, houses and even palaces, too! Earth and wood would have long since crumbled into dust and been recycled by natural processes. And there is nothing to suggest that he had no decoration in his dwellings, nor doors or screens to his caves, if such were deemed necessary. The beautifully executed cave paintings from many places in the world demonstrate that amongst the ancient race of men were those possessed of a fine aesthetic sense, as in present times.

Generally speaking, thatched and waterproof cottages are a more comfortable, less dismal and an altogether dryer environment than dark, damp, rock caves. Caves are rarely dry and many drip incessantly from water seeping through the earth above. Perhaps ancient man used them purely for storage purposes, as workshops or for religious and social occasions. In any case, there are so few caves. Certainly not enough to accomodate a thriving community of humans.

Some palaeontologists, preferring a neat linear perspective, even argue that Cro-Magnon man 'evolved' rapidly out of Neanderthal man only 50,000 years ago, whilst others point to evidence that Cro-Magnon man was, at least for some while, Neanderthal's contemporary and spread from Africa and the Middle East in a migration already underway 50,000 or more years ago. So even as little as 50,000 years ago, man's antecedents are unclear to us, whilst remains are few and far between. How, then, can we be so sure of our remoter past?

Massive movements of human populations across the face of our planet are a recurrent feature of man's history, as any human knows if he studies just a little of his own country's history. Our pale-skinned, Caucasian race are members of the Persian or Indian Aryan race, who are thought to have spread from the East many centuries ago. (In Sanskrit, *arya* means one of noble birth. And spiritually, to take birth as a human is to possess the noblest of all potentials: God-realization.)

In recent millennia, such migration has almost always entailed bloodshed and warfare and one wonders how well the Cro-Magnon and Neanderthal humans co-existed. 50,000–100,000 years ago was still the Kal yuga – though in an earlier phase. So perhaps they were kinder to each other than our own pale-skinned race has been to older, and often wiser, peoples. Difference in appearance, culture, thought processes and convention often generates mistrust, at least in modern times, so perhaps they too held prejudices and thoughts of superiority about each other. One wonders, for example, if they intermarried? There is some evidence for this. Romeo and Juliet is, after all, one of the oldest stories in the world.

And if that ancient race really did originate in Africa or the East, what colour were they? Supposing they were brown or black, then at least within the last few thousand years they have acquired a different and genetically transmitted skin coloration. For the typical northern Europeans are blond and fair-skinned, the mid-Europeans are of a predominantly mousy colour, while the southerners are dark-haired and olive in complexion. How? This can hardly have been by natural selection of random mutations.

It is certainly an advantage from the point of view of health to be fair in northern climes and darker where the sun shines more intensely. But how did man become so geographically adapted in such a short space of time? Is this an example of the environmentally stimulated emergence and transmission of genetically encoded characteristics? Does every human possess the genetic potential to be any colour? A colour which – given time – is brought out by environmental circumstances? Or has man been in Europe for far longer than we think?

Going further back in time, the remains of man become remarkably rare and there is little evidence of our existence even so 'recently' as a million years ago. All the same, just one unambiguously identified bone, footprint or artefact is enough to establish man's presence at that time. We have seen how the earliest fossilized birds and insects come from eras tens of millions of years from the period of their more common appearance.

During the Sat yugas, man is also said to be of a highly subtle, almost ethereal nature, drawing his energy like a ghost or astral being from the subtle energies of the life within him, and leaving few fossilizable remains. At least, if the ancient sages were correct and he really lives for 100,000 years, life here must be far less wearing at those times!

One of the major practical problems encountered in tracing man's ancestry is that apart from our brain size, there is very little in our skeletal structure to distinguish us from the apes. Complete skulls of ancient man or primate are rare and though one can, perhaps, distinguish an ape if one is lucky enough to discover his long arm bones, it is remarkably difficult, even in modern times, to tell whether a jawbone, a tooth, a piece of skull or a vertebra come from ape or man. So anything older than a few million years is almost automatically discounted as being other than human.

Moreover, if man was even two or three feet taller at some periods of the ancient past, then his arms and legs would have been longer. Perhaps enough to make a modern palaeontologist think that he was looking at an ape and not a man if all he had to go on was an arm – and especially if the dating did not match the preconceived evolutionary schedule for man's arrival. As a result, any findings of really ancient man may well have been misinterpreted. Back in the 1960s, for instance, Vincent Sarich of the University of California at Berkeley flatly declared that any fossil older than eight million years could not be human, not matter what it looked like. And the attitude still persists, reflecting the characteristic approach of modern palaeo-anthropology (the study of man's ancestry).

ANOTHER ODDITY CONCERNING MAN'S ARRIVAL

There is another odd aspect to the orthodox tale of man's arrival. As we have discussed, thoughout the fossil record we find evidence that extinctions and re-proliferations have occurred on a cyclic basis. The last great proliferation was at the start of the present cycle, the Pliocene, some 10 million years ago. The proliferation lasted for 2 or 3 million years, perhaps, but no radically new species have come into being since then. In fact, since the onset of the present ice age, for the last 1 million years or so, we have been losing species at an ever-increasing rate.

Yet, evolutionists would have us believe that man alone has bucked the trend of hundreds of millions of years and within a very short span of time, while either stasis or extinction ruled the day amongst all other species, evolution has gone ahead and produced the so-called (but self-styled) pinnacle of her success, man himself.

MONKEY OR MISSING LINK?

About 1700 fossil bone fragments, implicated by scientists in man's ancestry, have been discovered in Africa during this century. They span the last 4 million years and are the subject of continuous and considerable scientific controversy and confusion. One of the major problems is that the information that can be derived from the majority of these bones is so inconclusive that every new significant find results in a major, often radical revision of the evolutionary story. This underlines the point that the real differences between creatures is in their degree of intelligence and their level of consciousness, not in their bones.

The most prevalent evolutionary theory to emerge is that the line which led to man originated in Africa between 5 and 10 million years ago. So for the older bones, the question becomes simple: was the creature who once possessed them ape or human? Or something in-between?

The oldest of these bones belonged to a number of related species from the family *Australopithecus*, and Darwinian theory demands that one or other of them (or some very close ancestor) *must* be part of a human evolutionary lineage. They are simply the nearest thing around that even begins to fit the bill. Yet their nearest living relative is not man but the chimpanzee.

In the 1960s, the accepted idea was that our human ancestor was *Ramapithecus*, a 14 million year old Miocene primate. This implied a divergence of the ape and human lines of descent between 15 and 20 million years ago. *Ramapithecus*, it was thought, was already on the way to becoming human and nothing else. Evidence from the molecular biologists, however, showed that chimpanzees and gorillas possessed only a 1 per cent difference in their DNA from humans. This small difference, they argued, would have been far greater had man and apes diverged 20 million years ago. Man therefore could not have diverged from the apes so far back into the past.

Arguments in the 1970s were heated. On the one hand, the palaeoanthropologists relied entirely upon the structure of bones and teeth as evidence. On the other, the molecular biologists argued for a closer relationship between man and chimpanzee on the grounds of similarity in their DNA. But after more than twenty years of arguments, the palaeoanthropologists have finally stood down and nowadays, *Ramapithecus* is relegated, once again, to the status of a monkey. In fact, it is not even clear whether *Ramapithecus* has any modern descendants at all.

Perhaps more than any other branch of palaeontology, the study of humanoid fossils is largely a matter of interpretation. The emotional temperature, too, can run high whenever our ancestry is discussed — by scientists or anyone else. Such emotion and heated difference of opinion only arise when both the stakes are high and the evidence is inconclusive. In fact, quite apart from the arguments between the creationists and the material evolutionists, it is amongst the evolutionists themselves – those who all consider that man has evolved from the apes – that some of the greatest disagreements have arisen. These disagreements are largely concerned with which apes – ancient or modern – are our nearest relatives and whether some of the ancient finds were really ape or human.

Fossil fragments of various forms or species of australopithecine have turned up in Africa, spanning a period of roughly 1.5 million years, from about 3.25 million to 1.75 million years ago. They were small, about 3.5 feet in height, probably spent a good deal of time up in trees and could also be bipedal on the ground. They possessed large and powerful back teeth suitable for cracking nuts and chewing fibrous material, and lived off fruits, nuts, roots and other vegetarian fare. They also had small brains, not much larger – if at all – than the modern chimpanzee and gorilla.

The first discovery of an australopithecine fossil was made in 1924 by Raymond Dart in the limeworks at Taung in southern Africa and many other odds and ends have turned up since, including some more complete parts. 'Nutcracker Man', for example, was a skull uncovered by Louis and Mary Leakey in Olduvai Gorge, Tanzania, in 1959 and the 'Black Skull' was unearthed in 1985 by their son Richard Leakey with his colleague Alan Walker, on the shores of Lake Turkana in northern Kenya.

But perhaps the most famous of australopithecine finds was 'Lucy', an almost complete 3 million year old skeleton from Ethiopia, discovered in 1974 by Don Johanson in the Afar desert. Like all her kind, Lucy had a brain pretty much the size of a chimp and had adaptations which helped her to climb trees as well as (probably) to walk with a bipedal gait. She has been described as a 'bipedal chimpanzee'.

Most scientists readily concur that, in all respects, *Australopithecus* is far more like a chimpanzee than a human. So if man did evolve from an earlier version of *Australopithecus* then he has had to change far more than a chimpanzee in the last 5 million years. In fact, there are actually two species of chimpanzees – the common chimpanzee and the rarer Pigmy chimp. And Pigmy chimps are more frequently bipedal than the common species, bringing *Australopithecus* and modern chimps even closer.

Evolutionists presently disagree as to whether australopithecine specimens like Lucy are actually on the main line of human evolution or are a side branch that split off from an earlier ancestor. Much of the scientific debate centres on whether the australopithecines had thumbs and fingers. Unfortunately, none of the specimens come with the tiny bones that make up complete hands and feet. These could have told us much concerning her way of life and whether it could in any way have been human.

Human hands are remarkably sensitive, capable of making and manipulating the tools and equipment that our minds devise. Many creatures *use* tools. Even amoeba incorporate tiny sand grains into their cell wall, passing some on to their progeny when they divide. One of Darwin's famous Galapagos finches uses a cactus spine for winkling grubs and other small creatures out of crevices. And chimpanzees use sticks and stones for various purposes. But the actual *making* of tools is indicative of the discriminating foresight and planning which characterizes man. Before one makes a tool one must have a purpose and a plan in mind. The ability – and the hands to execute it – are therefore particularly crucial to any potential candidate for human ancestry.

It is not immediately obvious why the adoption of a bipedal gait should be linked to a higher intelligence. But it is certainly a human characteristic and it does free the hands to perform the manipulative functions our minds so cleverly concoct. Without our hands free we could not accomplish nearly as much as we do. In the evolutionist's mind, therefore, the route to being human necessarily includes acquisition of the ability to walk upright on your rear legs.

Apes are not as stable on the ground as humans, because their feet are also adapted for climbing trees. They have their big toes opposed to the other toes, for example, ideal for grasping branches and their hands are also well-adapted for a semi-arboreal life. Whilst on the ground they can walk on two legs, but for really getting about they go down onto all fours, walking or running on the knuckles of their hands.

But there are simply not enough bones available for us to know whether Lucy had hands sensitive enough to make tools or had feet adapted enough for her to have been comfortably and frequently bipedal. Australopithecines may perhaps have had cleverer hands than chimpanzees. But with a brain the size of a chimp, they are unlikely to have possesed the human degree of consciousness and foresight that would have enabled them to use those hands in a human fashion.

Consequently, the evidence remains inconclusive. And in any event, being adapted for living on the ground or even having clever hands would not automatically have made Lucy and her kin human.

Australopithecines also exhibited yet another chimp-like characteristic: they grew up faster. Their rate of growth can be determined from the growth layers found in tooth enamel, visible as lines which result from their seven or eight day growth cycle. Since the length of the cycle appears to be constant in primates, regardless of body size, it provides a neat in-built biological clock, enabling researchers to determine the age at death of many of the fossil hominids. It also enables them to calculate their rate of growth. And australopithecines grew up like chimpanzees.

For man, the possession of akash means that maturity entails far more than sexual growth. No other creature has a sense of morality and ethics. No other creature can learn quite so much and so widely as can man. No other creature possesses our kind of language. No other creature has so much choice in matters good or bad. Childhood and adolescence are meant to be a time when some of these fundamental human attributes are developed. The long period it takes for a human being to mature is indicative of all this. But Lucy and her kin grew up fast, like chimpanzees.

All the evidence, then, points to australopithecines being ancient relatives of the chimpanzee. Why then are they called hominoid? The answer is that they are the nearest that palaeoanthropologists can find to anything even remotely resembling a human ancestor. And given that man must (they say) have evolved from the apes, then the australopithecines are the nearest best fit. No wonder they debate whether they are on the main line of development or they split off some while earlier.

But to put an end to the debate, what we would really like is to meet one and to observe its mind and way of life. Five minutes would probably be enough to observe its degree of intelligence and consciousness. But this we cannot do from a few old bones! What is certainly true is that if there were any better candidates, then the australopithecines would be immediately dropped. In other words, the theory of their involvement in human ancestry exists entirely because of the evolutionary theory. And if that theory were dropped then the attempts to make the australopithecines more humanoid than chimpanzees would be immediately discarded.

HOMO HABILIS, HOMO ERECTUS AND HOMO SAPIENS:
MAN BY ANY OTHER NAME?

The case is entirely different when we study the clearly genuine relics of our own species. Dating back to times concurrent with the later australopithecines, up to 2.3 million years ago, palaeoanthropologists identify two 'species' of man: *Homo habilis* (handy or skilful man) and *Homo erectus* (upright man). The modern 'species' of human, which includes Neanderthal man, is known, of course, as *Homo sapiens*.

Predictably, some scientists disagree with this division, again indicating the paucity and inconclusive nature of the evidence. Since the sparse collection of African hominoid remains from between 1.6 and 2.3 million years ago exhibit considerable variety, they suggest that they really represent at least five distinct 'species' of *Homo*.

The first specimen of *Homo habilis* was found in 1960 in the Tanzanian Olduvai Gorge, while the first bones attributed to *Homo erectus* were discovered in Java, Indonesia, back in 1890–92. But at that time, the Dutch scientist Eugene Dubois preferred to think of them more in terms of an ape-like ancestor, no doubt to more accurately fit the missing link theory. He therefore dubbed the species *Pithecanthropus erectus* (erect ape man).

From the skeletons attributed to *Homo habilis*, most of them dated at between 1.6 and 1.9 million years ago, his height appears to have varied between 3.5 and 5 feet and from the archaeological evidence, he is believed to have made stone tools. But the debate surrounding the variant 'species' of *Homo habilis* is confounded, as ever, by the insufficient evidence and some scholars consider that some of the specimens attributed to *Homo habilis* are actually australopithecine.

Not only does it seem that *Homo habilis* made tools; it also seems that he was predominantly right-handed. Handed-ness is an entirely human characteristic and about 90 per cent of all human populations – whatever their nation or culture – are right-handed. No other mammals, not even chimpanzees, possess anything like it. They use both hands as they please. But stone tools from the Koobi Fora site on the east side of Lake Turkana in northern Kenya, dated at 1.5 to 2 million years ago, show all the signs of having been made by predominantly right-handed people.

Stone tools are made by flaking. For a right-handed person, a rounded parent stone is held in the left hand while a hammerstone is used to strike it with the right. At the same time, for a right-handed person looking down on it from above, the stone is slowly rotated clockwise and the flakes that fall from an originally rounded stone have a right-handed aspect: they have a part of the rounded stone on their right side only. Some apparently left-handed flakes may fall by chance or by random hitting, but the majority of flakes will be right-handed.

Seven of the Koobi Fora sites have been examined and all demonstrate the same higher percentage of right-handed flakes over left-handed. Additionally, in trials with two groups of undergraduate flint-knappers, 20 right-handed and 20 left-handed, the resulting flakes also reflected their handed-ness.

As with all crafts, the degree of refinement possible is considerable, perhaps reaching its zenith in the hundreds of small flint tools that have been discovered worldwide as far apart as Australia, India, Africa, Egypt, Sicily, France, and England. In the Indian caves of the Vindhya Hills, small crescent-shaped knives of flint and agate were found. And the first of several English finds, made in the last years of the 19th century in the moorland peat of east Lancashire's Pennine hills, were said to consist of hundreds of tiny flint tools – scrapers, borers and crescent-shaped knives no larger than half an inch. The craftsmanship of the flaking was so high that only under a magnifying glass could it be appreciated. These tools were clearly ornamental, perhaps for religious or other ritual purposes. They were art for art's sake alone and that is not the concept of an unintelligent people.

The making and using of tools tells us something else of great interest. Human brains – as well as hands and feet – are also left and right handed. The fine degree of control required for tool-making appears to be controlled by the left hemisphere and in this same hemisphere are found the areas which control human speech. So could *Homo habilis* also speak? Most like to argue that he could not, for if he could make tools and talk, the idea that he was not yet quite a man begins to evaporate, along with all evolutionary ideas of human origins.

But some scientists do believe that he could speak and Dean Falk of the University of Puerto Rico produced evidence in 1983 that in a cast made from the inside of one of the Koobi Fora skulls, there were impressions of an area known in modern humans as Broca's area, a part of the left hemisphere which controls the throat and mouth muscles during speech.

Unfortunately for palaeoanthropologists, the actual organs of speech – the larynx, tongue and throat – are all composed of soft or cartilaginous tissue, which does not usually fossilize, so the question remains a matter of dispute. There are also other aspects to the discussion, but there are certainly strong indications that the earliest known humans had all the essential human characteristics which we possess today.

The first signs of *Homo erectus* appear about 1.6 million years ago. He was considerably taller than *Homo habilis*, probably reaching heights of over 5.5 feet. Both *Homo habilis* and *Homo erectus* had larger brains than the australopithecines and it is certain that *Homo erectus* made tools, some of them of an exquisite and carefully executed design.

The most complete skeleton of *Homo erectus* was discovered in Kenya in 1984 by Richard Leakey's team and dated at 1.6 million years. Missing the feet, the hands, one arm and some other bones, the skeleton appears to be that of a boy aged about 12, who died on the banks of the River Nariokotome, a few kilometres from the western shores of Lake Turkana. He was strongly built and stood about 5 feet 5 inches high. There were no signs of disease, nor attack by carnivore, nor of any later scavenger, so the cause of his death remains a mystery.

Ancient man also used fire. Findings in 1988 at the South African Swartkrans cave by Bob Brain, director of the Transvaal Museum, and A. Sellen from the University of Capetown, seem to prove that an earlier form of man (possibly *Homo erectus*) also used and controlled fire at least up to 1.5 million years ago.

Prior to this discovery, archaeologists had thought that man did not use fire until his arrival in colder parts of Europe and Asia. There is no firm evidence that fire was used before about 300,000 years ago in these parts, although some sites suggest that it may well have been used as long ago as 700,000 years. The Swartkrans cave discovery therefore pushes back the date of man's earliest recorded use of fire by over a million years. Note, again, our lack of knowledge as to how our ancient ancestors really lived. One discovery changes a significant date by one million years.

Over 270 blackened bones, mostly from species of antelope but also single specimens of zebra, warthog and baboon, have been found at the cave, alongside stone tools and the ancient remains of man. One of the burnt bones was from an australopithecine, indicating that the ancient cousins of chimpanzees were possibly an occasional item of man's early diet, just as monkeys are for many forest tribes today. It seems ironic that a creature heralded by modern man as the closest known cousin of the missing link – if not the missing link itself – should be an item on the menu of early man. Presumably, man at that time did not consider australopithecines to be such close relatives, for there are no signs of cannibalism. From laboratory tests, the bones appear to have been burned in fires reaching over 400°C and they also appear at various levels in the deposits, indicating the regular use of fire over long periods of time.

No creature other than man is able to light and control fire. It requires a high degree of intelligence and the awareness of its potential results. In short, it requires the use of man's foresight, his akash. The man who built these fires, then, was a full man, though his technological skill may not have been so great as ours. But that is no definitive mark of humanity.

In general, modern man seems to be larger than his ancestors with a correspondingly larger brain – just as rabbits have larger brains than mice. But such criteria clearly do not indicate intelligence, per se, even amongst modern humans. No man is given a more responsible job because he has a bigger head than his fellows! Nor are brain sizes taken into account for the purposes of university entrance! Indeed, there is a considerable degree of divergence in brain size even amongst modern humans, varying from 850 to 1700cc, the average today being about 1450cc.

Brain size is more closely related to body size, to the physical sensory and motor aspects of the body, rather than to intelligence or level of consciousness. The bigger the body, then the bigger the physical control system required. An elephant has a bigger brain than any human, but that does not endow it with our human degree of intelligence and perception. What does seem relevant, to some degree, is the *relative* sizes of body and brain, and relative to the size of his body, man does possess a bigger brain than other creatures.

The brain, in any event, exists purely as the physical expression of the mind. But the mind lies in an altogether more subtle sphere of energy. And no scientist understands how brain and mind are 'interfaced'. There is absolutely no coherent and detailed model of brain and mind function. Whether one considers the mind and all aspects of self and consciousness to be mere vapours and by-products of molecules and electromagnetism, or whether one thinks of them as separate though integrated levels of being, there is no real understanding of brain-mind function.

Brain function and genetic processes are probably the two most complex and least understood areas of biology, as almost all scientists will readily agree. So to make any sweeping statements concerning the relationship between brain size and the level of consciousness is unwise. If one were to study any relative proportions, I imagine that a more important one to make would be the size of the body relative to the size of that part of the brain which is not associated with sensory and motor function. But even that delineation is by no means clear, for the two are so closely integrated. And in fossil specimens, with all brain tissue long since departed, we have no way of making such comparative assessments. In the absence of any real knowledge of how brain and mind are interfaced, the matter is fraught with difficulty and potentiality for error.

OUT OF AFRICA?

Since Raymond Dart's discovery in 1924, followed by those of the Leakeys, Johanson and others, Africa has been seen as the evolutionary birthplace of humanity. But this was quite different from the expectations of the early Victorian evolutionists. That white men should have had black ancestors was not an easy thought for them. Surely man would have originated in Europe, the hearth of civilization and the Industrial Revolution? Or perhaps in China, home of the most ancient known civilizations? Indeed when, in 1912, the fraudulent Piltdown Man was unearthed in Sussex, was this not really what everyone had always thought – that the first human had been an Englishman?

Why, though, do we find the earliest remains of our species in Africa? The answer is probably not that Africa is such a good place to live, but merely – borrowing a phrase from geologist Professor Bill Bishop – because it is a good place to die. It is our old friend again: a good place for fossilization. Or, bearing in mind the paucity of human remains even in Africa, a *comparatively better* place to die if you wish to leave a legacy.

The earliest discovery of human remains outside Africa was the Lantian find in China. Designated as belonging to *Homo erectus*, they are dated at nearly 1 million years. China's inaccessibility to the Western world has made it a difficult country in which to conduct research but in the 1930s, not long after the first major African find, excavations at the Zhoukoudian cave near Beijing resulted in what still remains the largest collection of *Homo erectus* fossils ever retrieved from a single locality. Sadly, these fossilized remains were lost during the Japanese occupation of China in 1941, but casts had been made in China and detailed descriptions produced. Furthermore, Chinese scientists are still making discoveries there.

The Zhoukoudian cave contains a collection of bones dating from 500,000 to 200,000 years ago, while sediments higher up the hillside contain far more recent fossils, dated at 20,000 to 50,000 years. How the fossils got into the cave is a matter of dispute. Some suggest that the cave was used by hyenas or other animals who had early man on their menu; others say that it was used as a dwelling. It could also have been employed as an occasional burial chamber or have even been inhabited, from time to time, by solitary humans.

Chinese discoveries are difficult to evaluate because of their un-availability to non-Chinese researchers, but there are two other ancient Chinese finds of relevance. Firstly, a partial skull was recovered from Dali, dated at 150,000 years, possessing a robust and smallish brain case, with a brain capacity of 1050cc, about the size of that possessed by *Homo erectus*.

Secondly, a partial human skull and much of the skeleton, too, was discovered at Jinnui Shan. This skull was thin-walled, with a brain capacity of 1400cc – larger than many modern humans. A more recent date for this fossil might, therefore, have been confidently expected by evolutionary theory, but not a bit of it. The skull is dated at 250,000 years old, 100,000 years older than the Dali find – an uncomfortable anachronism for those attempting to draw a straight evolutionary line of development from lower to higher.

The very existence of such ancient human communities outside Africa also causes problems for those attempting to trace a linear path of human development from African ancestors. *Homo sapiens* is the most recent of our kind to have appeared upon the scene. Considered by conventional evolutionists to be the most evolved of all the human species, he is not supposed to have arrived (albeit in 'archaic' form) until 250,000 years ago. After which date, say the theorists, *Homo erectus* was soon replaced by the new and improved *Homo sapiens*. Who then continued to improve until he became the fine specimen he is today. . . .

The fossil record is clear that *Homo erectus* and *Homo sapiens* were found both in Africa and China. *Homo erectus* also lived in Java (Indonesia), at least as far back as 700,000 years ago. In all localities, the two 'species' displayed regional variations, especially noticeable in the face and upper parts of the skull. In general, however, *Homo erectus* had a smaller brain capacity and a more robust skull, often sporting ridges, than his larger-brained, thinner-skulled and al-together more light-weight 'descendant', *Homo sapiens*.

Based upon this (very sparse) knowledge of man's ancient distri-bution on the planet, the essential problem faced by evolutionists is this: Did *Homo sapiens* evolve from *Homo erectus*, independently and by chance, yet more or less simultaneously, in three separate parts of the planet – China, Indonesia and Africa?

Or did *Homo erectus* first arise in Africa, spreading eastwards to China and Indonesia about a million years ago or earlier. But, subsequently, when 'archaic' *Homo sapiens* had arisen in Africa, he too spread eastwards, displacing the earlier communities of *Homo erectus*, about 250,000 years ago. And again, when respectable, modern *Homo sapiens* had arisen in Africa 50,000 years ago, he repeated the same pattern of migration, but this time going further and colonizing Australia?

The first proposition – modern man's simultaneous and parallel development in three parts of the planet – has become known as the multiregional theory, while the idea that we originated only in Africa has been dubbed the 'Out of Africa' theory.

In an attempt to decide between the two contending theories, scientists have studied the structure of the available skulls. If the three-waves-of-migration, 'Out of Africa' theory is correct, then the Chinese, Indonesian and later Australian fossils relating to these three waves should bear relationships to their *African* cousins – and not to the earlier fossils of their own country. If the parallel development theory is correct, then later races in those particular geographical areas should show marked similarities to their local forebears.

Predictably, the results are unclear. The Chinese, who are the only ones with full access to all the Chinese data, say that fossils such as the Dali and Jinnui Shan do possess characteristics in common with modern Chinese people, notably their relatively small, flat faces and delicate, high cheek bones. Effectively, they claim that the Chinese originated in China, not Africa. An understandable assertion.

Western scholars are divided in their interpretations. Some agree with the Chinese, others see more similarities to European and African fossils of 500,000 years or so ago. Additionally, they say that more recent fossils from the Zhoukoudian site, dating back only 40,000 years or so, bear stronger resemblances to populations from Africa and Australia than to modern Chinese. Based on the Chinese data, then, neither theory is conclusive.

The Indonesian and Australian fossil evidence, however, tells a different story. Java is famous in palaeoanthropological annals for providing the first finds of *Homo erectus* back in 1890–92, popularly known as Java man and dated at 700,000 years. Two other significant Indonesian finds have also been made, dated at about 400,000 and 100,000 years.

In Australia, the earliest remains so far discovered date back only 30,000 years, the best discoveries being – predictably – from areas where sediment could collect, notably Kow Swamp, Lake Mungo and the Willandra Lakes. It is assumed, therefore, that the native Australians migrated south from China and Indonesia not long before.

Cutting a long anthropological story short, the native Australian populations exhibit such a wide diversity in shape and size that some scientists have had to postulate at least two migrations into Australia in order to provide the continent with a wide enough mix of human features. And since, they say, these could only have been possible when New Guinea was a part of the Australian continent, they must have taken place about 50,000 years ago. The inclusion of New Guinea into the Australian land mass would have shortened the sea crossing, making it a feasible adventure for the presumed primitive craft of ancient man.

The first of these migrations came from Indonesia, bearing the heavier stamp of Java man, and more or less simultaneously a second migration of more slender humans came south from China. These two well-travelled communities then kept themselves apart for 40,000 years, only mixing in the last 10,000 years to create the modern aboriginal Australians. Other experts disagree, of course, suggesting that the Australian aboriginal population has diverged from one original migration, though the origin of this community is unclear.

It is here that the parallel development theorists encounter an extremely delicate problem. In the 'Out of Africa' hypothesis, any migration of *Homo sapiens* into Australia must have originated in Africa. But in the parallel evolution theory, while *Homo sapiens* migrated down from China, it was late survivors of *Homo erectus* who came over from Java. And the two species then interbred to form the aboriginals we know today. It is a delicate issue, for they appear to be saying that not only are the aboriginals partially descended from a more primitive form of man, but they are also contending that two species actually interbred – which means, effectively, that *Homo erectus* and *Homo sapiens* were not separate species at all.

The only way to get around the difficulty is to consider *Homo erectus* and *Homo sapiens* as variants of the same human species. There may have been more variations between them than amongst human variants today, but that is only because they were more isolated geographically and because the available fossils cover a long span of time. Consequently, there is more likelihood of variations.

And this is what some of the parallel development theorists have decided, though the available data is so limited, of course, that scientists will continue to debate the issue, unless or until something more decisive comes along.

MAN WAS ALWAYS HERE

Now this has all been a long story, but there are several points to it. Firstly, it highlights yet again the scantiness of the fossil data and the difficulty in interpreting it. Ancient man has lived in Indonesia for at least a million years, yet covering that long period we have only discovered three main fossil sites. In China and in Africa, his remains are also very few and far between. In Europe, he has left no fossils at all until comparatively recent times. So if we find so little in this cycle of the ages, are we likely to find evidence of his existence in ages past? Are we likely to recognize it even if we do? Especially if those who search do not believe he even existed at that time?

Secondly, it demonstrates the tremendous variability of the human species. We can see it in the fossil record and we can see it now in the world. Even an observant walk down a main street in some international city like London or New York will tell us how variable we all are. Thirdly, it shows that all our finds of human remains are indeed human.

Fourthly, it makes it clear that other interpretations of the fossil data are certainly possible, if not more likely. If man, for example, had been here all along, then there would be no need to propose all these extensive migrations out of Africa for a newly-evolved species, fresh and raw from nature's mixing pot. The 'Out of Africa' theory makes our human ancestry sound as if it had been issued like new brands of some household detergent, each improved version completely replacing the previous product on the shelves.

If one does not have to continually relate Chinese, Javanese and Australian fossils to assumed African forebears, it makes far better sense out of these regional finds. Extensive migrations will, I am sure, have taken place, adding to the confusion of later finds. Man has always been an adventurer. His akash gives him imagination and dreams of the future. He can project himself mentally into other situations and wander-lust may overtake him. Or other more pressing environmental or social changes may force him to move on. But the data is far more readily understood if we do not have to continually find routes and times for man to have travelled out of Africa – and only out of Africa.

Fifthly, the use of tools and fire by all variants of man shows quite clearly that the predominance of heavier cranial and facial features in the days of so-called *Homo erectus* is not to be construed as evidence of his being hairy, primitive and rather un-human. There is no evidence of this at all, though artists' impressions usually promote this fantasy. Having small, stout and robust features does not make you stupid. Nor does having a thicker skull. Most probably, they were perfect adaptations for their times. As we have said, there are still some tribes in India who possess thick brow ridges and they are as intelligent or stupid as the rest of us.

Finally, the fact that *Homo erectus* was around at roughly the same time in Africa, China and Indonesia, later changing to a more modern style, does not mean that he arose from one ancestor. I imagine that the changes have been partially automatic, due to the changing mood or mental atmosphere of the times and mediated through little understood genetic processes, as we have previously discussed. And certainly there will have been migrations, mixings and isolations to greater and lesser extents. This is the pattern of our history. Clearly, for all the modern races to have developed such distinctive features has required long periods of isolation from each other. But on the other hand, in just the last few hundred years the white-skinned races have spread to every continent of the world, often becoming the dominant race. In some instances, ethnic populations have almost totally disappeared. No doubt the case was similar when Cro-Magnon man ultimately took the place of Neanderthal man, though the two clearly co-existed for many millennia and may well have intermarried. And just as Java preserved one of the ancient types of so-called *Homo erectus* until only 100,000 years ago, similarly are there isolated races, such as the Australian aboriginals, who have preserved the characteristics of more ancient man.

But this does not mean that they are less evolved or less human than other races. Indeed, our modern civilization which prides itself so much on its material achievements is exactly that – more material. Man is a spiritual being, not a material machine. And on this scale, ancient man may have been inwardly more close to God and more spiritually evolved than modern man.

Even the making of tools, so eagerly heralded by palaeoanthropologists, may represent a descent into matter from a more spiritualized condition. Tools are first found nearly 2 million years ago. On the clock of the ages this fits perfectly with man's descent from the more spiritual yugas into times and conditions of greater materiality. Tools mean that he is expressing himself at a material level. And the more he turns his attention to material things, the more he forgets his Divine origins and nature, descending further and further into matter.

Similarly with the written word. It is not insignificant that it is materialistic civilizations which have developed the written word. laying so much store by it. Complex materialistic societies cannot exist without the written language, if you think about it. The ability to communicate via language is an essential attribute of man, but the written word is an outward crystallization of mental meaning. Like material tools and instruments it is essentially – or at least potentially – a descent into matter. Material things in themselves do not constitute the descent, but the more material a man's mind is, then the more he lays emphasis on the superiority of external things. The written word can thus open up the way to great discord, dispute and loss of spirituality.

It is so easy to assume without thinking that our way is best. But it may not be the case. Knowledge of the spirit, which is beyond words, is of far more value than the knowledge of this world. And a simple life definitely helps prevent the mind from descending into matter. So if the written or the spoken word, tools or any other material things, help only to focus the mind upon the realm of the physical senses, then we have become their slaves, not their independent users.

Man, then, has always been here. The evidence of the planet supports it and the experience of the mystic perceives that it is so.

EPILOGUE

TYING UP THE THREADS

Throughout both this book and its predecessor, *Natural Creation and the Formative Mind*, I have followed a number of parallel themes. In addition, the wealth of data available to draw upon concerning life and its creatures, both alive and in the fossil record, has meant that the best way to present the information has been by way of a pastiche – a sketch or scenario here, a discussion there. A full presentation of any one of these topics could have been enough to fill several volumes with detail which would have only served to confuse the main issue. Yet it has been necessary to consider all these topics, however briefly, for they have been of relevance to our theme.

The time, however, has come to pull these threads together and present a summary of the points I have been attempting to make in these two books. The third book, *Natural Creation: the Mystic Harmony*, then deals with more general aspects of the big wide universe in which we find ourselves.

The following, then, may be said:

1. Since all forms – outward or inward – are a part of a creative process from within-out, life and mind have not originated from dust and water. Dust, water and all gross physical forms are sensory phenomena arising due to the activity of Mind.

2. A mechanistic description of life and evolution fails to take into account the nature of Mind and consciousness. These are a part of the inward, vertical dimension of energy and life. They are a part of an ontological dimension. With our physical senses, we see only the external effects of patterns deeper within or higher up along this creative dimension of being and energy. Presently, physical science

deals almost exclusively with the realm of sensory experience – with the physical effects of more fundamental causes.

3.   The Life Force fuels or energizes. It represents the Primary Power or Energy, the Creative Word or Logos, the Creative Power of God manifesting the creation. The Word is one with God. The soul is the primary unit of being, a drop of God. In its essence, it is also one with both the Word and God.

4.   The greater or Formative Mind is the creator of space and time and all the patterns and rhythms appearing therein. The multitude of energies created thereby provide the patterns or blueprints for all physical, astral or causal manifestation. The physical bodies of all creatures are simply the projected images of more inward formative patterns of the Mind. The light in this cosmic movie projector is the Life Force, the soul or consciousness, itself. It both creates and illuminates the 'images in the movie projector', the 'hologram', or the stored blueprints, which then form the images on a 'screen' which we call physical bodies.

This system of energy manifestation is both multilayered as well as multireflective, reflecting in multiple ways within itself. It is a system of inwardly nested blueprints or patterns reflecting and projecting in an outward or downward direction. The physical universe and its bodies are the most outward or lowest point in this integrated Egg or Womb of the Formative Mind.

5.   Creatures are differentiated one from another by the structure of their more inward subtle or mental constitution. The physical body and the physical universe are thus an integral part of the greater Mind. This explains all psychosomatic, as well as miraculous and psychic phenomena, since they are all aspects of the same Formative Mind, functioning at different levels.

6.   The mind patterns surrounding each soul are integrated to the universal and formative sea of Mind, but are also individual. The individual aspects are created by the inward store of impressions, of karmas, the fine tracing of all past births, which automatically form and activate a physical body.

Thus, each individual creature has its own destiny or life to lead, whilst still remaining integrated within the total fabric of manifestation or creation. It is this past history which makes us all so different and so individual.

Just as each soul or spark of life is a drop in the great Universal

Consciousness, so too is each individual mind a part of the Universal or Formative Mind. 'As above, so below'.

7.   The hierarchical structure of Mind is a *real* dimension, a dimension of *being*, and as such that dimension can be travelled within our own beings. Consequently, whether one perceives individual events and individual creatures as being activated by random activity and chance or by the greater Formative Mind, depends upon where one's point of perception is on the ladder or dimension of Mind and consciousness.

The higher up we travel, then the clearer do things appear to us. This is the mystic experience – simply an enlargement of our present, physically confined state of being or point of perception. Reality is therefore better understood from a point of *being*, rather than through an analysis of physical substance or energy patterns. This implies that experience will always have more validity than words.

Substance only arises due to being. Ontological considerations must therefore come first if we are to gain an understanding of how even the physical universe is constructed. When one has risen above the Universal Mind, then one sees the soul, spirit or Life Force actuating the Mind. And further on, from God's point of perception, one sees everything as patterns, forming and disappearing in the great Ocean of His Being, Life or Consciousness.

However, simply having an intuitive realization that this is the nature of reality does not mean that we have actually achieved that high condition. We may not even have left our physical body, our physical mind and the physical universe.

8.   In the physical universe, the manifested power of the Life Force waxes and wanes. The periodicity given in Sanskrit writings is 4.32 million years, while the fossil record indicates a cycle of about 5 to 10 million years. We need not adhere dogmatically to the Sanskrit periodicity, since we do not know who wrote it, the degree of their mystic perception, nor whether the numbers have been changed by subsequent copiers of the manuscript.

Nor need we adhere religiously to scientific time-scales, for they are based upon an assumption of constancy in forces whose origin is not understood. This relates particularly to gravity and the forces holding atoms together or allowing them to disintegrate. The values of these 'constants' is presently arrived at statistically and by experimentally measuring their present values. Without an understanding of the basic principles underlying manifestation, we cannot assume their constancy over long periods of time.

Specifically, given that this great creative powerhouse of life appears to 'vary its output' according to a periodicity which is actually within the greater Mind, we cannot be sure that the values ascribed to the scientific 'constants' and upon which calculations of geological time are based, are always the same. There may be other factors, too, presently unknown to us, which influence the accuracy of these geological estimates. All the same, the time-scales are of interest, though not critical to the understanding of our thesis.

9. The first phase of this cycle, the Sat yuga, is the driving powerhouse of life on earth and, most probably, of life in the rest of the physical universe, too. It is then that new species are manifested by subtle creative processes, the full and exact details of which are not known. DNA and physical genetic processes will of course be intrinsically involved, but how they function at the present time is very much of a mystery to us. So how they function at that time is an almost total unknown.

The life forms themselves, especially man, will be involved in this creative regeneration since nothing comes from without. It is all integrated by the Oneness of the inner Ocean of Life and is spun into the appearance of manyness by the operations of the Formative Mind. During a Sat yuga, man is said to live for 100,000 years in a much subtler condition than at present, in greater harmony and creative co-operation with the natural law. Clearly he must be doing something constructive with his days.

Changes to all manifested patterns of life always arise within and proceed from living creatures themselves, according to their innate capacity. A sudden manifestation of new species like rain from the skies is not being suggested.

From the evidence of the fossil record, the regeneration appears to be quite sudden: after a preceding phase of extinction, there is a rapid proliferation which tails off. 'Sudden' is relative to geological time-scales. Probably all of the Sat yuga is devoted to the restocking of planetary species and the 'reconditioning' of the planetary biosphere. It is a time of spiritual housekeeping.

On the Sanskrit time-scales, the Sat yuga covers a period of 1.7 million years. On present scientific time-scales, it may well be more.

10. The Sat yuga merges imperceptibly into the succeeding yugas, these ages being only man's division for the convenience of our thinking. It is one, long continuous cycle.

As the great Springtime of the inner Life Force subsides, so too does the ability to generate new species, and life forms become more crystallized into set patterns. This appears in the fossil record as a time of stasis or equilibrium. The processes by which new species are formed then become hidden and we get glimpses of them only here and there.

11.   As the power of the Life Force further declines, this is manifested as increasingly difficult conditions of life and environment until species actually begin to die out. This probably begins to really appear noticeable during the Kal yuga, the last half million or million years of the cycle, depending upon the time-scale used and the possible cyclic variation of universal 'constants'. Some slow loss of species may even take place as a response to the decline of the Life Force as the Sat yuga slowly gives way to times of lesser subtlety.

The waning of the Life Force in a Kal yuga may also be mirrored in the onset of an ice age.

12.   The decline of the Life Force and of consciousness also dominates man's activities and thoughts and he loses sight of his Divine origin, even beginning to think that his life is nothing more than physical substance. His true nature is no longer immediately apparent to him.

The universal and natural appreciation of spirituality and life is increasingly lost until it becomes religion enmeshed in dogma, ritual and theological concepts.

Man becomes entangled in the grip of his emotions and the unconscious aspects of his mind. Any individual who expresses belief in the universality of spirit is likely to be labelled a dangerous mystic, a heretic, a vitalist and so on. This is despite the fact that such folk have rarely done anything to harm anybody. The harming – of both a mental and a physical nature – is usually done by the protectors of the 'faith' – religious, scientific, political, economic or whatever.

Sometimes the lack of awareness is such that the organization of physical life gets into the hands of the excessively intolerant and unconscious. Then the 'heretics,' who actually have so much more to offer, are killed, tortured, imprisoned or generally harrassed and ridiculed.

13.   At this point in the cycle, all of man's activities upon the planet reflect his lack of a genuine, uncluttered, spiritual perception and understanding. Indulgence in human weakness becomes fully acceptable, even built in to the social structure and considered a matter of pride and accomplishment. At the same time, man finds it necessary to develop his own laws because he has lost the wisdom to notice and

live in tune with natural law. Even if the majority understand the natural law, he still needs his own laws to protect himself against the excesses of the minority.

If he develops complex technology, this technology is then used to further his greed and ego, rather than enhance the spiritual quality of life. Life is taken to be of little value and man kills both his own kind and destroys the bodies and habitats of other living creatures without consideration of what he is doing. The rate of species extinction therefore increases rapidly. In reality, man should treat all other living beings with affection, love and understanding, as his brothers and sisters in life, sharing the vicissitudes of existence on the physical plane.

Man, who could be a wise and benevolent being, thus becomes a tyrant, and all creatures live in fear of him. He even lives in fear and apprehension of what his own kind may do to him.

14.   Ultimately, life becomes so intolerable that a threshold is reached and a new Springtime of the Life Force is released, flooding the physical plane with spirituality and consciousness once again. This is a return to the Sat yuga, whence the process starts all over again.

How fast this new Sat yuga arises is not known – whether it is within a few years or over the span of a thousand years or more.

15.   As regards the fossil history of these yugas, the record is most definitely present and quite indisputable, though many palaeontologists will no doubt refute this description, since they do not understand the nature of the Life Force and the role of the formative, cosmic Mind as the true origin of life and life forms. They wish to preserve their own point of view, intact. This is the nature of a habit or dogma-ridden mind.

16.   Because of continuous movements in the earth's upper layers, the continents and oceans have constantly risen and fallen. The land has many times become covered by the oceans and then re-emerged once again. Volcanic eruptions, erosion and occasional massive cataclysms engulf the earth, destroying and confusing its past geological and fossil history.

This understanding of plate tectonics has only become acceptable during the last twenty years, but past interpretations of the fossil record have not been seriously reassessed in the light of this new geological knowledge.

All the same, the evidence of cyclic extinctions and renewals is very clear.

17. During its long history, the earth has always maintained a full complement of the 8,400,000 tattvic configurations which constitute the basic species or 'super-species' inhabiting the physical plane.

According to environmental circumstances, the outward appearance of these super-species may vary, but not so the level of consciousness and the inner tattvic configuration of the creature. It is this which is the basis for our intuitive recognition that the species are placed upon an ascending scale.

The scale, however, is one of completeness in the subtle blueprint as a mental microcosm capable of contacting and comprehending the macroscosm. It is one of consciousness, not of biological complexity, nor of relative brain size, though these anatomical and physiological factors will to some degree reflect the structure and complexity of the inner subtle blueprint, the microscosmic 'equipment'. This is why man, possessing the inward integration of the akash tattwa, is (potentially) the most intelligent of creatures.

18. Akash gives discrimination, foresight and conscious appreciation of the relative positions of everything in life. Without this, we could not plan ahead and weigh up the possible outcome of events and actions, express or understand language, be spontaneously inventive on a regular basis, or do any of the things which are uniquely human.

Akash also permits us to know the true nature of our own *self* or *being*. An incorrect perception of who and what we are, we experience as our false self or 'ego'. Inwardly, this also includes knowing our position relative to God and being able to meditate on the Creative Word and to realize Him, within. This is actually the highest purpose or unique characteristic of human life.

19. The similarity between species does not indicate that all bodily forms have arisen 'horizontally' or physically from a common ancestor, nor does it demonstrate parallel evolution – the independent and chance generation of the same good idea on a multitude of separate occasions.

It demonstrates that all the physical forms of living creatures are derived from the same subtle substance, in the same essential fashion. All are projected images. The similarities and differences between creatures arise because of similarities and differences in the tattvic patternings.

These inner patterns are an integral part of the Formative Mind structure which, like the soul and God, has both individual as well as universal or cosmic aspects. This integration of all individual minds into the universal is responsible for the continuous and integrated flow of life here — all creatures continuously moving and reacting with each other, through their individual minds, yet forming the integrated *whole* of nature.

This is the way the individual karmas are worked out, the physical domain being entirely devoted to the fulfilment of karmic 'debts' and — especially in man's instance — the creation of new karma. Our akash is a two-edged sword — for 'good' or 'evil'. 'Good' is what takes us towards God, towards the Life Force; 'evil' is whatever takes us away from that higher consciousness.

20.   The particular variations in the conditions of life here are entirely created by a combination of the individual minds of all the souls drawn to this planet. We all go round and round on the wheel of birth and death. Hence, at the end of one cycle, the conditions of the new cycle will bear similarities to the past cycle, since the same minds will still be involved, though inhabiting different bodies. Through the ubiquitous presence of the Formative Mind all souls are all joint shareholders or co-creators of the physical world in which we live.

This explains why the remains of life forms in the fossil record — while often showing a marked jump or phase shift after one extinction — still appear to be part of a continuum with the previous set of species. And some species even appear never to become extinct and to continue through with little or no re-creative work being applied.

21.   The degree to which species may change outwardly is not unequivocally apparent from the fossil record, but there is certainly no evidence at all of major shifts. Bacteria did not become seaweed, amoebae and other invertebrates; spiders did not become insects; fishes did not become amphibians; reptiles did not become birds and mammals; apes did not become man. Missing links between such forms have remained missing; not a single one has ever been found.

The degree of external variety which may be expressed by each subtle, tattvic configuration or super-species may perhaps be considerable, but will not go beyond certain boundaries. These boundaries are essentially mental and subtle in character, relating to the ecological niche of the super-species and the atmosphere of the time and place.

Though the fossil record may be misleading, there appears to be more variety amongst warm-blooded vertebrates in the external expression of a super-species than amongst reptiles, amphibia, fishes and invertebrates. For example, some of the dinosaurian species may now be represented by our modern birds, both being expressions of the same super-species – both essentially having the same character and level of consciousness and occupying the same niche in the complete ecology of nature.

22. The true natural ecology is an ecology and integration at the level of the subtle tattvic configurations or microcosms. It is a complete ecology of mind and consciousness, such that all possible levels and expressions of consciousness are always simultaneously present. Hence, it is maintained that representatives of all super-species have always been present on the planet, including man.

23. The number of species (or super-species) described by mystics is 8,400,000, which are said to have always existed on the planet. Scientists are very unsure of the number of species that may be described according to taxonomic criteria, but it is probably in excess of 30,000,000 at the present time. Counted throughout geological history this number may well exceed 3000,000,000, but this is only a guess. It could be more, though it is unlikely to be less. Hence, there is considerable justification for suggesting that a number of the outward forms that we call different species are actually representative of one super-species.

24. The processes by which changes in the outward expression of the super-species are manifested are not those of chance or random genetic mutation and natural selection of the fittest to survive. DNA and genetic processes are deeply complex and have yet to be unravelled. They are also responsive to what we call 'environment'. Keys to understanding some of these processes are demonstrated by atavisms such as hens' teeth and horses' toes, which show that the super-species' expressions of even more than 65 million years ago are not lost but are still stored within the genetic system. They remain purely in potential form.

Whatever changes take place are a reflection of the individual minds of all the souls involved, themselves integrated into the greater Formative Mind. The species present at any particular time are all reflections of the mental mood of those times. Although DNA and genetic processes are involved, the more primary pattern-maker lies in the subtle energies of the Mind and within the super-species blue-prints. It is these subtle, mental energies which actually determine how the DNA is configured at the physical level.

25. The 'survival of the fittest' – as a mechanism – is a purely horizontal or physical perception. It therefore fails to address the

question as to *how* such an arrangement could have arisen and what actually determines this apparent 'competition' between creatures. From the horizonal, slit-window view of things, one can say that such a process is in operation, but it is incorrect to suggest that it is a primary force by which inert dust and water have self-organized themselves into a multiplicity of living forms. There is another dimension to the whole affair which must be considered.

26.   In any event, more than DNA is involved in the manifestation of gross physical forms. Physical bodies also possess subtle, etheric forms which act as dynamically active blueprints working in concert with DNA activity. It is also necessary to re-appraise all molecular function at subatomic and even vacuum state levels if one is to really comprehend genetic processes and the means by which overall bodily integration and manifestation come about.

We may think, as children, that electricity comes out of a hole in the wall, in some 'self-organizing' manner. But later we discover that all these holes in the wall are fed by one main electrical input to the house. This is of help in understanding how we have a ramification of electrical wall sockets, but it would be a mistake to assume that the true source of electricity was the main domestic input.

Similarly, DNA is only a link in the formative chain, an end-point on the vertical, ontological dimension of Mind and energy patterning. After all, something has to give form and energy to DNA and all the subatomic particles of which it consists.

Any necessary changes to the DNA are brought about through the hidden workings of this inner Mind. Hence, the right adaptations to outer form and function as well as inner, mental behavioural patterns are all integrated. Creatures *do* respond genetically to their 'environment', because both 'environment' and the inner mental being are part of one integrated energy system of the greater Mind.

27.   Man has conceived millions of opinions and concepts in his mind concerning the nature of reality. Yet that Reality lies within ourselves, remaining quite unruffled by all our thoughts and ideas about it. The myriad beliefs and ideas of religion, philosophy and science bear extensive witness to the fact that, generally speaking, man does not know what on earth is going on. They also testify to his never-ending quest to understand the how and why of things.

By thought, we cannot fully appreciate Reality. We can only experience it by contacting our own real essence, the same Life Force which lies within each and every one of us. This is the only way to know how and why things are put together. Until then, everything remains just a working hypothesis. Dogma and expanding conscious-ness cannot co-exist. Dogma will always decline as understanding and inner experience increase.

CONCLUDING

I have put forward a radically new description of our planetary history as regards its life forms and geology. I make no apology for this, for the time is ripe for new perceptions and I am also a child of the times.

I have suggested that an entire dimension is missing in conventional scientific descriptions and explanations of the universe. I have also raised more than just a question mark over what we really mean by evolution. What is it that evolves – or have we only been observing outward physical manifestations of *change*? I have not disputed the evidence for this change; rather I accept wholeheartedly the clear geological and palaeontological evidence.

But I see no signs in it of full-scale, materially based evolution, of all creatures evolving from one common ancestor. This is pushing the evidence beyond its capacity. But it is true that there have been great changes. This is not in dispute.

But the means by which change is mediated are not those of chance mutation, natural selection and survival of the fittest. Nature is not so superficial or banal in her processes. There are subtle, formative processes at work both in creation as it appears now and as it has been moulded this way and that with the passage of time.

All scientific 'explanations' which describe fundamental order or repeating patterns, and yet resort to chance and self-organization as the essential driving forces, are missing the perception of this onto-logical dimension of energy manifestation. This is the condition of almost all modern science.

Interestingly, modern psychology alone has an inkling of this inner dimension when it is observed that outward behaviour and even 'chance' events are manifestations of and are directly related to the content of our inward psyche. Both Freud and Jung spoke of mind as *psychic energy* and it was Jung himself who first gave credence to the phenomenon of synchronicity. But the time was not right for the full meaning and implications to become clear.

If we can grasp the reality of this inward, 'vertical', ontological dimension of the Formative Mind, of how energy patterns are manifested from within-out, then the physicist, the healer, the doctor and the psychologist – even the astronomer and the astrophysicist and all who seek to analyse and understand the nature of physical existence – can all begin to talk to each other in a coherent and common language.

Then, too, can we begin to unravel – if indeed it is really necessary – the true saga of change which our planet and the whole universe have undergone and will undergo. Then we will glimpse how superficial are our ideas that all mind and consciousness have arisen from inert dust. We will see that our ideas have been totally upside down. With a perception of the hidden dimension, our view of science, evolution and our whole life takes on a radically new perspective.

In the last book in this series, *Natural Creation: The Mystic Harmony*, we look at some other aspects of the natural world in the light of this new perception. Again, we find that this approach illuminates and explains matters in a most revealing fashion. This is then followed by many personal accounts of mystic experience, together with a full description of the mystic hierarchy of creation.

GLOSSARY

Palaeontological and geological terms are not included in this glossary since they are defined on their first occurrence in the text and can be found by consulting the index.

akash Literally, sky, firmament, ether. Esoterically, *akash* is the inward focus or plane of energy potential out of which the physical universe is created. It is the hidden energy which fills all space and out of which the other four tattvic states are derived or manifested, like bubbles, waves or patterns on an ocean. In gross physical terms, it is the all-pervasive vacuum or space of the physical realm, of which even apparently solid substance almost completely consists.

In its subtle form it is linked into man's inner being. Since it is all-pervasive, it gives him a mental appreciation of how things are put together. It also gives him a human identity or a perception of his place in the scheme of things. It provides an awareness of space and time. Thus our human discrimination, foresight, intelligent perception and so on are all attributable to the existence of the *akashic* element in our make-up.

Man's inner being is generally disturbed by the outward and scattered tendencies of the mind and senses. Consequently, he has lost consciousness of his true Self, the soul. Man's experience has become restricted to the physical realm and his sense of self has become correspondingly confined to the individual mind, working at the physical level. The place of the true Self has thus been usurped by the little, illusory self or ego.

astral region The astral realm lying between the causal region (above) and the physical universe (below). The heavens to which the devotees of most religions aspire lie within the astral realms.

Brahm   'Lord' or 'ruler' of the region of Universal Mind.

Brahmanda   Literally, 'Egg of Brahm'. Refers either to the causal region of Universal Mind, or to the astral and causal realms combined.

causal region   The highest region of the Mind; the region of the Universal Mind; the source of illusion; the blissfully intoxicating realm comprising the finest mental essences, tattwas or energies, the seed or blueprint forms of time, space, causation and duality as we experience them in dense, crystallized manifestation in the physical universe.

chaurasi   The wheel of 8,400,000 species or bodily forms in which a soul may take birth whilst in the physical world.

Creative Word   *See* Life Force

DNA   Deoxyribonucleic acid. The main constituent of the chromosomes of all living organisms (except some viruses), playing an important role in protein synthesis and in the transmission of hereditary characteristics.

Egg of Brahm   *See* Brahmanda

Formative Mind   *See* Mind

God   The primal, self-existent Being and source of everything. *Also called* the Father, the Lord, Ocean of Being, Ocean of Life, Universal Consciousness, the Source, the Supreme Being and by many other names throughout the world.

God-realization   The state of consciousness of a soul that has completely merged into God.

greater Mind   *See* Mind

Kal   The Negative Power; Satan; the lord or ruler of the Universal Mind; Brahm.

karma   The law of the greater Mind by which souls, under the influence of their individual minds, are brought back into physical birth after physical death. It is an automatic and natural law of cause and effect which exacts strict justice rather than mercy and forgiveness. The record of karma is held within the Mind as the impressions in seed form of all thoughts, actions and desires ever entertained or performed by a soul. Karma is of three kinds:

1. **Destiny karma** – the events of life which are fixed at the time of birth and which have to be undergone. They are the effects, good and bad, of previous actions, thoughts and desires from previous lives. Destiny is etched into the complex, energetic fabric of our human mind.

2. **New karma** – new actions and desires, performed or entertained in the present life, which become seeds or mental impressions for the destiny of future lives.

3. **Stored karma** – in one lifetime, we may gather more new karma than can be paid off in just one future life. Any balance of this 'unused' karma goes into 'storage'. Over the span of aeons, this store of karma becomes a great weight upon the soul, keeping it bound to the wheel of birth and death. This continues indefinitely, until the soul has the good fortune to meet a Master who has come from beyond the realm of karma and has the power to release souls from the Mind, by taking on responsibility for the payment of this vast debt.

Karma also means 'sins' and, from a mystic point of view, the 'forgiveness of sins' actually means help and guidance in the clearing of this great mountain of stored karma by a contemporary, living Master who is divinely qualified and appointed to do so. Such a Master inwardly connects or re-tunes the soul to the Creative Word or Logos – which is the real Master. It is the absorption of the mind and soul in the sound and light of the Creative Word which cleanses it of all past karmas and ultimately draws it back to God, beyond the realm of Mind and Maya (Illusion).

individual mind   A drop or ray of the Universal Mind, with which every human is endowed. It contains the seeds of an individual's destiny and records the new impressions due to actions and desires performed in the present life, as well as providing the characteristics of memory, intellect, discrimination, thought, emotion, personality, ego or identity, instinct and so on. *Also called* human mind or physical mind.

Life Force This term is used in many ways by different writers. In this book, it refers to the creative power of God in the creation; His primal emanation, from which all other emanations are derived. It is the Primal Vibration, underlying all other vibration and movement in the creation, both within and without. Nothing exists, at any level in creation, without this incessant movement. And just as our senses can perceive certain physical vibrations, so too do our inner mind and soul possess the capacity to *hear* this Primal Vibration inside, in mystic experience. The inner light also comes from this Primal Sound. Also called: Logos, Nous, Word, Creative Word, Sound Current, Audible Life Stream, Life Stream, Music of the Spheres, Divine Music, Divine Sound. This life-giving current, as heard in the region of the Universal Mind, is called Aum or Om, in the Vedas.

Logos *See* Life Force

Maya Literally, 'illusion'. First arises in the region of the Universal Mind as a web of patterns and rhythms over the face of pure spirit. It is illusory because the mind takes these patterns and rhythms as the reality, losing sight of the One Creator within all things. The sensory world of the physical universe as well as the higher regions of the Mind are thus all Maya – illusion.

Mind or mind A general term, sometimes referring to the individual or human mind, sometimes to the Universal Mind and sometimes to any or all aspects of the Mind as it is found within the three worlds of the Mind. The higher aspects of the Mind, lying between the individual mind and the Universal Mind are also referred to as the Formative Mind or the greater Mind. Mind, when spelt with a capital 'M', refers to aspects above the individual mind. With a small 'm', it refers to the individual or human mind.

mysticism The study and practice of philosophies and techniques leading to the ascent of the soul and mind from the physical body. The highest mystical experience is the union of the soul with God. Hence, a mystic is one who is able to leave his body whilst still living, and the highest mystic is one who has attained God-realization. Such a one may also, but not necessarily, be appointed to perform the duties of a perfect Master.

physical universe The region of dense matter and crystallized physical forms, where Mind reigns supreme, though largely unrecognized, remaining concealed within forms. The realm in which the soul, under the influence of the mind's attractions and tendencies, takes birth in successive bodies, together with corresponding destinies, both of which accurately reflect the character of the individual mind.

Prakriti Primal Nature. The prototype, blueprint, seed or ultra-fine subtle mental pattern, originating in the region of the Universal Mind, which becomes what we call 'nature' in the physical creation. Prakriti is the subtle source or pattern from which the planetary biosphere or ecosystem is derived or reflected.

Pralaya Dissolution. According to some Indian mystics, the three worlds of the Mind are periodically dissolved every 1000 cycles of the three yugas. This period of creation is known as a Day of Brahm. After a quiescence lasting the same span of time (a Night of Brahm), the three worlds are said to be recreated and so the cycle continues. After 1000 such cycles, both the spiritual creation beyond the Mind, as well as the Mind worlds themselves, are all dissolved. All creation temporarily ceases, until a new cycle is commenced.

Puranas Literally, the 'old ones'. Any of a class of ancient Sanskrit writings not included in the Vedas, said to have been compiled by the rishi (yogi or sage) Vyas.

reincarnation The incarnation of a soul in successive physical bodies, human or otherwise, due to the influence, tendencies and involvements of the mind. *Also called* transmigration or metempsychosis. *See also* karma.

Self-realization The mystic knowledge of the soul that it is pure soul, only attained when the soul gains release from all aspects of the Mind, on rising above the Universal Mind.

soul A term used throughout the ages in reference to many psychological and spiritual aspects of a human being. Mystically, the soul is said to be a drop of the Divine Ocean, constituting our true Self and innermost essence.

three worlds of the Mind The three worlds ruled by the Universal Mind, viz. the physical, astral and causal realms.

Universal Mind The power that rules the three worlds of the Mind:

the physical, astral and causal realms. *Also called* Satan, Negative Power, Brahm, and by many other names throughout the world.

Sanskrit An ancient language of India; the language of the Vedas, of Hinduism, and of an extensive scientific and philosophical literature dating from the the first millennium BC. The oldest recorded language of the Indic branch of the Indo-European group of languages, recognized as such in the eighteenth century from a comparison of Greek and Latin with Sanskrit. The historical basis for this relationship is unknown.

sat Literally, 'truth', specifically Divine truth; that which endures, rather than that which changes and is subject to dissolution.

tattwas Energy essences, primary elements. First manifesting as ultra-fine mental essences, blueprints or energies in the region of the Universal Mind, the tattwas appear as reflections at the physical level and are involved in all aspects of physical living, gross and subtle.

Vedas Literally, 'Divine knowledge'. The four principal holy books of the Hindus, written by their great sages and mystics in ancient times.

Upanishads Literally, 'to sit near or close to' or 'setting at rest ignorance by revealing the knowledge of the Supreme Spirit'. Thus it also means esoteric doctrine or mystical teachings. Specifically, the Upanishads are a class of Hindu writings, there being 108 in number, whose aim is to reveal the secret or mystical meaning of the Vedas.

yugas Literally, 'ages'. According to the Hindu sages, the physical universe is said to cycle through ages of great spirituality (Sat yugas) down to ages of great spiritual poverty (Kal yugas). The span of one cycle lasts 4.32 million years. Just as spring comes after winter, a Kal yuga is followed by a Sat yuga.

BIBLIOGRAPHY

Books, papers and articles quoted or from which material has been drawn are all listed below. A few others of related interest are also included.

Anomalies and Strange Artefacts

Corliss, William R., *Ancient Man: A Handbook of Puzzling Artefacts*; The Sourcebook Project, Glen Arm, MD 21057, USA, 1978.

The Reader's Digest, *Strange Stories, Amazing Facts*, The Reader's Digest Association, London, 1976.

The Reader's Digest, *Mysteries of the Unexplained*, Reader's Digest Association, New York, 1982.

Evolution

Anderson, Ian, *Chinese Unearth a Dinosaur's Graveyard*; New Scientist, November 12 1987.

Anderson, Ian, *Darwin May Founder on the Great Barrier Reef*; New Scientist, October 20 1990.

Anderson, Ian, *Dinosaurs Breathed Air Rich in Oxygen*; New Scientist, November 5 1987.

Anderson, Ian, *Fetal Fragments Suggest Warm-Blooded Dinosaurs*; New Scientist, September 24 1987

Anon., *Oldest Complete Amphibian is Scotland's*; New Scientist, April 4 1985.

Bakker, Robert, *The Dinosaur Heresies*, Penguin, London, 1986.

Bowler, Sue, *Lucky Escape for Europe's Oldest Flying Insect*; New Scientist, May 18 1991.

Bunney, Sarah, *Another Cousin Joins the Family Tree*; New Scientist, August 14 1986.

Bunney, Sarah, *Fossil Fingers Point to New Ideas on Evolution*; New Scientist, June 2 1988.

Bunney, Sarah, *Modern Man Not so Modern*; New Scientist, January 20 1990.

Bunney, Sarah, *Neanderthals Weren't So Dumb After All*; New Scientist, July 1 1989.

Bunney, Sarah, *The Origins of Manual Dexterity*; New Scientist, November 28 1985.

Bunney, Sarah, *Our Most Complete Ancestor*; New Scientist, September 5 1985.

Bunney, Sarah, *When Humans First Came Home to a Real Fire*; New Scientist, January 14 1989.

Bunney, Sarah, *Will the Real* Homo Habilis *Please Stand Up?*; New Scientist, October 29 1988.

Cherfas, Jeremy, *Extinction and the Pattern of Evolution*; New Scientist, October 3 1985.

Darwin, Charles, *The Origin of Species*, J. M. Dent & Sons Ltd, London, 1928.

Davidson, John, *The Search for the Missing Link in the Theory of Punctuated Equilibria*; Scientific and Medical Network Newsletter, Summer 1988.

Dayton, Leigh, *Step-wise Extinctions Preceded Demise of Dinosaurs*; New Scientist, July 7 1990.

Eldredge, Niles, *Life Pulse*, Facts On File Publications, London, 1987.

Eldredge, Niles, *Time Frames*, William Heinemann Ltd., London, 1986.

Foley, Robert, *Hotbed of Evolution; BBC Wildlife Magazine*, November 1988.

Foley, Robert and Robin Dunbar, *Beyond the Bones of Contention*; *New Scientist*, October 14 1989.

Gould, Stephen Jay, *Hens' Teeth and Horses' Toes*; W. W. Norton & Co., London, 1983.

Hecht, Jeff, *Fossil Birds Force an Evolutionary Rethink*; *New Scientist*, November 3 1990.

Henblest, Nigel, *Geologists Hit Back at Impact Theory of Extinctions*; *New Scientist*, April 29 1989.

Jeram, Andrew, *When Scorpions Ruled the World*; *New Scientist*, June 16 1990.

Leggett, Jeremy, *The Biggest Mass-extinction of Them All*; *New Scientist*, June 10 1989.

Lewin, Roger, *Neanderthals Puzzle the Anthropologists*; *New Scientist*, April 20 1991.

Long, John, *The Extraordinary Fishes of Gogo*; *New Scientist*, November 29 1988.

Lowenstein, Jerold and Adrienne Zihlman, *The Invisible Ape*; *New Scientist*, December 3 1988.

Lucas, Spencer *The Rise of the Dinosaur Dynasty*; *New Scientist*, October 6 1990.

Malet, Daniel, *Night of the Tenrec*; *BBC Wildlife Magazine*, February 1989.

Maudsley, Brian, *Defenders of the Reef*; *New Scientist*, April 28 1990.

McNamara, Ken, *Survivors from the Primordial Soup*; *New Scientist*, December 8 1990.

Morris, Simon Conway, *Palaeontology's Hidden Agenda*; *New Scientist*, August 11 1990.

Pitman, Michael, *Adam and Evolution*, Rider, London, 1984.

Rampino, Michael, *Dinosaurs, Comets and Volcanoes*; *New Scientist*, February 18 1989;

Stork, Nigel and Kevin Gaston, *Counting the Species One by One*; *New Scientist*, August 11 1990.

Stringer, Chris, *The Asian Connection*; *New Scientist*, November 17 1990.

Taylor, Ian T., *In the Minds of Men*, TFE Publishing, P.O. Box 5015, Stn. F, Toronto M4Y 2T1, Canada, 1984.

Genetics and Evolution

Cherfas, Jeremy, *Bacteria Take the Chance out of Evolution*; *New Scientist*, September 22 1988.

Lewin, Roger, *In the Beginning Was the Genome*; *New Scientist*, July 21 1990.

Scott, Andrew, *Messages in Evolution*; *New Scientist*, July 25 1985.

Geology and Earth Sciences

Anon., *How the Himalayas Arose from a Clash of Continents*; *New Scientist*, May 26 1988.

Anon., *Volcanic Plumes Rise in the Mantle*; *New Scientist*, October 14 1989.

Bowler, Sue, and Rob Butler, *Mountain Building under the Microscope*; *New Scientist*, April 13 1991.

Morgan, Nina, *The Fires that Cracked a Continent*; *New Scientist*, June 8 1991.

Press, Frank and Siever, Raymond, *Earth*, W. H. Freeman and Company, New York, 1986.
Petford, Nick, *Granite on the Move*; *New Scientist*, June 15 1991.

Miscellaneous
Hessler, Robert, Peter Lonsdale and James Hawkins, *Patterns on the Ocean Floor*; *New Scientist*, March 24 1988.
Postgate, John, *Bacterial Worlds Built on Sulphur*; *New Scientist*, July 14 1988.
Shakespeare, William, *The Complete Works of Shakespeare*, ed. Peter Alexander, Collins, London, 1951.

Mysticism and Mystical Experience
Charan Singh, Maharaj, *Spiritual Heritage*, Radha Soami Satsang Beas, Beas, India, 1983.
Jaimal Singh, Baba, *Spiritual Letters*, Radha Soami Satsang Beas, Beas, India, 1958.
Rumi, Jalalu'ddin, *The Mathnawi*; translated by R. A. Nicholson, first published by Luzac & Co., London, 1926. Presently published by Cambridge University Press, Cambridge.

New Science and Mysticism
Davidson, John, *Subtle Energy*, C. W. Daniel & Co., Saffron Walden, 1987.
Davidson, John, *The Web of Life*, C. W. Daniel & Co., Saffron Walden, 1988.
Davidson, John, *The Secret of the Creative Vacuum*, C. W. Daniel & Co., Saffron Walden, 1989.
Davidson, John, *Natural Creation and the Formative Mind*, Element, Shaftesbury, 1991.
Davidson, John, *Natural Creation: The Mystic Harmony*, Element, Shaftesbury, 1992 (to be published).

Organization and Order in the Universe and Living Systems
Anon., *How Living Things Keep the Planet Cool*; *New Scientist*, September 2 1989.
Edwards, R., M. C. Ibison, Julian Kenyon and Roger Taylor, *Light Emission from the Human Body*; *Complementary Medical Research*, Spring 1989.
Lovelock, James, *The Ages of Gaia*, Oxford University Press, Oxford, 1988.
Lovelock, James, *Gaia*, Oxford University Press, Oxford, 1979.
Popp, Fritz-Albert, *On the Coherence of Ultraweak Photon Emission from Living Tissues* in *Disequilibrium and Self-Organization*, ed. C. W. Kumister, Reidel Publishing Co., 1986.
Popp, Fritz-Albert, and Walter Nagel, *A Physical Electromagnetic Model of Differentiation*; *Cytobios*, 37 71–83, 1983.
Popp, Fritz-Albert, Ke-Shue Li and Walter Nagel, *A Thermodynamic Approach to the Temperature Response of Biological Systems as Demonstrated by Low Level Luminescence of Cucumber Seedlings*; *Z. Pflanzenphysiol*. Bd. 114. S. 1–13, 1984.
Popp, Fritz-Albert, Walter Nagel, K. H. Li *et al.*, *Biophoton Emission*; *Cell Biophysics*, Vol. 6., 1984.
Sheldrake, Rupert, *A New Science of Life, The Hypothesis of Formative Causation*, Blond and Briggs, London, 1981.
Sheldrake, Rupert, *The Presence of the Past*, Collins, London, 1988.

INDEX

FURTHER INFORMATION

Details of further books by the same author, as well as books upon allied topics, are available from:

WHOLISTIC RESEARCH COMPANY
Bright Haven,
Robin's Lane,
Lolworth,
Cambridge CB3 8HH,
England.

Please send four second-class postage stamps (£2.50/$5.00 overseas) for a booklist.

THE SCIENTIFIC AND MEDICAL NETWORK

The Scientific and Medical Network is an informal international group consisting mainly of qualified scientists and doctors, with a seasoning of psychologists, engineers, philosophers and other professionals.

The Network came into existence in 1973 and now has around 700 Members in 36 countries. It questions the assumptions of contemporary scientific and medical thinking, so often limited by exclusively materialistic reasoning.

By remaining open to intuitive and spiritual insights, it fosters a climate in which science as a whole can adopt a more comprehensive and sensitive approach.

The Network does not embrace the unorthodox for its own sake; it is not "anti-establishment", but its Members support the freedom to develop any worthwhile field of study, even if this means moving beyond what is currently considered scientifically plausible.

The Network nevertheless encourages intellectual discrimination and is wary of the consequences of ill-founded and over-enthusiastic claims often made in the areas of pseudo-science.

The purpose of the Network is to explore concepts that go beyond generally accepted ideas. In doing this, it puts like-minded individuals in touch with each other, thus encouraging an exchange of ideas and information which often leads to valuable new friendships. Members share a common concern with the essential questions about the meaning and value of life.

For details of membership, events, publications etc., contact:

The Scientific and Medical Network
9 Julier House, Pera Road, Bath BA1 5PA, England
Telephone/Fax: 0225-334526